PUBLICATIONS OF THE
NATIONAL BUREAU OF ECONOMIC RESEARCH,
INC.

NUMBER 24

STRATEGIC FACTORS
IN BUSINESS CYCLES

STRATEGIC FACTORS

IN BUSINESS CYCLES

JOHN MAURICE CLARK

WITH AN INTRODUCTION BY

THE COMMITTEE ON RECENT

ECONOMIC CHANGES

A PUBLICATION OF THE

NATIONAL BUREAU OF ECONOMIC RESEARCH

IN COOPERATION WITH THE

COMMITTEE ON RECENT ECONOMIC CHANGES

NEW YORK : 1935

Reprinted 1949

Reprinted 1949
AUGUSTUS M. KELLEY, INC.

PUBLISHED BY SPECIAL ARRANGEMENT WITH
NATIONAL BUREAU OF ECONOMIC RESEARCH, INC.

LITHOGRAPHED IN U.S.A.

INTRODUCTION

BY THE COMMITTEE ON RECENT ECONOMIC
CHANGES

––––––

IN 1921, in the midst of the early post-War depression, the President of the United States called a national Conference on Unemployment to deal with urgent emergency problems. Out of this Conference came a series of important investigations, each sponsored by committees set up by the Conference.

In 1927 a continuing committee of that Conference was brought together under the chairmanship of Herbert Hoover, then Secretary of Commerce, designated as "The Committee on Recent Economic Changes of the President's Conference on Unemployment." Its purpose was to make a comprehensive fact-and-figure picture of the results of the working of economic forces during a major business cycle, assembled in the form of a descriptive record with statistical measurements, which should reveal the developing pattern of our economic evolution.

In order that this project might be carried out in a thoroughly scientific spirit, and be utterly free from partisan bias, the National Bureau of Economic Research, Inc. was enlisted by the Committee to assemble, assimilate and organize the factual and statistical material for study and interpretation. For

v]

this undertaking a group of fifteen of the most competent economists in the country was assembled by the National Bureau of Economic Research. To the broad background knowledge of this collaborating group the National Bureau added its wealth of statistical data and its facilities for progressively measuring the operation of economic forces, reflecting the actions of millions of human beings engaged in the normal processes of living.

In 1928 Arch W. Shaw succeeded Mr. Hoover as Chairman of the Committee on Recent Economic Changes, and early in 1929 the Committee's first report was brought out, a two-volume work covering the period from 1922 to 1928, entitled *Recent Economic Changes in the United States,* intended as a record, partly statistical and partly descriptive, of the ascending curve of the cycle which started after the depression of 1921 and carried through 1928.

When, a year later, the country entered upon the descending curve of the major cycle under observation, the part that public works might be expected to play in stabilizing our national economy was engaging the attention of thinking men. Inasmuch as this represented a field where a statistical picture could be made with reasonable promptness, and one which would fit into its broad program, the Committee sponsored a study, which was prepared at the National Bureau of Economic Research under the

[vi

direction of Dr. Leo Wolman, and published as *Planning and Control of Public Works*.

In 1932 the developing pattern of our economic experience was further disclosed by the publication of a work by Dr. Frederick C. Mills entitled, *Economic Tendencies in the United States*. This book, published cooperatively by the Committee on Recent Economic Changes and the National Bureau of Economic Research, summarized and extended the record covered by the two-volume report already described. In this work Dr. Mills essayed the important task of bringing out the characteristics of the tendencies prevailing during the period preceding the current economic depression, in comparison with the tendencies prevailing during the period preceding the World War. This served to clarify many economic relationships which had previously been little understood.

In this program the Committee and its collaborator, the National Bureau of Economic Research, have been concerned chiefly with making a quantitative analysis by means of facts and statistics, picturing as they do the movement of commerce and industry—ships crossing the seas with cargoes of imports and exports, freight and passenger trains rumbling across the continent, the daily transactions in banking houses, stock and produce exchanges, wholesale establishments and retail stores—all representing the reality of life and the relation of industry to industry and individual to individual. Without such a statistical and descriptive record as had been undertaken, representing the 'measurables' of our economic life, little progress could be made in the analysis or understanding of the motives and operations that underlie and affect the movement of economic forces.

All statistical measurements must of necessity be on a common basis if comparison is to be possible. In the statistical record compiled over the whole period covered by the Committee's program, whatever monetary units have been used have been in terms of dollars based on a constant relationship to gold. Early in 1933 the United States went off the gold basis. The Committee recognized this as a natural stopping point for its undertaking, and it determined to bring to a head as rapidly as possible all of the separate studies which formed its program of publication, thus fulfilling its mission at a time when the results would be of the most timely interest and service.

In line with this decision, there will follow as rapidly as they can be completed and prepared for the press, a study of "Profits" by Dr. Ralph C. Epstein; a study of "Prices" by Dr. Frederick C. Mills; a report on "Wages and Consumption," by Dr. Leo Wolman; a report on "Industrial Trends" by Dr. Willard L. Thorp; and possibly one or more additional reports or surveys.

[viii

Meanwhile, the Committee sponsored a special study, from the descriptive and statistical record which had been assembled, to endeavor to disclose, so far as might be possible, what factors play an active role in throwing the economic mechanism out of balance and what factors adapt themselves passively to the changes produced by the active factors. It is this phase of the Committee's exploration which explains the present volume. While the statistical and factual record of the cycle was being made by the collaborating group of economists, Dr. Clark was a regular attendant at the meetings of the group. He participated in the discussions, studied the wealth of factual and statistical material which had been assembled, and assimilated much of the picture of our economic life which it reflected. Then, viewing the whole picture objectively, he essayed to make an appraisal and draw certain conclusions.

The present volume is the result. Intended to achieve a perspective on the pattern of our recent economic experience, it shows something of the evolving design and, in careful fashion as becomes a work by so eminent a student of economic theory, examines into the general direction the pattern is taking.

While Dr. Clark is responsible for the conclusions herein set forth, the Committee on Recent Economic Changes is pleased to offer this report of his findings as a valuable and timely contribution to current economic thought. Indeed, the Committee hopes that it may prove to be helpful in relating yesterday's economic experience to tomorrow's economic needs. For out of his intensive study of the pattern of our recent economic life Dr. Clark has endeavored to isolate what he terms the "strategic business factors"—strategic because they seem to have a causal influence upon the business cycle and are possibly susceptible of conscious control by the community. Highly suggestive, also, is his analysis of the character of and requirements for national economic balance, and the discussion of the means and possibilities of attaining and maintaining it.

The Committee is glad to have the opportunity of presenting an analysis of this character. It is also glad to add its emphasis to Dr. Clark's call for an improvement in the quality and quantity of the country's statistical services. But it realizes that effective results can be achieved only by putting to work the results of scientific analysis and continued statistical investigation in the realm of practical affairs. What is perhaps more needed at the present time than anything else is the development of means of coordinating and utilizing the experience of men of affairs and the results of economic research.

It is the Committee's belief that economic research itself is made more fruitful through contact between economists and men who are more familiar with business than with text books, for whatever scientific analysis has to contribute to human wel-

[x

fare must be done through the channel of practical application. Among the things which the Committee views with most satisfaction is that its work has made at least a modest contribution toward the achievement of some such union. In the carrying out of this work it has had the generous support of the Rockefeller Foundation, the Economic Club of Chicago, the Carnegie Corporation, and various socially-minded groups and individuals, whose support it here gratefully acknowledges.

Recognizing the timeliness of Dr. Clark's report, the Committee has been led to hasten its publication that it may serve the immediate need of clearer perspective. It is presented, not as a full and matured expression of the Committee's own collective viewpoint, but as the findings of an able thinker upon a broad problem of great significance at the present juncture in our social-political-economic life. It leads up to the great question that we face as a nation: which factors are and which are not amenable to purposive control by public or private agencies?

Arch W. Shaw, *Chairman*	John J. Raskob
Renick W. Dunlap	Samuel W. Reyburn
William Green	Louis J. Taber
Julius Klein	Daniel Willard
John S. Lawrence	Clarence M. Woolley
Max Mason	Owen D. Young
Adolph C. Miller	Edward E. Hunt,
Lewis E. Pierson	*Secretary*

November, 1933

RELATION OF THE DIRECTORS
TO THE WORK OF THE NATIONAL BUREAU
OF ECONOMIC RESEARCH

1. The object of the National Bureau of Economic Research is to ascertain and to present to the public important economic facts and their interpretation in a scientific and impartial manner. The Board of Directors is charged with the responsibility of ensuring that the work of the Bureau is carried on in strict conformity with this object.

2. To this end the Board of Directors shall appoint one or more Directors of Research.

3. The Director or Directors of Research shall submit to the members of the Board, or to its Executive Committee, for their formal adoption, all specific proposals concerning researches to be instituted.

4. No study shall be published until the Director or Directors of Research shall have submitted to the Board a summary report drawing attention to the character of the data and their utilization in the study, the nature and treatment of the problems involved, the main conclusions and such other information as in their opinion will serve to determine the suitability of the study for publication in accordance with the principles of the Bureau.

5. A copy of any manuscript proposed for publication shall also be submitted to each member of the Board. If publication is approved each member is entitled to have published also a memorandum of any dissent or reservation he may express, together with a brief statement of his reasons. The publication of a volume does not, however, imply that each member of the Board of Directors has read the manuscript and passed upon its validity in every detail.

6. The results of an inquiry shall not be published except with the approval of at least a majority of the entire Board and a two-thirds majority of all those members of the Board who shall have voted on the proposal within the time fixed for the receipt of votes on the publication proposed. The limit shall be forty-five days from the date of the submission of the synopsis and manuscript of the proposed publication unless the Board extends the limit; upon the request of any member the limit may be extended for not more than thirty days.

7. A copy of this resolution shall, unless otherwise determined by the Board, be printed in each copy of every Bureau publication.

(Resolution of October 25, 1926, revised February 6, 1933)

CONTENTS

CONTENTS

PART THREE

GENERAL MOVEMENTS, 1922-1929

PART FOUR

SPECIAL FEATURES OF THE LAST CYCLE

PART FIVE

ANOTHER APPROACH: THE
MEANING AND REQUIREMENTS OF BALANCE

     [xiv

CONTENTS

xv]

STRATEGIC FACTORS
IN BUSINESS CYCLES

PART ONE

THEORETICAL APPROACH

The Nature of the Study

THE reader should be warned at the start that this study is not exclusively or mainly devoted to the current depression, but is a study of business cycles in general, as they have been experienced during the period for which fairly comprehensive and organized statistical records have been gathered. The special features of the present catastrophe are rather briefly dealt with in Part IV, and the trends of the post-War period leading up to it in Part III. By setting the crisis against the background of experience some well-founded idea may be gained of the extent to which it resembles other depressions, the extent to which its extraordinary severity and persistence are due to unique causes that may not reappear, and

3]

the extent to which they are due to changes in the economic system that introduce new elements with which we shall have to reckon in the future, and which may make future cycles more serious than those of the recent past. The peculiarly grave and threatening character of the present emergency needs no proof. As to how close it has brought us to a complete collapse of our economic system economists, like others, can only conjecture. When such questions can be definitely answered, it is always too late to make use of the answer.

The origin and purpose of this study have been explained in the introduction. The special objective assigned was the attempt to select, among the many factors involved in business cycles, a limited number which have especial strategic importance. The task is not primarily one of statistical description nor of statistical analysis in the usual sense. It is perhaps better described as an application of theoretical analysis to an unusually comprehensive array of concrete data. Thus, while the study deals with statistical materials, it makes no attempt to present a complete or voluminous statistical picture of the history of business cycles. Other studies of the latter character are under way; and it would be neither useful nor proper to attempt to duplicate or anticipate them.

In trying to pick out factors of special significance, the question arises on what basis significance is to be

[4

judged. It may be judged from the standpoint of an objective diagnosis seeking to learn what brings about the conditions we observe, and suffer from; or it may be judged with a more pragmatic eye to controlling these results. The two approaches are not wholly distinct, since results can often best be controlled indirectly, via their causes, and can never be controlled without taking these causes into the reckoning. But the ultimate purpose justifying such an investigation is to help toward doing something to improve conditions; and toward this end, causes we cannot control do not have the same grade of significance as those whose action we can modify. They still have to be reckoned with, but in a different and more limited fashion.

Let us say that variations of weather, acting on agriculture, cause changes in supplies of raw products; and that in our economic system these cause changes in prices and in demands for other products, and so play a part in the general business cycle. The weather itself we shall not, in the present state of our meteorological knowledge, attempt to control; but we may search the economic system for factors responsible for the economic disturbances that come about, changes in weather being taken for granted. And having found factors about which something can be done, we shall focus attention on them. The weather, if we could learn enough about it, might tell us how to time some of our safeguarding measures; but not what measures to take. Thus we may fairly say that the weather has only a secondary grade of significance. The possibility of control, then, is one of the keys—perhaps not the only one—to the human significance of causes. For this reason it will be kept in mind throughout our study. On the other hand, details as to ways and means of control are not our present concern. They constitute the next step.

The special purpose this study may serve can be expressed in another way. Theoretical studies give us causes that are too few and too simple, such as over-production, under-consumption, over-saving, or failure to distribute to laborers their whole product or enough of the whole product of industry to enable them to buy the things they have produced. Inductive studies, on the other hand, reveal so many factors at work, so completely interrelated, that we are likely to come to the conclusion that everything is both cause and effect, and everything is the result of nearly everything else, or that all features of modern industrialism are jointly responsible for the business cycle. The attempt in the present study is to steer a course between these two extremes, including anything which a well-rounded survey of the facts can suggest, but selecting those factors which seem to have the greatest strategic importance, if any can be picked out. A factor may be said to have strategic importance if it has real power to control other factors, and to determine the general character of the result; and it has peculiar strategic importance if, in addition, we have power to control it; if it is not, like the weather, beyond the reach of anything we can now do.

The field of study will be construed somewhat broadly. The most clearly marked cycles are relatively short wave-like movements of general business, which in this country vary from two to five years in length, with an average length of about forty months. But it would be arbitrary to limit our study to these short cycles and still more arbitrary to focus attention on their usual course. Differences between successive short cycles are important, and may yield evidence of the existence of longer cycles, or at least of longer movements. And any movements are significant which manifest phenomena similar to those that make the problem of business cycles such a serious one. Lack of equilibrium, unemployment and inability to use all of our existing powers of production, or even a reasonably large proportion of them —these are all properly parts of our study, in whatever forms we find them.

The materials upon which this essay is based are, for the most part, those collected by the National Bureau of Economic Research, together with studies made by a special staff consisting of members of this Bureau and others, engaged in an investigation of the cycle ending with the current great depression,

and working in collaboration with the Committee
on Recent Economic Changes. These studies have
been discussed in joint meetings of the special staff
and the Committee. Among the materials of the
National Bureau of Economic Research, the most
extensive use has been made of a set of series especially prepared on a common pattern devised by Dr.
Mitchell for the purpose of affording comparable
pictures of cycles of different lengths. A brief description is here given of the essential features of the
scheme on which these series were prepared. It is
necessarily somewhat difficult and technical, but the
reader is asked to be patient with it, since it is necessary to an understanding of the nature of the evidence underlying the main findings of this study.

More specifically, the object of these specially prepared series was to make possible a composite picture
of the average cyclical pattern of each single series—
pig iron production, car-loadings, etc.—in the face
of two outstanding difficulties. The first arose from
the very different lengths of the successive cycles of
general business, and the second from the further
fact that the single series have their own cycles which
do not agree exactly with the cycles of general business, and are also of different lengths.[1]

[1] For a brief description of these specially prepared series see the article
on "Business Cycles" by W. C. Mitchell in the *Encyclopedia of the Social
Sciences*. A fuller development will appear in Dr. Mitchell's forthcoming
second volume on *Business Cycles,* which will also be published by
the National Bureau of Economic Research. It would be clearly in-

[8

The problem of differing lengths of different
cycles is met by dividing each cycle up into the same
number of 'stages'. One of three months represents
the point at which the trough is reached and expansion begins, another of three months represents the
point at which the peak is reached and recession begins, while each individual expansion and recession
is arbitrarily divided into three equal parts, which
will of course be longer in a cycle of four years than
in one of two. Thus each cycle is divided into eight
stages, or nine if we include the revival which marks
the end of that cycle and the beginning of the next.
This is done both for the cycles of general business
and for the 'specific cycles' which appear in the particular series, and which do not have the same timing as the general business curve, though some of
them follow it very closely.

The movements of each series—for example, pig
iron production—are then tabulated in two ways.
First, the average rates of pig iron production in the
successive stages of the general business cycles are
recorded (in terms of percentages of the average

appropriate to publish these same tables and charts in the present
essay, and this may serve to explain why the evidence on which this
study rests is not presented in full. Short of this, the writer has endeavored to indicate the basis of his statements by describing the behavior of the series. And in order that such descriptions may be
understood, the character of these special series must be explained.
The reader who wishes fuller verification is referred to Dr. Mitchell's
forthcoming book.

9]

value for the cycle) and second, a similar record is made of the rates of pig iron production in the successive stages of the cycles marked off by the high and low points of pig iron production itself, which may not come at exactly the same times as the high and low points of general business. The second table gives the 'specific cycles' of pig iron production itself, while the first table gives the behavior of pig iron production during the successive phases of the 'reference cycle' or cycle of general business. Finally, the successive cyclical curves, both reference and specific, are averaged into a composite picture of average behavior for a series of cycles.

As a matter of interest we reproduce Dr. Mitchell's table of standard reference dates for the United States.[2] The dates, based upon a study of business annals and the best statistical indicators of business activity available, purport to show the month and year of successive revivals and recessions in general business activity. As Dr. Mitchell says:

> it cannot be claimed that the reference dates are more than fair approximations to the central points in a long succession of turns that occur in the economic activities of a nation.
>
> . . . . Quite apart from doubts whether we have made the best choices of reference dates, we recog-

2 *Recent Economic Changes*, II, 892 (National Bureau of Economic Research, 1929).

STANDARD REFERENCE DATES FOR BUSINESS CYCLES, UNITED STATES

| Expansion | | Contraction | | Duration in Months | | |
Revival	High	Recession	Low	Ex-pansion	Con-traction	Full Cycle
January 1855 to June	1857	July 1857 to December	1858	30	18	48
January 1859 to October	1860	November 1860 to June	1861	22	8	30
July 1861 to April	1865	May 1865 to December	1867	46	32	78
January 1868 to June	1869	July 1869 to December	1870	18	18	36
January 1871 to October	1873	November 1873 to March	1879	34	65	99
April 1879 to March	1882	April 1882 to May	1885	36	38	74
June 1885 to March	1887	April 1887 to April	1888	22	13	35
May 1888 to July	1890	August 1890 to May	1891	27	10	37
June 1891 to January	1893	February 1893 to June	1894	20	17	37
July 1894 to December	1895	January 1896 to June	1897	18	18	36
July 1897 to June	1899	July 1899 to December	1900	24	18	42
January 1901 to September	1902	October 1902 to August	1904	21	23	44
September 1904 to May	1907	June 1907 to June	1908	33	13	46
July 1908 to January	1910	February 1910 to January	1912	19	24	43
February 1912 to January	1913	February 1913 to December	1914	12	23	35
January 1915 to August	1918	September 1918 to April	1919	44	8	52
May 1919 to January	1920	February 1920 to September	1921	9	20	29
October 1921 to May	1923	June 1923 to July	1924	20	14	34
August 1924 to October	1926	November 1926 to December	1927	27	14	41
January 1928 to June	1929			18		

nize that recession and revival are changes in the condition of business which take much more than a month. They are not turning points, but turning periods. It is probable that on the average more than a year elapses from the time when the activities which respond most promptly to changes in business prospects turn upward or downward, to the time when the most sluggish activities respond to the changes which have already taken place in other parts of the economic system. To date one of these turns by a single month is therefore arbitrary. But we need some set of bench-marks in time by which to record the sequence in which the specific cycles of different business factors make their cyclical turns. The reference dates serve that purpose.

The specific cycles of pig iron production, for example, approximate so closely in respect of timing the cycles of general business that there is little difference in that respect between the two curves. But there are large discrepancies between the specific cycles of construction contracts or volume of stock exchange transactions and general business cycles. The former show large leads with peaks occurring, on the average, well ahead of the peaks of general business. And the fact that the peaks of the reference cycle curves for these series are considerably lower than the peaks of their own specific cycles registers

[12

the fact that their peaks occur at different stages of successive general business cycles. If there were a consistent and uniform lead, the amplitudes of the specific and reference cycles would be the same.

When such discrepancies appear, it is a signal to the student to turn from the composite pictures of average cycle patterns to a study of the behavior of the series cycle by cycle. Indeed, the writer has found it desirable to do this wherever it was a question of comparing the behavior of different factors which bear a vital relation to one another. For this purpose the writer has used the device of charting the behavior of one factor through a series of cycles, and below it the behavior of related factors through the same series of cycles. These charts themselves are not presented in this study, largely because the transition from one cycle to the next makes this type of chart confusing to the eye. The conclusions drawn from them are used, since they serve especially to show whether resemblances in the average cycle patterns of different series represent truly consistent behavior in which each single cycle exhibits the same resemblance. In what follows, attention is thus paid not merely to the average patterns but also to the variations from cycle to cycle.

Framework of a Theory

It may be worth while at the start to outline in the most general terms the form which the results of this study are to take, leaving it to later sections to put material into this framework. First, we should understand that there are no causes that are aboriginal in the sense that they have not themselves causes; but there are some that may be treated as originating forces for our purpose. There are, on the other hand, the responses of the business system in the form of rising or falling prices, the reaction of profits to changes in volume of production and of volume of production to changes in profits, the ordering of increased capital equipment to satisfy an increasing demand, etc. Some theories of business cycles run mainly in terms of originating forces, others in terms of the responses of the business system. It appears, however, that cycles cannot be regarded as results of one or the other of these groups of forces exclusively; they are joint results of the two groups and of their interaction.

The 'originating forces' are taken to include such things as wars, the effect of the weather on crops, certain elements in the processes of change in consumers' wants and, with some qualifications, inventions and the discovery of new goods. Secular changes in price-levels would be included, and especially deflections or changes in the direction or rate of change; together with the causes which bring them about.

It is necessary, however, to avoid confusing changes in consumers' wants, of an 'originating'

[14

character, with changes in effective demand in the market, or the development of invention of processes or goods with the rate at which these are actually installed, applied or exploited in industry. Changes in effective demand are mainly the results of the fact that in prosperous times people have more income to spend on new goods and more confidence to expand purchases on credit, and so buy more. These conditions result in turn from changes in the rate of productive activity. They are thus, in the main, part of the system of business responses. In the same way the rate at which new capital is actually invested in installing new types of equipment to utilize new inventions, and the rate at which new goods are marketed, or even the times when they are placed on the market, are all the results of the prospects of business profits, which vary with the varying phases of the business cycle itself.

The originating forces underlying these factors do not appear directly and unmodified in the statistical record, but they are nevertheless important. If they were acting on an economic structure with radically different types of response from those of the present form of business organization with its pseudo-individualism and its partial freedom of enterprise and limited competition, they would presumably produce results bearing little resemblance to those we now witness.

Even steadily progressive changes may be sources

of disturbance if the adjustments they make necessary are sluggish or encounter resistance, allowing pressures to accumulate until there is a more or less sudden giving way. It is possible that the great collapse of prices in the last three years is a case in point, representing the final breaking-down of resistances to the forces of post-War deflation, which may have been gathering strength progressively for seven or eight years previous to 1929. The resistances have taken various forms. There were measures for the valorization of specific commodities. Currencies were restored to a gold basis by the 'gold exchange' system, whereby multiple burdens were placed on the gold reserves of those countries whose exchanges were used as means of stabilization of the currencies of other countries. Systems of trade barriers and exchange restrictions have multiplied in a warfare of mutual defeat, ultimately ending in a general crippling of export markets for basic commodities entering into international trade.

Another possible case is the development of labor-saving machinery and processes. This has almost certainly made necessary larger adjustments than actually occurred in wages, in the length of the working day, in consumption and in the development of new goods. Such situations may give rise to recurrent disturbances of an equilibrium which was only apparent, and under cover of which tension had been increasing. This appears to have been happening,

[16

for example, throughout the period from 1922 to 1929. As another example, the great increase in durable goods used has, as we shall see, aggravated one of the most powerful elements of instability in our system, and may be responsible for a lasting change in the length and severity of business cycles.

The term 'originating' does not mean that the forces so described are necessarily of superior importance for the purposes of our study to the other group described as 'business responses'. Of the 'originating causes' some may be unavoidable, like the uncertainties of the weather, or even desirable in the sense that it would not be desirable to take the steps which would in practice be necessary in order to remove them, like the irregularities inseparable from invention. On the other hand, the factors concerned with the responses of the business system may be the factors we can change, and so utilize as working causes in the attempt to improve conditions.

Furthermore, it seems almost certain at the start that the factors which account for the effects of disturbances taking the particular forms they do, and producing cycles with their fairly rhythmic swings, will be factors concerned with the responses of the business system. We have apparently had cycles just as long as we have had this type of business system.[3]

[3] See Wesley C. Mitchell, *Business Cycles: The Problem and Its Setting* (National Bureau of Economic Research, 1927) Chapter II.

17]

Moreover, some of the originating causes, such as wars and crops, clearly do not follow the same rhythm as the shorter business cycles; as to the others, there is no sufficient reason for thinking that they do, and every reason for thinking that they do not. Some new inventions mature very quickly, others slowly, while major developments in the way of new wants may require from a decade to a generation to reach their full potentialities. If these forces produce the familiar business cycles, or play a part in producing them, it is because they are acting on a particular kind of business system, which reacts to them in particular ways. As already remarked, on a different system they would have different effects. Our examination of the detailed statistical materials affords no reason for modifying this conclusion.

As revealed by these studies, the responses of the business system seem to form a closely-knit sequence of cause and effect, in which a state of over-contraction appears to set in motion forces leading to over-expansion, and this in turn to over-contraction once more. In these swings, movements tend to be self-reinforcing rather than self-limiting, until they have gone so far that a marked reversal becomes inevitable. This is so true that it has proved possible to construct theories of the self-generation of business cycles by the business machinery itself, which have more verisimilitude and have gained wider acceptance than those theories which interpret the timing

[18

of the cycle as wholly governed by outside originating causes, such as weather. And in any case these latter theories, granting their truth, cannot explain the particular characteristics of the cycle without reference to the system of business responses. Sunspots might affect human affairs in a variety of ways, but only in collaboration with a particular business system could they conceivably bring about stock exchange booms or widespread unemployment among construction workers.

Whether the theories of self-generation are true or not it is not necessary at this time to discover. There are always independent disturbing influences at work, and they modify the resulting course of events. But it is significant that there is much less variation in business cycles than in the outside influences which act upon them. Major or minor wars, in which the country in question is either a belligerent or a neutral, expanding or contracting domestic farm production coordinated with like or unlike movements of foreign production, upward or downward secular price trends—all these occur in an indefinite variety of combinations, while the new goods and new processes which form the foci of successive waves of expansion change from decade to decade. But at whatever varied points and in whatever varied forms such 'outside' factors have their first impact on the business system, the resultant is to initiate or modify expansions and contrac-

19]

tions which spread rapidly through the system as a whole, and which produce very similar symptoms. Cyclical movements of prices go on through rising or falling secular trends, though the relative lengths of the upward and downward cyclical movements are affected. Basic industries, factory employment, general retail and wholesale trade, credit and securities markets—all show essentially similar movements. All this argues that the responses of the business system are more important in determining the results than the particular character of the original disturbances, even if one grants provisionally that without some kind of outside disturbance business cycles would not be initiated in the first place, or would not continue their more or less regular succession of ups and downs.

The indicated probability is that the average period of these upward and downward swings is determined by the character of business responses, for example, the time required to finance capital expansions and to construct new factory units or new apartment buildings. The variations in the timing of these movements appear to arise partly from changes in the conditions governing these responses directly, and partly from the random behavior of the outside or originating causes. We must also not forget the possibility that certain types of response may have different periods from others, with the result that changes in the timing and

[20

severity of cycles may be in part due to the varying conjunctures of responses with different normal periods. For example, among the more mechanical features having to do with the construction of capital equipment and the using up of stocks of goods, some of the more important may have periods the combination of which tends naturally to produce a cycle of about 40 months, while the more violent psychological brainstorms represented by the stock market mania of 1929 and the 'new era' delusion which went with it, and similar waves in the past, may require more time to work up their full momentum—perhaps something like ten years. They are, of course, subject to interruption by such outside disturbances as wars.

In general, the 'originating' causes may be provisionally assumed to have two effects. The first is to keep the responses of the business system from dwindling away to zero, in case they would naturally do so in time if left to themselves. Whether they would do so or not is impossible to prove and is in any case non-essential, since it is not allowed to happen. There are continually-renewed disturbing impulses. The second presumptive effect of these 'originating' causes is to induce variations in the timing and severity of the resulting cycles.

Within this framework of theory, itself subject to modification as we proceed, we may search for causal factors of peculiar significance. They may be defined as those which, by variations in their characteristic behavior, can bring about significant differences in the course of business prosperity and depression. The ones most worthy of study are those which actually do vary, or which could be made to vary—in other words, are subject to control. The most useful thing to find would be an element which was always present, whose behavior made a vital difference to the resulting course of business, and which could be controlled. But if a factor is always present, and regularly behaves in the same way, it becomes impossible to determine its significance by the inductive method of observing the difference that is made according as it is present or absent or varies in its behavior. As a result, the more abstract theoretical method may become necessary. And among factors that are not always present, or that vary their behavior from cycle to cycle, the multitude of factors and variations is so great, and the number of systematically observed cycles so small, that the methods commonly characterized as inductive face almost insuperable difficulties in attempting to isolate the significance of particular factors by correlating their variations with variations in the course of business. The data appear to be just approaching the state in which such methods, handled with the utmost care, may yield some useful results with respect to a few among the many questions which the business cycle raises.

[22

PART TWO

TYPICAL CYCLE PATTERNS

―――――

Introduction

THE statistical record of business cycles, voluminous as it is, is still too incomplete to afford a systematic test of all the principal theories and the principal causal factors suggested by them. If we wish to test the theory of over-production in a literal form, the figures for stocks of goods are not sufficiently complete or systematic for the purpose; they merely afford suggestions. If we shift to the theory of under-consumption, figures of consumers' purchases are even more fragmentary.[1] If we go on to theories of under-saving or over-saving, or the theory of discrep-

―――――

[1] An adequate test of this theory would require other data also. But figures of consumers' purchases, if not alone sufficient for the purpose, are clearly necessary.

ancies between saving and investment, we find that real figures of savings are almost non-existent, since the data on savings bank deposits represent too small and too special a fraction of this flow to have great significance, and issues of new securities afford only indirect evidence. Data on the spending of savings for actual goods are also not sufficiently complete and detailed to be useful in checking any theory that rests upon a discrepancy between this very large flow and another about equally large. Figures of production are far more satisfactory, as are those on international trade and on banking, though in the latter the difficulty is one of interpretation, since credit issued for different purposes has very different meanings. It may be supporting a boom, or extending first aid to victims of a crisis. Hence any suggestions as to the more significant causal factors derived from the statistical records must not be regarded as exhaustive; one must expect rather that other factors will be added by the development of more complete records, if this development can outrun the impatience of industrial nations to do something decisive to remove or control the phenomenon under examination.

Another difficulty is that of establishing causal importance in a bare record of a sequence of events such as the one before us. Not only are no two cycles exactly alike; no two are alike in all but one probable causal factor; so that it is impossible to

establish the causal effect of any one factor exactly
by the method of formal induction. And if it were
possible, we should have only a record of this factor
in connection with a particular combination of
other factors; with a different combination its effect
would in all probability be different. Hence the
scrutiny of the record, by itself, will yield suggestions rather than proof.

Perhaps the chief evidence as to which are the
disturbing factors in the record is presented by two
characteristics of the series: their timing and their
relative amplitude of fluctuation. Series whose up-
and down-turns consistently precede those in other
series are suspect as having some causal significance,
if they are of such a character as to make this interpretation rational. And series that consistently fluctuate much more violently than the rest are similarly
suspect, on the same terms. In addition, factors
whose behavior is irregular are not to be ignored,
if there is any basis for judging their effect.

Indeed, a study of business cycles may be divided
into two inquiries: a search for the universal factors
and another search for the occasional ones. Or we
may search for the causes applicable to all cycles
and then search separately for the factors responsible for the mildness of some and the severity of
others. In advance, it is impossible to tell which
inquiry is the more significant; but at any rate, the
second is not to be ignored.

25]

The Factor of Timing: Introduction [2]

In studying leads and lags, it is almost inevitable to use the general 'reference cycle', or period of expansion and contraction of general business conditions, as a common standard in terms of which to report the relative timing of the various series. But it is also necessary to remember that this 'reference cycle' is after all only a composite picture; and that in all strictness the significant factor is the relation of the timing of each series to that of all the other specific series with which it may have some fairly direct connection. A series with an unusually large lead, however, with respect to the reference cycle, by that fact must have a lead over most of the specific series that go to make it up.

In this study of timing one result which stands out is that, of the series presenting the movements in various forms of production, those whose timing agree most closely with that of the 'general business' cycle are, for the most part, the so-called 'basic industries'—pig iron, steel ingots, coke, machine-tool shipments and producers' goods in general. Production of consumers' goods shows more variation from

2 In dealing with leads and lags, the writer has, with one exception, based his conclusions on the three-month periods marking the stages of recession and of recovery already referred to (see pp. 8ff. above). This was done in preference to using the highest and lowest single months, chiefly because the latter procedure involves difficulties with double peaks, and does not do justice to the difference between short, sharp peaks and lower but longer ones.

[26

the general cycle, while the movements of agricultural production show little or no relation to it. This may, of course, be a comment on the importance attached to these 'basic industries' in fixing the dates of the general business cycle; but even so, the conclusion is, not that these basic industries are given undue weight, but rather that their fluctuations are so much more pronounced than the average that they, with other series moving in sympathy with them, tend to dominate those series whose timing is radically different. This conclusion is strengthened by the fact that they move in closer agreement with each other than do other series. They· seem justly to assume a place of central importance in the general business cycle.

Timing: Construction

The largest and some of the most clearly prevailing leads are found in the construction industry, as exhibited in building permits issued and contracts let. Their movements are followed, with minor discrepancies, by the production of structural steel, Portland cement, oak flooring, baths and lavatories— in short, materials and products serving the construction industry.

The average cycle pattern for construction contracts awarded shows a clear lead of a quarter-cycle at down-turns and a larger lead at up-turns. There are, however, marked differences of behavior be-

27]

tween different cycles, and between different sections of the industry. Industrial construction shows the most regular timing, most nearly synchronous with the general business cycle, and the largest amplitudes of fluctuation. It manifests a tendency to lead on the up-turn but not on the down-turn. Commercial construction also manifests no tendency to lead on the down-turn but shows an average lead of more than a quarter-cycle at the up-turn, of the three general business cycles in which commercial construction manifests a definite trough. In the last two cycles there is no trough deserving the name, one exhibiting almost continuous rise and the other almost continuous decline. Commercial construction is thus more irregular than industrial, showing less conformity to the general business cycle, and also has milder cyclical fluctuations. Public works and utilities (recorded for two cycles only) manifest no tendency to lead or lag.

Residential construction has the largest irregularities, particularly in the last two cycles, combined with a large average lead. In residential contracts awarded (value, recorded for five cycles, 1915-31) there seems to be a clear tendency to an average lead of a quarter-cycle, though with a considerable dispersion around this average. It is this tendency which is mainly responsible for the tendency of total construction to lead general business, and entirely responsible for the tendency to lead at the peak. In

[28

the last cycle the curve of residential construction has no real peak, only a brief and slight interruption of its downward swing. It shares with commercial construction the responsibility for the peculiar behavior of the combined construction series in the last two cycles, the first showing an almost uninterrupted rise and the second an almost uninterrupted decline.

The grand resultant is a composite curve characterized by considerable irregularity. The behavior of total contracts awarded during the general business cycles of 1912-14 and 1915-19 is fairly regular, leading the curve of general business by a few months, and showing a rise in the final years which appears to record mainly the effect of the War on money values, rather than an increased physical volume. In the next cycle, that of 1919-21, construction has a double peak, better described as a plateau occupying the entire expansion and the down-turn stage of general business, the subsequent up-turns occurring mid-way of the general business contraction. The cycle of 1921-24 shows a mild peak or plateau occupying the latter part of the general business expansion, and a higher, briefer peak mid-way of the general business contraction. Of the last two cycles, 1924-27 and 1927-32, the former shows a rise throughout and the latter a decline throughout, both interrupted by a mild peak occurring at the same time as the down-turn of general business.

29]

In the latter cycle, of course, these series do not show a definitive end of the phase of contraction.

To sum up: in two cycles construction reaches its peak some time before the peak in general business activity; in one there is a double peak or plateau extending over the entire business expansion; in one a mild peak somewhat before the peak in general business activity and a higher peak mid-way of general business contraction; and in the last two there are mild construction peaks at the peak of general business activity, superimposed upon a larger movement upward throughout the 1924-27 cycle and downward throughout the succeeding cycle. Thus construction reached a major peak during the very mild depression of general business that separated the last two cycles. The peak of construction and the trough of general business both appeared in mid-winter of 1927-28 (it must be remembered that these cyclical movements are reckoned after the seasonal fluctuation, with its pronounced winter decline in construction, has been eliminated). The unusual behavior of construction at this time may have been responsible for the fact that this depression of general business was so unusually mild. The typical pattern, barring the exceptional features of the last two cycles, shows a peak or plateau somewhere in the expansion phase of general business, and a lead of about a quarter-cycle on the subsequent up-turn.

[30

In the total figures two features stand out. One is the tendency to lead, which would be more plainly evident if cyclical movements were measured as departures from secular trends. The other is the ten-year wave which dwarfs the three short-cycle movements from 1921 to 1931. This wave manifests itself in the fact that the various series of all sorts quite typically have a descending trend in this present cycle: a slight rise and a large drop; whereas they typically showed the reverse in the two preceding cycles: a large rise and a slight drop. Industrial construction, however, appears to be dominated by the short-cycle movements rather than by this ten-year wave. The irregular or random forces (from the standpoint of the short-cycle) would appear to have acted mainly on branches of construction other than industrial.

The behavior of production and sales of structural steel, Portland cement, oak flooring, baths and lavatories is consistent with that of building contracts, showing in general a considerable lead, and larger activity on the up-swing of the general cycle than on the down-swing. A tabulation of leads and lags as compared with what seems in each case the most relevant construction-series indicates a fairly normal distribution, with more than one-third of the down-turns and up-turns synchronous with those of the relevant construction series, and lags very

31]

slightly more numerous than leads.[3] A similar tabulation of leads and lags as compared with the general business cycle (omitting the two last cycles as abnormal) again shows more than one-third of the cases synchronous while in nearly all the rest the construction material leads. Again the tendency to lead is clear. Incidentally, these construction materials suggest the ramified effects of building activity.

To sum up, the large lead in construction activity suggests strongly that this industry has a peculiar causal significance. The irregularities of its behavior indicate that there are 'originating causes' at work, mainly outside the field of industrial construction. This last follows the timing of the general business curve more closely and regularly, but the great intensity of its fluctuations still indicates a peculiar causal importance (to be discussed in the following section). The lead it exhibits on the up-turn, though not on the down-turn, is also highly significant. And the peculiarities of the behavior of construction during the last three cycles, taken together, suggest that it may be one of the industries which, at times at least, follows longer cycles than those of general business and is only slightly modified by these shorter business cycles; and that in any case the variations

[3] For example, Portland cement was correlated with public works and utilities, also with industrial construction; baths and lavatories were correlated with residential construction; structural steel with total construction.

in its behavior from one general business cycle to another may be one of the important influences determining the differences between these cycles themselves. It is worth noting also that residential construction—which is in the class of consumption goods—shows the largest and most frequent lead, as well as the greatest irregularity, so that the evidence of an originating causal role—so far as we can speak of such a matter in this connection—is strongest for this section of the industry.

This pattern of behavior is not difficult to rationalize on theoretical grounds. It is a phase of the general principle of intensified fluctuations of derived demand for durable goods. That is, demand for new supplies of durable goods fluctuates more intensely than demand for the current services these durable goods render. This principle we shall encounter at several points in the following discussion and it is therefore worth stating with some fullness.

The basic force at work can best be seen in a simplified example.[4] If there is a stock of 100,000 units of some durable commodity with a life of twenty years and a secular rate of increase of 4 per

---

[4] The writer has developed this principle in Business Acceleration and the Law of Demand, *Journal of Political Economy*, XXV, 217-35, March, 1917; also in *Economics of Overhead Costs* (University of Chicago Press, 1923), pp. 389-94. Cf. also criticism by Ragnar Frisch, Capital Production and Consumer-Taking and subsequent discussion with the writer: *Journal of Political Economy*, October, December, 1931, April, 1932.

cent per year (figured in compound-interest fashion), then to maintain that rate of increase for the current year will require about 7,360 new units: about 3,360 for replacing those built twenty years previous and 4,000 to furnish the current year's increase. The previous year's output, on the same basis, would have been 7,077 units. Now if in the current year the stock increases by 8 instead of 4 per cent, current output will have to be 11,360, which is 54 per cent above the 7,360 which we may call 'normal' for the year, and 60 per cent above the previous year's output. On the other hand, if in the current year the stock increases, but by 3.717 per cent instead of 4 per cent, current output will not increase over that of the previous year. If the stock increases by a less amount, current output will decline. If the stock is barely maintained, current output will shrink to 3,360, which is 54 per cent below normal and 52½ per cent below that of the previous year. If the stock is allowed to decrease 3.36 per cent by failure to make replacements, current output will shrink to zero. Evidently a change in the growth of the stock, representing a change in the growth of the rate of use, calls for a much more intense change in the current production of the commodity.

If the commodity is shorter-lived, like an automobile, and the element of replacement is correspondingly larger, the principle remains the same, but the quantities are different. If we have a stock of 100,000

[34

automobiles in the hands of users, with a life of seven years and increasing at an annual rate of 10 per cent, then normal production for the current year is about 20,500; about 10,500 to replace those made seven years previous, and 10,000 to provide for normal increase. The previous year's normal production would have been something over 18,600. Then if the rate of increase of the stock rose to 20 per cent, the current output would rise to 30,500, which is 49 per cent above normal and 64 per cent above the previous year's output. If the rate of increase of the stock declines from 10 to 8.1 per cent, increase of current output will cease entirely. If the stock ceases to increase, current output will fall to 10,500 which is 49 per cent below normal and 44 per cent below the previous year's output. If the stock decreases 10.5 per cent through the cessation of all replacements, current output shrinks to zero. Here again fluctuations in the movement of the stock give rise to intensified fluctuations of current output, though the intensification is less marked.

One of the most significant features of this relationship is that it is not necessary for the stock of goods to decrease in order to bring about a decrease of current output. A moderate decrease in the rate of growth is sufficient.

The actual behavior of production as affected by this principle is complicated by several other factors. One thing which is likely to happen is a temporary reduction in the rate of scrapping, because old units are kept in service longer. This means that the existing stock of goods suffers a decline in average quality because the average age of the units has increased. To the extent that retirements are postponed in dull times or speeded up in active times, the result is an even greater intensification in the movements of current output corresponding to given fluctuations in the number of units in service.

By way of illustrating the operation of these factors, the production of automobiles decreased from 5,621,715 in 1929 to 1,431,494 in 1932, while the number of registrations, taken as an indication of changes in number of cars in service (though slightly overstating the absolute numbers) declined from 26,545,281 to 24,136,879.[5] Thus a decline of nearly 75 per cent in annual production corresponded to a decline of only a little over 9 per cent in total number in use. If figures were available showing the number of cars which merely stood unlicensed in the owners' garages or backyards, the total number might show no decrease at all, although production had gone on at a rate far below a normal replacement basis in 1931 and 1932.

Furthermore, while retirements of cars from use, as deduced from licenses taken out, did not actually

[5] See *Facts and Figures of the Automobile Industry, 1933*, published by the National Automobile Chamber of Commerce.

decline during the depression years, they did fall far behind the rates of production recorded seven years previous, when the cars were being produced which would normally have been retired during 1930-32. During 1928 and 1929 the reverse was the case, retirements exceeding the production of seven years previous. Thus during the boom the average age of cars decreased somewhat through a relative speeding-up of retirements, while during the depression average age increased through an opposite movement. The same effect appears to a less extent in comparing retirements for 1924 and 1925. The essential figures are shown in the accompanying table.[6]

Another complication arises because fluctuations in demand for products or services are not instantly followed by the precisely appropriate fluctuations in stocks and current output of the durable goods required as means to make the products or render the services. There are lags, errors of estimate and competitive duplications of apparent demand, which play a role in the actual outcome, and the changes in demand are themselves complex, partly causes and partly results. They are partly matters of chang-

[6] *Facts and Figures of the Automobile Industry, 1933.* An accurate estimate of normal retirements should, of course, be based on a distributed lag, rather than on production in one year only. This would not, however, change the essential showing on the point at issue, the chief effect being to make the comparison of retirements in 1924 and 1925 less striking.

PRODUCTION AND SCRAPPING OF AUTOMOBILES

	Production for domestic market	Total scrapped or replacements	Excess or deficiency of scrappings. Cf. production of 7th year previous
1917............	1,793,792		
1918............	1,123,515		
1919............	1,850,982		
1920............	2,051,164		
1921............	1,555,984		
1922............	2,417,587		
1923............	3,799,788		
1924............	3,310,018	1,151,381	—642,411
1925............	3,837,841	1,670,337	+546,822
1926............	3,908,854	1,824,230	—26,752
1927............	2,935,577	2,110,214	+59,050
1928............	3,776,583	2,516,868	+960,884
1929.´..........	4,625,354	2,772,838	+355,251
1930............	2,950,980	2,884,228 *	—915,560
1931............	2,148,917	2,904,262 *	—405,756
1932............	1,251,205	2,900,000 *	—937,841

ing taste, but their cyclical fluctuations are mainly dependent on fluctuations in incomes, which in turn reflect fluctuations in productive activity, thus completing a vicious circle. The sensitiveness of different commodities to such changes in income depends partly on their durability and partly on the degree to which they represent necessities or luxuries.

Building construction, for example, is both a necessity and a luxury; but as there are always sufficient buildings to house the population in some fashion, current additions are concerned mainly with

* The compilers note that these figures may include cars merely stored.

the relative luxury element of more adequate and modern accommodations. And for the same reason the time when any given house-dweller enlarges his accommodations is peculiarly optional, liable to epidemics of postponement, or to concentrations which bring about particularly active seasons of building. A dwelling is also customarily rented or bought on credit; consequently the ability to pay an additional $50 for rent this month, together with confidence in the continuation of this happy state, can give rise to a demand involving an immediate expenditure of, let us say, $6,000 in construction. In fact, the increase in construction may be more than this, if we take into account the possibility of building in excess of demand, causing some of the older accommodations to stand vacant and making the total amount of additional investment in housing construction perhaps materially larger than the increase in capital cost or value of accommodations which tenants are actually occupying and paying rent on.

On the other hand, if there is at the moment an over-supply left from a recession immediately preceding, the first increase in demand may not absolutely necessitate any new building in order to satisfy it. However, even in such an event, the existing buildings will not be entirely up to date, and the demand for housing of this character will call for some new construction. It will also stimulate work of repair and remodelling as well as speculative building in advance of demand, both of which tend to fall behind their normal condition in a depression. Moreover, the areas in which the recovery of demand is strongest are not likely to coincide exactly with those in which previous activity has left the largest over-supplies. Thus a revival of demand is likely to produce a considerable immediate effect on construction work, even though there may be in the aggregate a considerable amount of vacant space, and even though the full effect of the revival may not be felt until this over-supply has been considerably reduced.

Thus a given increase or decrease in consumer-demand for housing, measured by the income the consumer stands ready to devote currently to this purpose, naturally results under ordinary conditions in a much larger increase or decrease in volume of expenditures on the production of the goods that are to satisfy that demand. This outcome may, of course, be modified if reviving demand finds a considerable surplus already on hand. It naturally requires, further, that the construction industry shall have sources of funds to carry on the work: funds whose increase or decrease is not limited by the movements of consumers' income. This requisite is supplied by an elastic credit system. Easy credit, combined with an optimistic and speculative spirit, may tend to push expansion beyond its logical proportions as dictated by actual demand.

[40

Finally, as partial explanation of the *lead* in construction work, we should note that the demand for construction in excess of replacements is logically the heaviest, not when consumers' incomes are the largest, but somewhere near the time when they are *increasing fastest*. Thus a lead of approximately a quarter-cycle in construction work, as compared with the general course of consumers' incomes, is logical even if construction does not anticipate the growth of demand but merely synchronizes with it. Even if it really lags a trifle behind its logical timing, it can still show a substantial lead in its actual peaks and troughs. Thus a boom in construction may be at one and the same time a result of recovery in consumers' incomes from a low point and a cause of further recovery through the increased spending power arising from the increased volume of work done. This does not preclude, of course, the possibility of increased construction work being undertaken as a result of optimism and a general speculative spirit, giving rise to a greater readiness to build ahead of current requirements. The same considerations apply, in the reverse direction, to the process of recession.

This principle, as already noted, is a general one applying, *mutatis mutandis,* to all durable goods and to capital equipment. In the latter case, however, another step is involved. An increase in output of consumers' goods has, in addition to the work of

41]

making them, a further effect in the shape of a demand for more capital equipment, if existing equipment is not in every way adequate. This demand for capital equipment fluctuates more intensely than the output of the goods it serves to produce; but the total amount involved is likely to be much smaller; the average annual expenditures for replacement and extension of capital equipment are likely to be not more than, for example, 10 to 20 per cent of the annual output of the goods they serve to make.[7] A change from a 3 to a 6 per cent annual increase in the output of the commodity might cause as much as a 40 or 50 per cent increase in the smaller figure representing the requirements for production of capital equipment, and a change from a 6 to a 3 per cent annual increase in the commodity might cause a corresponding decline in the requirements for output of durable means of production. In the case of capital equipment, also, the existence of excess capacity at the moment when revival begins is likely to have more effect in retarding the revival of the derived demand than in the case of residential construction. Equipment can often produce up-to-date goods even though it is not itself completely up to date, or can do so with minor changes. Production of goods entering into general capital equipment, as

[7] The precise figure is not essential. The ratio between total output of capital goods and consumers' goods clearly falls between these limits.

we shall see, shows the phenomenon of intensified fluctuation but not the large lead that characterizes construction work.

A further and very significant feature of this principle is that it does not require, to bring it into operation, that the original movements of ultimate consumers' demand shall be actual alternations of rise and fall. Fluctuations in the rate of growth are sufficient to start the process of intensification. These may then cause absolute rises and falls in the work of supplying the demand, or of supplying the durable equipment needed. And these in turn naturally bring about absolute rises and falls in total consumers' purchasing power, with resulting rises and falls in the actual observed demand for commodities in general. Thus this principle is of peculiar strategic importance in explaining how alternate rises and falls can be generated out of tendencies whose original form and character need not contain any positive shift from upward to downward movements. It may also be of some help in explaining the duration of the swings, in view of the time required for equipment to catch up with growing demand, or for demand to catch up with equipment. This matter of duration will be left for further study, when we shall be in a position to build this principle, as one element, into a more rounded theory. It does not in itself suffice to explain all the observed movements, and its action is clearly modified by other factors.

Timing: Durable Luxury Goods

Another class of goods exhibiting some lead as compared to the general business cycle is that of durable luxury goods. For the purpose in hand this group may be broadened to include goods which may not in themselves be clearly luxuries, but which are of such a character that the buying of a new one at a given time to replace an old one which could be made to serve longer might fairly be classed as a luxury purchase in a considerable proportion of cases. The dominant commodity of this class is passenger automobiles, for the production of which monthly data are available. Some slight indications, however, point to the conclusion that fur coats and some other goods of this class behave in a somewhat similar way. However, not all these other commodities are bought on the installment plan to the extent that automobiles are, and hence effective demand is not so free to expand beyond present realized income. A given increase in consumers' current willingness to pay does not have the opportunity to cause to the same degree an intensified increase in gross production and sales of the goods themselves.

Passenger automobiles, like houses, are both a luxury and a necessity, though the luxury element

[44

is presumably larger. The high-priced car is clearly a luxury; but so also are many replacements of moderate-priced cars, when made earlier than necessary. One would normally expect hard times to bring about a shift of demand from higher-priced to cheaper cars, coupled with a general postponing of replacements and new purchases. The purchase of a car is postponable; probably to a greater degree even than the provision of housing space. Most new cars are bought to replace used cars which still have a considerable amount of wear left in them. And if the car is a first purchase, the owner could usually get on a while longer as he had previously, without a car.

Furthermore, the credit system of purchase may bring it about that a given increase in consumers' monthly income devoted to this purpose can furnish the basis for a much larger immediate increase in effective demand for the product. This may ramify into a further increase in consumers' incomes before the original purchaser has liquidated his original obligation. If demand were steady, of course, the monthly flow of income into the payment of installments due would balance the monthly volume of new sales; but any fluctuation brings about a discrepancy, and the essence of this problem is fluctuations, especially the way in which initial fluctuations —which may arise from an indefinite variety of causes—produce cumulative effects which may bring about consistently repeated cycles of general business activity. If the volume of installment credit is increasing, purchases are exceeding the volume of income currently absorbed by them; and *vice versa,* when outstanding installment credit is being liquidated. And either condition tends to give rise to a self-reinforcing movement. Purchases in excess of income tend to increase income somewhere in the economic system, via increasing production, while if purchases fall short of income, this tends to reduce income somewhere in the system by reducing production.

In any case, production and sales of passenger automobiles show not only fluctuations decidedly more intense than the average, but also a decided lead as compared with the general business cycle. The average lead is 3.8 months at the peak and 3.3 months at the trough, but in one cycle out of four recorded there is a lag of 7 months at the peak. Trucks show still more violent fluctuations and a decidedly smaller lead, especially at the peak. Here the prior impulse seems to come from consumers' goods.

The principle of a derived demand dependent on the *rate of growth* of the primary demand applies here as in housing, though to a less extent, since the stabilizing element of need for replacements is a larger part of the picture. Automobiles, being shorter-lived than houses, come that much nearer the type of currently consumed goods, and the ele-

[46

ments of lead, and of intensification of fluctuations, would therefore both logically be less marked.

Timing: Consumers' Goods in General

Evidences of leads and lags as between consumers' and producers' goods in general are probably too slight to support conclusions as to definitely established patterns of behavior; but they do point in certain directions. The Standard Statistics Corporation's index of general industrial production shows a lead at the down-turn in two out of five cycles, as compared with the general business cycle, and a lead at the up-turn, also in two cycles out of five, while the various samples of retail sales point, on the whole, to a slight tendency to lag. Wholesale trade, with some irregularities, seems on the whole to move a trifle more promptly than retail trade; while the volume of production of consumers' goods shows some indications of moving more promptly than either wholesale trade or the production of producers' goods. It exhibits a clear lead of several months in the series compiled by Dr. Leong and this is quite consistent from cycle to cycle.[8] To repeat, these indications are too slight and characterized by too many irregularities to afford a basis for definitive conclusions.

[8] See "A Comparative Study of the Indexes of Production," *Journal of the American Statistical Association*, September, 1932, pp. 256-69, for a published version of this study, which version is not, however, put into the form of 'reference cycles' and 'specific cycles'.

47]

These observations, as far as they go, tend to the conclusion that general consumer demand does not lead, but follows the movements in production of consumers' goods—that it moves up or down mainly because changes in the rate of production have increased or decreased the current purchasing power of the workers. This would leave the causes of the movements of production still to be explained. There is also clear indication that the relations of retail to wholesale trade, and of wholesale trade to production of the goods dealt in, are affected by fluctuations in dealers' stocks, and that dealers begin to go cautiously before the actual down-turn of consumers' buying. This is adequate to explain the lead shown by production of consumers' goods; and would also tend logically to make production fluctuate somewhat more than retail sales. But in view of the irregularities in the series, the inference that this happens in every cycle would be, to say the least, premature.

Production of producers' goods might logically show a similar lead but does not. This may be taken to indicate that the tendency to lead is neutralized by the lag due to the time required to finance and carry through capital expansions, and to carry output to completion.

It seems clear that we have at least two forces at work at the same time, playing into each other's hands, so to speak, and modifying or reinforcing each other's action. Consumers' buying power depends on the rate of production: this is an ever-present and dominant factor from which there is no escape. Movements of dealers' stocks are less certain and regular. They may strengthen this major force or may partly neutralize it, but on the whole it seems probable that their effect tends to increase disturbances. When dealers buy faster than they sell, production tends to move faster than retail sales, and this is likely to mean that people are receiving more income than they are spending, and can promptly increase their expenditures, with cumulative effects.

Neither the records of consumers' income nor those of retail purchases are sufficiently complete to make possible a conclusion as to whether either leads the other. Movements of industrial payrolls seem to synchronize quite closely with those of retail sales. Industrial payrolls may be presumed to be more prompt in their movements than salaries or interest and dividend disbursements; and on this ground it might be presumed that total consumers' income lags somewhat behind the movements of retail sales, rather than leading them. But this would be conjecture, rather than a definitely indicated conclusion. Expenditure of income from speculative dealings in securities might well reverse it. Verification must await more complete figures. Of the fig-

49]

ures available, many cover too few cycles to be very significant.

Timing: Industrial Production and Prices, Employment and Payrolls

Physical production of consumers' goods appears to reach its peaks and troughs ahead of the corresponding movements of prices. Producers' goods do not exhibit this phenomenon in unmistakable form, but they have another characteristic which bears a close family relationship to a lead. Physical production has its most rapid increase in the first part of the up-swing, the rate slowing down before the peak is reached, while the financial volume of production is swollen by rising prices at a fairly uniform rate throughout the rise. Not all producers' goods show this phenomenon; bituminous coal production increases more rapidly in the final phases of the up-swing, anthracite coal shows an even rate of increase throughout, and coke shows only a mildly greater rise in the early phases of the up-turn than in the later. Zinc shows an even rate of increase, lead behaves rather ambiguously, while oak flooring, lavatories and baths show a lead at peak and trough rather than any changes in the rates of increase or decrease during expansion or contraction. Pig iron production (observed for 13 cycles), steel ingots (3 cycles), copper (8 cycles), Portland cement (3 cycles), and machine-tool shipments (4 specific cycles

[50

covering 5 reference cycles) all show a more rapid increase in the earlier stages of the expansion period. Fabricated structural steel shows both a lead and a more rapid increase in the early stages of the expansion period. The general curve of industrial production also shows a definite tendency toward a greater rise in the early stages of the expansion period.

Figures of factory employment seem to show a similar tendency toward greater increase in the early phases of the expansion in the average cycle pattern, except for the Federal Reserve Board's series, covering only three cycles. But this behavior is not consistent from cycle to cycle, and hence cannot be regarded as a well-established feature of the typical cycle. One might anticipate a less marked tendency in this direction in these employment series, presumably because they include consumers' goods. Payrolls, on the other hand, show on the whole the opposite tendency; that is, they increase slightly more rapidly in the later stages of expansion, and decrease slightly more rapidly in the later stages of contraction. These tendencies do not appear in all cases. But in the New York State factory employment and payroll indexes, where the figures are presumably comparable, covering the same four cycles, employment shows a large and definite tendency to rise more rapidly in the early phases of expansion, and payrolls a small but definite tendency to rise more

51]

rapidly in the later phases of expansion, indicating probably a considerable lag in the response of wage rates. This is complicated, however, by the factor of part-time and over-time. A more widespread policy of splitting up employment by shortened work-days in dull times might alter the character of this curve. Numbers employed would be prevented from falling so low in mid-depression; and hence would naturally not rise so steeply in the early stages of expansion. Thus the shape of the curve might be reversed. But this policy does not seem to have been carried far enough to transform the curve, in the recorded cycles.

This behavior of payrolls sheds some light on the theory that depressions are due to a failure of industry to increase its distribution of incomes as fast as its output of consumers' goods. Apparently there is such a discrepancy during the up-swing of the business cycle, but it is on the whole slightly greater during the early part of the rise than during the later part. If this is an important factor in bringing on the recession it must be delayed in its action, being temporarily neutralized perhaps by expansion of stocks and perhaps by expansion of credit, so that its effect comes to a head when these neutralizing factors have exhausted themselves.

The question arises: do these facts indicate that producers' goods have greater initiatory importance than consumers' goods, since it is in producers' goods that a preliminary tapering-off of rates of growth manifests itself before the general recession? The inference seems natural, but against it stands the fact that this tapering-off is on the average slight, and the further fact that it does not affect payrolls and hence involves no corresponding tapering-off of personal incomes. Nor does it govern the movement of prices. It is an interesting symptom, but the evidence at hand does not prove that it is in itself an important causal factor in the typical cycle pattern. In this respect the lead in physical production of consumers' goods is probably more significant. But it does seem significant that, for a given class of goods, it is at the stage farther removed from the consumer that the initiatory movement takes place—that is, at the stage of production rather than retail selling—if the available figures are representative.

Stocks of Goods

The story told by stocks of goods is decidedly confused. In a general way, those nearer the consumer tend toward a positive correlation, rising as business rises and falling as business falls, while those nearer the source of production show the opposite tendency. In the first group may be named department store stocks, cotton at mills (with a large lag) and steel sheets, while in the second group are petroleum, cement, iron at furnaces, sugar and refined copper. The line of division is none too clear, and some

53]

stocks follow a more complicated pattern. Cotton in warehouses fluctuates far more than cotton at mills, and as compared with the latter may about equally well be regarded as an inverse cycle with a large lead or a positive cycle with an equally large lag. As compared with cotton consumption, cotton in warehouses shows an inverse cycle with a definite lead. The inverse cycle is natural, since the growing of cotton does not follow the cycles of manufacturing activity that govern its consumption; hence active manufacturing tends to draw down the stocks. The apparent lead may point to a delayed reaction of manufacturing activity on cotton growing. A depression may lead to reduced cotton-planting which would not take effect on the crop until near the peak of the next expansion.

In the cycle culminating in 1929, stocks of goods seemed on the whole to show positive cycles, indicating a behavior tending to intensify fluctuations of consumers' demand in the process of passing them on to the producers of goods and materials. That is, in the boom, producers were working not only to supply an active consumer demand, but to increase stocks also. This may further indicate an unusual piling-up of unsalable stocks in the prosperity phase of the cycle: in other words, literal 'over-production' such as is not commonly found. If this behavior were more marked in this most recent cycle than in previous cycles, this fact would constitute one factor contributing to its unusual violence and persistence. Stocks which show a negative correlation would seem to have the opposite effect: that is, they would seem to be used to make ultimate production more stable than volume of consumers' purchases. They would indicate that producers work to stock when demand is slack and so maintain employment. In few instances do stocks appear to be so handled as to produce a genuine stabilizing effect of this sort for an industry as a whole, whatever single enterprises may do. The movements of stocks thus seem to have, on the whole, an unstabilizing influence, tending to intensify fluctuations of business activity. This is an influence responding to business moods and susceptible of control by business policy, not wholly governed by physical forces. But the total volume of stocks, at those points where they show a positive correlation with production, is typically not large; so that there may well be doubt whether their fluctuations, when compared with the annual output, produce a decided effect on the typical business cycle.

Some effect there probably is, but the data do not suffice for an estimate of its importance in quantitative terms. Statistics on stocks need to be fuller and especially to be more differentiated, so as to show separately stocks of materials in the hands of those who are waiting to sell them, and in the hands of those who have bought them and are waiting to use them in further production; also stocks of intermediate products and finished goods classified on similar principles, distinguishing, so far as possible, finished products in the hands of manufacturers, wholesalers and retailers. If possible, a line should be drawn between stocks whose amount registers a willingness to buy and those whose amount reflects inability to sell. The 'consumer's inventory' of durable goods is not to be ignored but will be difficult to reach statistically.

Timing: Dealings in Securities

The stock market is generally credited with being one of the leading forces of disturbance, and if priority of movement is the criterion the evidence of its complicity is strong. In this field data are available for systematic analysis of a larger number of cycles than is possible for many other classes of data, and the type of behavior indicated may be regarded as correspondingly well established. It is a pattern with considerable diversities of timing; but not sufficient to destroy the well-marked type-form.

Volume of sales of stocks exhibits, on the average, about a quarter-cycle lead as compared with the general business cycle. This means that on the average sales reach their maximum mid-way in the upswing of the general cycle; but in point of fact, this peak sometimes occurs near the beginning of the general up-swing, sometimes near the end, and in

1929 it occurred a few months after the down-turn of general business. This last, however, was exceptional behavior, characterizing a very exceptional cycle. Dealings in bonds show an even greater lead.[9]

Prices of securities lag behind volumes of sales, but lead as compared with the general business cycle. Prices of preferred stocks and of bonds (the latter taken as the inverse of bond yields) show approximately a quarter-cycle lead; those of common stocks a smaller lead. In other words, the volume of sales runs high during the boom that carries prices up to their top level. The lag of common stocks as compared with bonds records the well-known shift from the less speculative to the more speculative securities as the boom proceeds, and the return to more conservative issues as depression deepens.

The large lead exhibited by dealings in stocks places them in a class with construction and the various special series directly related to it. There is, in particular, a rather remarkable and suggestive similarity between the average cycle pattern for sales of stocks and of fabricated structural steel. In both cases there is a lead of about a quarter-cycle as com-

---

[9] This series may also be represented as an inverse cycle with a short lag, though this would tend to obscure the relationship between the movements of bond and stock sales. In the separate cycles the typical behavior (about one-third of total cases) is a lead of one cycle-stage in bond sales as compared with stocks (each cycle being divided into eight stages). About an equal number of cases show a larger lead, and almost none show an unmistakable lag.

57]

pared to the general business cycle. In both cases the peak regularly comes at some time during the up-swing of general business, but at different times in different cycles, with the result that the composite picture (the average cycle pattern) shows a plateau instead of a peak. In both cases the trough comes, on the average, about midway of the down-swing of general business. And in both cases there is one cycle showing an exceptional behavior. In the 1921-24 cycle fabricated structural steel shows a double peak, the higher one occurring midway of the down-swing of general business. The inference is that special conditions during our immediate post-War reconstruction lent greater persistence to the upward movement, much as special conditions in 1927-29 prolonged the stock market boom past the peak of general business, contrary to the usual behavior of stock exchange trading. If priority of sequence is valid evidence of causal responsibility, the case against stock speculation is strong.

The *rationale* of the connection between stock speculation and the general business cycle may seem self-evident, but it is not utterly simple. Stock speculation, like other things, may appear as both cause and effect. And for at least one essential feature of the story factual evidence is badly needed. A revival in the securities markets has been construed as a direct result of business depression, in that business has so little need or productive use for funds that they flow into the market for securities already out-standing—first favoring the least speculative issues, as befits the mood of the moment. Money at such times is cheap. This condition implies that savings are in excess of investment, in the Keynes termi-nology. This is not because savings have increased, but because investment has fallen off so much more sharply.

The upward movement of securities tends, of course, toward revival of business confidence, and is in turn stimulated further by such a revival. As it continues, it produces several effects. The strength-ening market makes the issuance of new securities more attractive, at the same time that reviving con-fidence and business activity increases the desire and need of corporations to obtain increased capital by new issues. Possibly the time this process requires may be one reason why the forces of supply and de-mand in this case, instead of working toward an equilibrium, operate with an initial inertia and a final momentum that regularly bring about over-swings.

The growing speculative demand for securities operates with borrowed funds to a far larger extent than the original conservative demand for the less speculative securities. It is the stock-speculator who deals on margin more than the bond-investor. Thus the demand for securities is one of the growing group of demands which tends to outrun the volume of funds taken currently for the purpose from the personal incomes of the purchasers. Business and the stock market are now competing for funds, and money rates rise, but the profits of a rising stock market are so attractive that the rising money rates do not promptly check the speculative demand, though ultimately they may help to do so if the movement is of the ordinary sort and has not gone beyond the control of the forces of reason as did the boom of 1928-29. Call money rates seem to be highest typically after the peak of stock prices and on the decline, and often register the urgency of threatened speculators struggling to hold on.

To use the concepts employed by Keynes, a rising stock market is initiated in a period in which savings almost certainly exceed investment: the same condition that, in his theory, brings about a low general price level.[10] And the reaction occurs at a time when investments presumably exceed savings: the condition which, according to the Keynes theory, brings about high general prices. This latter discrepancy is probably intensified by the use of some part of the stock market profits to purchase consumers' goods; though there are no data to test whether such a movement exists, or how great it may be.

The behavior of the stock market in the last cycle

[10] See pp. 88, 91 for discussion of the probabilities as to the relative behavior of savings and investment. The writer's conclusion on this point does not rest on statistical evidences, for he has found no adequate evidence bearing on the question.

[60

was out of the ordinary in that the stock market boom went to fantastic and irrational heights in 1929, and continued extraordinarily long. Instead of beginning to subside well before the general business peak, it continued upward, tending presumably to reinforce the peak of general business, and did not reach its peak until several months after signs of a down-turn in general business were recorded. Thus, so far as speculation is a causal factor, it did its utmost to make the last cycle unusually violent.

Timing: Agricultural Production and Prices

The timing of agricultural activity is markedly different from that of industry and trade; and while it shows no regular leads or lags it should be treated in connection with the general subject of timing, especially as various theories have traced the origins of the business cycle to agricultural fluctuations. Agriculture appears to have its own cycles, whose timing has no clear or regular relation to the cycles of general business. This is true whether we consider physical production, prices at the farm, or the product of the two, which may be taken to measure the total purchasing power which agriculture generates and has to offer in the general market. Agriculture sometimes moves in harmony with the general business cycle, sometimes in the reverse direction and sometimes in quite an unrelated way. One writer has added a third element to the analysis

61]

by calculating the total purchasing power of agriculture *in terms of non-agricultural products;* and with the help of this quantity has attempted to establish an Agricultural Theory of Business Cycles.[11] But the correlations remain fragmentary and unconvincing.

This does not mean that agriculture has no effect on the business cycle, or no responsibility for its occurrence; far from it. It simply means that agriculture is not a regularly acting force, tending typically and regularly to help initiate the recovery, or stimulate the revival, or in any other way to play habitually the same role in at least a predominant number of cycles.

But a theory of business cycles must be concerned not merely with forces arising within the cycle itself, or in regular timing with it, but also with forces arising outside the regular course of the general business cycle and of a random character in respect of timing relative to the phenomenon we are studying at present. We live in an economy exposed to such 'random' forces; and one in which many kinds of disturbance tend not to be self-limiting at once, but to act in a cumulative and self-reinforcing way for a considerable time and until the movement has gone so far that a return swing naturally follows. Without this characteristic of our economic system,

11 See an article under that title by M. D. Anderson, *American Economic Review,* September, 1931, pp. 427-49.

there would in all probability be no cycles, but merely random fluctuations. If, being what it is, the system were exposed to no 'external' or 'random' disturbances, it might in time reach a state of equilibrium in which again there would be no business cycles. This last is an unprovable conjecture; but whether true or not, the cycle as we know it is the resultant of the combination of random disturbances and an economic system which transmits their effects cumulatively. There may also be forces which do not fit well into this twofold classification; but in any case, both the 'random' and the strictly cyclical forces are to be regarded as of the essence of the actual phenomenon. The random forces are not to be disregarded merely because there is no discernible correlation between their timing and that of the business cycle itself.

They may, indeed, include those causes which have the most obvious claim to be regarded as originative in character; though this means little more than that they originate outside the endless circle of causes and effects set in motion by the business cycle itself. They are presumably originative only from the standpoint of our somewhat arbitrarily delimited problem. In their own nature they are no more aboriginal than any other forces we can discover—they in turn have their causes.

There are perhaps two main ways in which agricultural fluctuations may logically be supposed to

influence the general course of business. One is that
plentiful and cheap raw products are a stimulus to
the activity, or at least to the profitableness, of the
industries using them. Among the relationships of
this sort which could be traced are those between
wheat and flour milling, meat animals and slaughter-
ing and meat packing, wool and woolen manufacturing, hides and leather products, cotton and cotton textiles. However, the cyclical fluctuations of
factory employment in food products are so very
slight that apparently the total disturbing influence
that can be traced to agriculture in this branch of
manufacturing, at least, is of superficially negligible
magnitude. It is, of course, conceivable that outside
disturbances of tiny magnitude are all that is required by the type of business cycle theory indicated
above.

The other way in which agriculture would logically be expected to influence general industrial and
commercial activity is by means of the greater or less
purchasing power that it throws into the market for
consumers' goods and farm equipment. The effects
of this element in the total flow of purchasing power
are not easy to isolate. Production and sales of farm
equipment might be segregated, and general retail
sales in rural districts would throw light on the matter. Mail-order sales, supposed to go largely to farmers, are apparently more influenced by the general
business cycle than by agricultural conditions,

[64

though analysis of these sales by districts might reveal a more positive dependence on the prosperity of the farmer. In any case, this theory of the effect of agricultural purchasing power is somewhat discounted by the possibility that the increase in farmers' purchasing power is partly at the expense of that of other groups. This is especially probable so far as farmers gain through increased prices of their products. Agricultural prosperity is likely, however, to increase the power of farmers to buy equipment on credit without subtracting an equal amount from the corresponding power of other groups. And we must remember that small impulses of this sort may still be important. To sum up: the influence of agriculture on general business is not traced in the data so far analyzed but may be susceptible of some degree of tracing by additional studies.

Timing: Foreign Trade

Foreign trade in relation to American business cycles contains elements of both cause and effect. Our imports respond quite closely to our domestic business cycles. Increased industrial activity here augments demand for raw materials from abroad, while the resulting prosperity enhances our buying power, part of which flows to imported products. Capital funds might naturally be expected to flow increasingly to this country when it is in a business boom, thus balancing and making possible an increase of commodity imports, relative to exports.

Exports are subject to a complex of forces arising both here and abroad and affecting different products differently. However, as might be expected, there is a considerable degree of general correspondence between the movements of our exports and the course of general business cycles in the importing countries. These cycles are, as is well known, longer than ours and differently timed. Though major disturbances affect the entire industrial world to a considerable extent, still, seldom or never are all the main countries to which we export simultaneously in the same stage of their business cycles as we are in ours. And some of our largest exports are of a sort to be affected by our own agricultural productiveness as well as by changes in foreign demand. Hence it is natural that exports, while showing some slight correspondence with our business cycles, show a still larger measure of independent action.

Fluctuations in export demand, as distinct from fluctuations due to larger or smaller supplies of exportable products in this country, are an element in stimulating or depressing domestic production and trade. And they are, to a considerable extent, among the random or irregular forces. In the decade following the World War our balance of trade was subject to conditions which were not only radically different from those prevailing before the conflict, but also decidedly abnormal in the sense that there is little or no possibility of their continuing and constituting a state of equilibrium, even of the moving variety. The sudden reversal of our position from a large debtor nation to a creditor nation, closely rivalling Great Britain, created a situation such that an export balance of commodities, to which our economy is accustomed and geared, was sustained only by continued and large exportation of capital funds, largely on what may fairly be called a distress basis. Europe was not borrowing on the normal basis of increasing productivity in an economy sound and solvent to start with, which could therefore make its borrowing self-sustaining with no ill effects.

This condition could not, in the nature of the case, go on indefinitely. Either foreign borrowing power would become exhausted or the amounts due us on interest account would pile up to a point at which our export balance of goods would be cut down, and ultimately be turned into an import balance. In fact, a sharp break was brought about as a result of our own exaggerated stock market boom, which attracted funds into our stock market both from this country and from abroad. This weakened the financial structure abroad, already working on too slim a gold margin; and brought into the foreground the disturbing fact that foreign countries owed amounts on short time which, if called in, could not be paid and could wreck their financial structures completely. While this was the more serious effect, a more immediate one was the cutting down of our exports of goods. This movement occurred prior to the decline of imports and of business in general; and this order of sequence was unusual, since our imports usually move more sharply than exports in response to our domestic state of expansion or recession. This initiatory decline of exports must be reckoned a special contributing factor in the present depression.

Timing: Banking

In the field of banking, clearings and the volume of deposits show a lead in the average cycle pattern, as is natural in view of the large part the stock market plays in the demand for credit and in the volume of payments in large clearing centers. Interest rates, on the other hand, tend to lag, especially at the downturn of the general business cycle. It is perhaps significant that loans and discounts in general show a lead as compared with interest rates. One conclusion that may be drawn is that interest rates are more a passive than an active or originating factor, though it is pertinent to add that high interest rates at the peak and just after may have some effect in starting trade downward, while easy money in the early stages of a revival may be an important facilitating cause.

In the last cycle, the timing was different from this general type. Interest rates led general business

[68

slightly on the 1927-28 up-turn and on the 1929 down-turn, while loans and discounts showed no lead on the up-turn and lagged on the down-turn. Thus interest rates in this case led loans and discounts. The fact that they were declining sharply before the peak of the stock market boom indicates that the repressive force of the credit system was relaxed rather than tightened at the point where expansion was becoming critical. Funds from non-banking sources were pouring into the call-loan market in ways which the bankers felt themselves unable to control.

Corporate Incomes

Net earnings of corporations are available for five cycles, not counting that beginning in 1928, but two are disturbed by the War and the immediate post-War deflation. Of these, the cycle of 1914-19 shows a rise in net earnings throughout the course of the general business cycle, while that of 1919-21 shows a decline throughout, both for the totals and for most of the separate industrial groups. Of the other three cycles, all exhibit quite normal behavior, except that in one case—in 1912—this series lags behind the down-turn of general business. Corporate incomes fluctuate with the general business cycle, but much more intensely, the slump from the peak of 1929 being especially cataclysmic. All this is natural and well known. The chief peculiarity of the post-War

69]

period is revealed in the record of the construction industry, where corporate incomes showed an uninterrupted rise through the two cycles 1921-24 and 1924-27, and then declined almost throughout the succeeding cycle. In other words, this industry, as we have already seen, rolled three cycles into one, with a length of ten years or more. The non-availability of monthly figures of corporate incomes is undoubtedly responsible for the fact that they do not show the short-cycle movements which appear as slight interruptions of this long-cycle swing in the figures for contracts awarded.

The behavior during the War period serves to indicate that corporate incomes are affected by price movements as well as by the fluctuations of trade activity: that is, by those larger price movements which go beyond the very moderate cyclical ups and downs. The latter amount to about ten per cent on the average. The up-swing of prices from 1919 to 1920 brought no corresponding rise in corporate incomes, possibly in part because of an unusually large rise in wages.

Dividend and interest disbursements, as is well known, are far steadier than corporate incomes, surplus and undivided profits being so used as to act as equalizers. Of the last thirteen general business cycles (omitting that beginning in 1928) four do not appear at all in the dividend records, indicating that reserves are sufficient to iron out minor depressions completely. Dividends show a marked cyclical lag (as might be expected) and also a strong up-trend. In the last depression they actually increased for a short time after the general business curve had started downward, and maintained themselves for well over half a year before the depletion of reserves forced them to follow the general downward swing. While these figures may not be highly accurate, the character of the story they tell is so strongly marked that it can hardly fail to reflect the general run of the facts.

General Conclusions as to Timing of Series

Some general conclusions may at least tentatively be drawn from the timing of the various series. Some of the apparently conflicting tendencies may be partly reconciled by the proposition that, as between goods of similar durability, consumers' goods tend to move more promptly. But as between long-lived and perishable goods, the long-lived goods appear to take the lead. Construction, especially residential construction, shows a great lead. Automobiles, especially passenger cars, show a lead. Production of consumers' goods appears to move ahead of sales for consumption, and there are some indications that wholesale trade leads retail. Thus there is some ground for a tentative conclusion that, as between the same goods at successive stages of production and distribution, the stages farther removed from con-

71]

sumption show the prompter movements. This proposition, however, is not to be regarded as definitively established. Movements in purchases for consumption are, in the nature of the case, a dominant force; but we have seen that even if impulses originate here, the relation between consumers' purchases and the production of goods is such that the resulting movements in the production of goods to meet the purchases may behave in the way described as 'leading', the effect appearing to precede the cause. But this productive activity also governs consumers' incomes, becoming in turn a cause returning on itself with intensifying force. The actual expansions and contractions of consumers' purchases are largely results of changes in productive activity.

Another indication is that bank rates are acted upon more than acting, with a possible exception in the last cycle. Movements in volume of bank credit initiate the conditions bringing about changes in the rates. These movements in volume of credit may at times act as initiating forces, as when idle funds tend to stimulate the markets for securities, but it is not so clear that they act in this way directly on the actual work of producing and selling commodities. Here the volume of credit seems to respond in the main to the demands of the volume of trade. It is an important enabling cause or condition, but hardly an initiating one in the typical case. And experience points to the conclusion that the power of

[72

bank rates, and indeed of other banking weapons of control, is rather limited in face of the large task of stimulating business when it is depressed, or repressing it when it is stimulated.

Some still more general points may be noted. Physical production series of the more general sort show a very widespread tendency to a short lead on the up-turn of the general business cycle, with a very slight rise toward the end of the cycle.

Series for prices and sales show only slight and spasmodic traces of this feature, except for commodities already noted as having a special tendency to lead. And series representing incomes, payrolls and dividend and interest disbursements do not show it at all. Whatever the impulse to revival in the general economic field, it seems to appear earliest in physical production.

Further development of some of these points may wait until we have examined the evidence that may be drawn from the amplitudes of the fluctuations, as distinct from their timing.

Amplitudes of Fluctuations: Production

In production three groups stand out: construction and related industries, automobiles and producers' goods in general. In these three groups are to be found the great bulk of the fluctuations in production that are above the average in amplitude. Professor Mitchell has estimated that about one-sixth of our normal national income goes into the production of producers' goods (capital equipment and non-residential construction, including public works). The addition of residential housing construction and automobiles would bring the fraction up to the neighborhood of one-fourth.

The average cyclical fluctuations of these series as a group can best be judged from their behavior during different stages of the 'reference cycle' or general business cycle, since in some of these branches of production their own individual cycles show considerable irregularities of timing. On this basis they consistently show fluctuations well above the average for all branches of production, and they contain among them (along with closely related series) substantially all the production series that show such exceptionally large fluctuations. This last fact, together with the further fact that these series contain some of those most consistent in their timing, tends to the conclusion that the aggregate impact of the fluctuations of these groups is of peculiar weight and importance. Indeed, if one adds its secondary and tertiary effects, ramifying through the business system, it may well dominate the general movement.

Accurate measurement of the aggregate fluctuations of this group of series would require the construction of special indices for the purpose. Such analysis as the present writer has been able to make, using the existing series, leads to the conclusion that the aggregate fluctuations of this group, conservatively estimated, are certainly not less than 30 per cent on the average of the upward and downward movement.[12] This in itself would account for a fluctuation of 6 to 7 per cent in the national dividend, in commodity terms; without taking account of its secondary reactions on the production of other types of goods.

In striking contrast to these large disturbances are the very moderate fluctuations in the physical volume of retail trade. Copeland's index of retail trade for the three cycles 1919-27, deflated by a cost-of-living index number, indicates fluctuations of approximately 7 per cent, 5 per cent and virtually zero, or an average of a little over 4 per cent. As indicated by Dr. Kuznets' study[13], the physical volume of wholesale trade probably fluctuates more than this. In view of the pitfalls involved in measuring physical production by deflated dollar values, no great importance should be attached to these precise figures; but the general range of magnitudes they indicate is clear. Production of producers' goods fluctuates vastly more than retail trade.

But when we turn to the estimates of physical volume of production made by the National Bureau

[12] For details of this analysis, see the Appendix at the end of this volume.

[13] Simon Kuznets, *Cyclical Fluctuations: Retail and Wholesale Trade, United States, 1919-25* (New York, Adelphi, 1926).

of Economic Research, classified into consumers' goods: durable, semi-durable and non-durable; and producers' goods: capital equipment, durable goods and non-durable goods, we find that the intensity of cyclical fluctuations apparently depends not so much on whether the goods are for consumers or for producers, as upon their durability. The figures cover the period 1922-29, by whole years. While they are not comparable with the more elaborately analyzed cyclical series, they show that durable goods in both major groups, including capital equipment, experienced cyclical fluctuations several times as great as non-durable and semi-durable goods.

The conclusion that a major part of the responsibility for the business cycle focuses in this group of industries does not mean, of course, that the impulses responsible for movements necessarily originate there; for the chain of causes is endless. But if in any way this group of productive activities could be regularized, it would seem that the business cycle would be reduced to proportions that would no longer constitute a major evil in our economic system.

Any attempt to deal with these disturbing elements must take account of the conditioning factors of credit and capital funds which furnish the purchasing power to sustain these movements, and of the corresponding movements of prices for the particular commodities making up these groups. In

[76

general, the movements of volume of security trading, of prices of securities, and of new securities issued, are such as would be expected, showing large positive fluctuations, with volume of security trading showing a large lead and security prices a smaller one. Available data on new securities issued indicate an exceedingly strong cyclical movement. As to prices of commodities, parallel tables of prices and of physical volumes of production, made up of identical commodities, would make possible interesting comparisons, which would reveal whether prices of the various types of goods move in harmony with physical volumes of production. They might also throw some light on the question whether the movements of prices are obstructed in some instances by artificial policies of stabilization, and whether prices are thus stabilized at the cost of allowing a greater · fluctuation of output than would take place if prices were allowed to move in a more natural way as demand fluctuates. Competent observers have no doubt that this has been happening during the recent great decline in business.

The reasons why the group of products with which we are dealing shows more violent fluctuations than the average have already been dealt with. They rest mainly on the durability of these classes of goods and secondarily on the fact that wherever the volume of durable producers' goods increases in response to an increasing demand from consumers, it requires

77]

a larger percentage increase in the immediate flow of production of new producers' goods to bring about a smaller percentage increase in the total volume of such goods in the hands of those who use them. For the same reason the current production of durable producers' goods ordinarily increases by a larger percentage than the flow of products to the ultimate consumer. The total effect is summed up in saying that fluctuations in consumption, or in consumers' current expenditures, are passed on in the form of more intense fluctuations in the producers' expenditures on the durable means of gratifying these consumers' demands; and even changes in the rate of growth of consumption may bring about positive ups and downs in the resulting expenditures of producers. Since each expenditure constitutes someone else's income, the result is a widespread fluctuation of incomes and a corresponding fluctuation in consumers' subsequent expenses. Thus slight disturbances are self-multiplying.

On the side of the supply of funds to finance the expansion of producers' goods, there is the probability—which may be taken as a moral certainty—that as the national income increases in the up-swing of the business cycle, consumers' expenditures increase less rapidly than the total income, and savings available for expenditures on producers' goods (or for advances on the making of durable consumers' goods) increase more rapidly. But the most decisive factor on the side of purchasing power is the elasticity of the credit system, since it makes possible increased expenditures for producers' goods without correspondingly limited outlays for consumption—in short, an increase in total expenditures not limited to income derived from previous production. When credit contracts, the opposite effect is produced. The importance of this factor cannot be overestimated as an essential link in the chain of causes bringing about cyclical expansions and contractions of general business.

Thus the intensified fluctuations in these groups of goods are susceptible of rational explanation. And this machinery of intensification may be regarded as one of the primary causes of the character of the typical business cycle.

Amplitudes of Fluctuations: Incomes

Contributory to this whole situation is the fact that wages and salaries fluctuate less than the total national income, and profits more. Thus in a time of great activity, wages and salaries constitute a smaller fraction of the increased national income than in a time of depression. And while an increased part of the profits is put into reserves in prosperous times, even this is not hoarded as cash, but is invested—in equipment, inventory or securities. It constitutes a part of the disproportionate flow of social

79]

income into producers' goods which takes place in the period of prosperity.

These reserves furnish a margin which makes possible the stabilization of dividends, and their intensified fluctuations constitute the reverse side of the stable-dividend policy. And it is evident that the result is not to stabilize total purchasing power, but rather to concentrate the fluctuations on the kinds of things corporate surpluses are spent on, or invested in. In the first instance, the income distributed to consumers in the form of dividends is stabilized; but, as we have seen, the unstabilized activity in the creation of producers' goods results in violent ups and downs in the incomes of a quite different group of consumers. So the total of consumers' income in the nation still fluctuates. And the total flow of purchasing power into goods of all sorts may conceivably fluctuate quite as much as if there were no such attempt at stabilizing that part which flows through the channel of dividend payments.

These are factors the relative amplitudes of whose fluctuations would tell us far more than we now know, if only we could measure them with sufficient comprehensiveness and precision. Do consumers' expenditures fluctuate more or less than personal incomes? Do savings and expenditures for producers' goods follow a parallel course, or are there important discrepancies? Do savings exceed expenditures for producers' goods during recession and depression,

[80

and do expenditures for producers' goods exceed savings during expansion and prosperity? To these questions no exact statistical answer can be given.

In the first place, production of goods fluctuates more than incomes disbursed to individuals. This class of income (estimated by years only) appears to fluctuate approximately as much as retail sales, though the lack of monthly figures of income makes a close comparison impossible. However, there is *a priori* reason for believing that consumers' expenditures on the whole fluctuate slightly less than personal incomes and that savings fluctuate more, while expenditures on capital fluctuate more than savings, and total expenditures of all sorts fluctuate more than income. This last proposition is supported by the way in which credit expands in boom times, indicating an increase of actively used purchasing power in excess of income. But the question is complicated by the ambiguous character of purely speculative gains, which should probably be reckoned by themselves as a kind of income separate from that derived directly from the processes of production. As to the greater steadiness of consumers' expenses, the conclusion is supported by the general fact that the production of consumers' goods fluctuates less than the comprehensive index which includes both consumers' and producers' goods, while retail prices of consumers' goods fluctuate less than the average of all prices.

81]

But there are cross-currents and eddies in the movement. Some with a liberal margin of income may spend pretty much according to their desires and let the fluctuations of their income show mainly in their savings; and others with no margin at all may be forced to draw down their savings or buy groceries on credit, or both, as soon as depression reduces their income. All these are spending more steadily than they are earning.

At the same time others are accused of hoarding or are said to be skimping consumption during the depression and saving to the utmost while they still have jobs, because they do not know how soon they may join the ranks of those without incomes. And others are tempted into bargain hunting in the security markets. Still others are making the payments due on goods bought in better times on the installment plan, and making no new installment purchases. These are all spending less steadily than they are earning, increasing their savings or reducing their indebtedness at just the time when incomes are falling off.

There seems little doubt that the main current is made up of those who spend more steadily than they earn, and that those who earn more steadily than they spend constitute an eddy or group of eddies not sufficient to neutralize the main drift. There may be an initial stage in a depression in which consumers' purchases of postponable goods and luxuries

[82

shrink more than their incomes, and this stage may be important.[14] But once the depression is well under way, incomes in general shrink more than the possible amount of these easy economies in luxury buying. The funds free for investment bargain hunting are scant, as witnessed by the continued low prices of securities; and as for hoarding by those who still fear to lose their jobs, they have little enough money free for that. Funds free for reducing installment indebtedness are also necessarily limited. Hence, in default of fuller and more accurate statistics we may provisionally assume that consumption (or rather consumers' current expenditures for consumption goods) is steadier than personal income.

The statistics further bear out the logical conclusion that this relative steadiness is mostly found in the realm of necessary and perishable goods. Durable goods, and moderately durable goods in the luxury class, show great fluctuations. These are the goods in which a shrinkage of income causes the heaviest contractions of expenditure. In fact, goods may be divided into two classes: those in which expenditures are steadier than income and those in which they

14 Dr. W. I. King considers this the dominant movement, holding that expenditures fluctuate vastly more than incomes and that this is the chief 'immediate cause' of business cycles. (*Proceedings, American Statistical Association*, March, 1932, especially pp. 222-4.) It is unfortunate that there is not adequate statistical evidence to test either this proposition or the other which seems to the present writer more probable.

are less steady. The second class includes capital goods as well as durable consumers' goods and luxuries. If all goods were in the first class, business cycles would be, at most, mild affairs. The conclusion seems inevitable that the main responsibility centers in the second class of goods.

They are also (as already noted) the goods in which a loss of confidence, or a weakening of the mood of optimism characteristic of a boom period, may cause a contraction of expenditures even before incomes have actually begun to decline. To this extent they may be regarded as active or initiating factors in the movements of general business activity. Even at this point in the cycle, however, though some consumers may decrease their purchases of some commodities before their individual incomes begin to shrink, there is likely to be some prior shrinkage of production and income in those branches of business which show the greatest lead in the average business cycle pattern.

The fact—if it be a fact—that expenditure for consumption is steadier than production and income may represent one of the forces setting limits on the cumulative effects of disturbances, which have been noted as one of the central causes of the cyclical behavior of business. If every reduction of productive activity at any point caused an equal reduction of expenditures, diffused throughout the economic system, resulting in a further reduction of

[84

production and so on, there would be no logically assignable limits to the lengths to which such contraction could go, short of a breaking-away from the profit system and a shift to one of self-sufficing production or barter. It is significant, indeed, that precisely this has happened, locally and on a small scale, in the present emergency.

But if a reduction of production, and of income, is followed by a *smaller* reduction of expenditures, then the series of derived effects is a dwindling series of the type which should have a finite, not an infinite sum. If, for instance, a contraction of production were followed by a contraction of expenditures only one-half as great, then the sum of an infinite series of such reductions would result only in doubling the amount of the original contraction. And if we imagine business at any moment suffering from the first phase of one original contraction, plus the second phase of an earlier one, plus the third phase of a still earlier one, and so on, the result would be the same: the original contraction would be doubled and no more. Or if the derived contractions were three-fourths of the original ones, the total effect would be larger, but still limited. What probably happens is that the fraction representing the dwindling of the derived effects is variable from one phase of the cycle to another.[15]

[15] Since writing the above, my attention has been called by Mr. M. C. Rorty to a paper by R. F. Kahn entitled "Public Works and Inflation",

This same feature of the greater steadiness of expenditures as compared with incomes plays an important part in Dr. Warren M. Persons' theory as one of the forces tending to bring depression to an end, and initiate the resumption of activity.[16] Excess inventories are reduced by the purchases of consumers who are drawing on their savings or credit, with the result that purchases by dealers revive.

It is obviously a necessary condition of this process that excess inventories should be cleared before these consumers' savings, or their credit resources, are exhausted. And it seems quite possible that if the depression, with its cutting down of incomes and its frozen inventories, is unusually severe, the savings and credit resources may be exhausted first. If this should happen, it seems only natural that the depression would fail to be checked in the usual time, but would go on into a deeper and more prolonged phase, waiting the coming of other forces of revival. In such an event, the strain might be

Journal of American Statistical Association, Supplement, March, 1933, which applies the idea of a dwindling series of finite sum to the secondary effects of a public-works program, taking account of various elements responsible for the 'leakage'. He estimates the additional secondary or induced expansion of employment, for Great Britain, on various bases, at ¾, 1 and 2 times the number directly employed. For the United States he considers the induced employment would be larger.

16 See *Forecasting Business Cycles* (New York, Wiley, 1931), Chapter II, especially pp. 22-5.

said to have exceeded the limits of the normal elasticity of the business structure and become a thing of a different sort—as indeed seems to be the case today. When this happens, revival may wait for some other force of recovery—perhaps for a slower process whereby the shrunken volume of savings of the relatively well-to-do, exceeding the still-more-shrunken volume of capital expenditures, finally produces an upward turn in the securities markets. This may revive confidence and lead to increased expenditures by producers and consumers alike. Or recovery may wait upon some outside originating force or forces of a favorable nature.

Another factor which must not be forgotten in seeking for causes of the cumulative expansions and contractions, as well as of the limits set upon them, is the elasticity of credit. As we have seen, it is mainly this factor which makes it possible for total expenditures to move independently of total incomes previously received, and thus to initiate and strengthen these cumulative movements. Expansion of credit makes it possible for expenditures to increase beyond incomes already realized, and so to lead to an increase of production, leading in turn to a subsequent increase of incomes. This is clearly very different from what could happen if the expenditures which limit production were themselves limited to income derived from prior production. Limits on the expansion of credit presumably bear a share of

87]

responsibility for setting limits on the resulting industrial expansion. And contraction of credit means that expenditures are smaller than incomes already realized, with the result that subsequent incomes are smaller. In this case, while the contraction of credit may to some extent be the moving cause of the contraction in expenditures, it seems more likely to be a result, taking up the slack as expenditures shrink. This is partly borne out by the fact that bank credit frequently shows no absolute contraction in a business recession.

Statistics seem to afford no way of testing the causal importance of this element. As an enabling cause of rapid expansion, if other forces are working in that direction, it appears to be of vital importance: an essential element. But as an independent moving factor, the writer is inclined to assign it mainly a contributory influence, only occasionally rising to first-rate significance. Easy money enables people to obey the impulse to buy more goods and securities, but does not seem likely in most instances to furnish the moving impulse if there are no other circumstances tending to create it.

The business cycle is a vicious circle with no beginning this side of the origin of capitalistic production and no end until a way is found of breaking into the circle at some point and controlling its hitherto-endless sequence. Perhaps the chief reason for not regarding consumers' expenditures as con-

[88

stituting the factor of most strategic importance is that they do not seem to afford the most promising point for breaking into the circle with measures of control. Consumers' income is a more promising lever to work with, but even here crude efforts might easily neutralize themselves or worse.

Amplitudes of Fluctuations: Prices

One of the well-known discrepancies in the business cycle is constituted by the greater fluctuations in wholesale prices than in retail prices or costs of living. Is this of important causal significance? Does it, for instance, bring about automatically a discrepancy between production and purchasing power such as many theorists take to be the central cause of the whole phenomenon? The fact might be urged that during a recession this discrepancy in price movements brings about a shrinkage in the money incomes derived from the earlier stages of production, while the prices that have to be paid when these incomes are spent for consumers' goods show no corresponding shrinkage. Thus the purchasing power of incomes is automatically reduced.[17] The reverse happens during business expansion. It appears that the effect of this discrepancy in price movements is disturbing.

The causal problem remains untouched. What

[17] Income in this case must probably be taken to include individual business profits.

causes the decline in wholesale prices at the beginning of a depression, or what causes the previous rise? Furthermore, this series of movements cannot be realistically discussed apart from the movements in volume of trade which go with them. Prices decline because demand has weakened; and weakening demand commonly manifests itself first in a falling-off in volume of sales. This falling-off in sales is commonly a proximate cause of the decline in prices.

It is also one of the keys to understanding the effects of the price-deflation. It operates in conjunction with losses due to depreciation of inventories bought at earlier and higher prices; and serves to aggravate this element by forcing dealers to hold their inventories longer. Another element is the fact that many wholesale deliveries are made, not at current market prices but at prices fixed in earlier contracts. Thus, when the wholesale market falls, the average price governing actual transfers of goods does not fall as far or as promptly as the open-market price. No one of these factors would perhaps be sufficient to answer the question why dealers do not make profits instead of losses when the wholesale prices they have to pay decline so very much more than the retail prices they receive. Taken all together, however, they suffice to explain the outcome.

The discrepancy between the movements of wholesale and retail prices is a result and symptom of the fact that the depression strikes hardest at the

[90

points farther removed from the ultimate consumer; and it becomes, of course, part of the mechanism by which the effects are transmitted and their incidence apportioned among different groups. But it is hardly in itself an initiating cause.

Amplitudes of Fluctuations: Profits

The intensified fluctuations of profits constitute another obvious and significant factor, closely related to the movements of prices. The traditional function of profits and losses is to direct economic resources into the creation of the goods that are most in demand, and to bring about the absorption of business by the most competent producers and the weeding-out of the incompetent. A marked increase of profits over the entire business field is, from this standpoint, a curious phenomenon, seeming to imply that commodities in general are more in demand than before, or that the supply is short. As human needs remain about the same from prosperity to depression, and as the general increase in prices and profits occurs at precisely the times when goods are plentiful rather than scarce, this curiosity gains the character of an anomaly. High prices and high profits are an index, not of general scarcity but of general plenty. They serve to urge the producer to increase his production to the utmost at precisely the time when he is already turning out more than can, in the nature of the case, be continuously absorbed. It seems evident that the function of profits is suffering some sort of a perversion, and that this is one of the central and strategically important factors in the business cycle.

One cause of such a perversion is to be found in the movements of prices, together with movements of costs which do not keep pace. Interest burdens are fixed by contracts, many of which run for long terms of years, while even on the shorter ones the rates of interest do not rise and fall sufficiently to compensate for the effect of changing prices. Wage rates are also sluggish in their responses—earnings, of course, move with the volume of employment. Furthermore, since much indirect labor is of a character that does not vary proportionately with fluctuations of output, an increase of production carries with it a less than proportionate increase in the number of labor-hours necessary to turn it out. Hence an increase of output, if not neutralized by an actual fall in prices, has of itself the effect of increasing profits; and this is precisely the signal which business is accustomed to interpret as a sign that conditions are such as to justify further expansion. Thus profits fall in the class of cumulative, rather than self-limiting, forces; and this fact tends to destroy their value as a governor of general business expansion. If an expansion is indicated, and business responds to the signal, the signal does not grow weaker as the presumed need is met, but stronger.

This is not the place to attempt to elaborate pro-

[92

posals for dealing with these matters; we seek merely to establish the practical and strategic importance of this set of causal factors by showing that they can be reached by things men can do to modify their action. Something can be done about them. Moreover, in devising policies it is essential to distinguish sharply between the 'internal economies' of full utilization, which depend on the principles of overhead costs and not on changes in the market rates of wages or prices of materials, and the external forces arising in the general market. It is probably useful to have producers under a spur to operate their individual plants at full capacity in order to derive the economies of full operation. An economy where plants operate reasonably close to capacity is not necessarily an economy in which markets are chronically glutted. This incentive to full operation may be so handled, it is true, as to work towards increased instability; but probably it can also be so conditioned as to work towards greater stability.

Business men may simply regard the peak periods as their sources of greatest profits, and subordinate other things to the attempt to do as large a volume of business as possible at those times, living through the dull periods as best they can. This attitude tends to perpetuate instability. A truer reckoning would indicate that the burden of idle overhead through the dull periods is chargeable to the peak business as a cost of standing ready to handle it when it comes;

93]

and this burden makes the peak business very expensive, even casts some doubt on its real profitableness. When this is realized, the business interest in stabilization becomes clear.

But this interest is still not fully reflected in the methods of accounting appropriate to separate enterprises. This is chiefly because individual businesses may also shift a considerable burden of idle overhead to other businesses by curtailing their purchases. The cost of goods and materials is a direct and variable cost to them, but it contains a large element of overhead cost for the businesses which make the goods and materials. A consolidated income account for business as a whole would have a larger proportion of constant or overhead costs than do the separate accounts of the individual businesses, and when business thinks in terms of its fortunes as a whole it will have a correspondingly greater interest in stabilization than is apparent on the surface of the ordinary methods of cost reckoning.[18]

Thus the fact that the profits of a business show an intensified increase in response to an increase in the output of that business constitutes a force which may work toward stability or toward instability. The outcome depends on whether business thinks and acts in old-fashioned individualistic terms or in terms

[18] The writer has dealt with this question at more length in his volume, *The Economics of Overhead Costs.*

of its long-run and collective interests. But there seems to be no ambiguity as to the effect of a condition in which the market behaves in such a way as to increase one producer's profits by reason of the fact that *all the other producers* are expanding their operations. This almost certainly makes for instability and cumulative intensification of movements.

PART THREE

GENERAL MOVEMENTS, 1922–1929

Introduction

BEFORE the advent of the current type of statistical analysis, theories of business fluctuations ran in terms of a period of about ten years. The more recent methods have revealed cycles which, in this country, have an average length about one-third as great, though with considerable variation from cycle to cycle, ranging from about two to five years. One reason for this change may be that the older methods of observation revealed only the more obvious and spectacular movements, commonly accompanied by great waves of speculation and a widespread breakdown of the banking system, while the more delicate statistical analysis now available reveals more basic industrial fluctuations which do not always

[96

produce such spectacular symptoms, visible to the man in the street. On the other hand, there have been changes in the character of business cycles themselves. And it may well be that factors having relatively short natural periods have been increasing in importance as compared to others whose natural periods are longer. If so, traces should still be visible of these more slowly acting forces. And some present-day students still consider that there is evidence pointing to the existence of longer cycles, combined with the shorter ones. Thus it is particularly pertinent to examine the movements over longer periods.

In doing this for the post-War years the writer was much assisted by material presented by Professor F. C. Mills in *Economic Tendencies in the United States*,[1] covering the period 1899-1929, with emphasis on the last eight years. The organized series of the National Bureau of Economic Research were also a main reliance. While still provisional as to the length of the recession beginning in 1929, they give an adequate picture of the decade 1921-31, covering almost the whole of three short cycles.

In this analysis it seems significant that this entire three-cycle period exhibits a surprising number (though not all) of the features that characterize the typical single cycle. In most series it shows two cycles

[1] (National Bureau of Economic Research, 1932), a study sponsored by the Committee on Recent Economic Changes.

with large rises and small declines followed by one cycle with a small rise and large decline. In construction, as already noted, there is a practically uninterrupted rise during the whole of the first two cycles and a practically uninterrupted decline during the greater part of the last cycle. For this decline, residential construction is responsible.

The Stock Market

In stock exchange speculation the striking feature is not a repetition of three similar cycles, but successively rising waves culminating in a veritable mania. This, in connection with the intervals that have separated comparable fevers in the past, suggests strongly that there are psychological elements in this phase of business which have a longer natural period than some of the other elements, such as those connected with the time concentrations of expansion of capital equipment. One cycle of three years and four months appears to be too short for the working up of one of these more extreme forms of market brainstorm, including the process of forgetting the lessons supposedly learned from earlier experiences of the same sort. A 'new era'—or a new era psychology—cannot be successfully launched in three years.

Another line of explanation of the stock market boom is based upon the quantity of free funds seeking investment and constituting the demand for securities, relative to the supply. Expressed in an

[98

extreme form, this explanation states that the boom was simply due to the unprecedented quantity of savings seeking investment that accumulated in the prosperous period of 1922-29. According to this view, a rise in prices was a mathematical necessity, since the supply of securities into which these funds might flow, though large, was still limited. There can be little doubt that savings during this period were an increasing proportion, and probably an unprecedentedly large proportion, of an unprecedentedly large national dividend. A contributing factor, whose importance cannot be measured, was the retirement of the Federal war debt at a rate of over $800,000,000 a year, tending to increase the volume of free funds seeking re-investment. This fully neutralized the increase in state and local debts during the same period, and left free for private investment funds which would otherwise have been absorbed by increased issues of state and local bonds. Cheap money rates and the expansion of bank credit strengthened the movement, and are thought by some to have been the initiating and determining factor. The total was sufficient to finance a large export of capital and an enormous increase in our domestic capital equipment, and to leave something over for sheer speculative inflation of security values.

The effect of such a surplus of savings, if we assume that it existed, constitutes an interesting theoretical problem. A buys securities from B, and B

99]

spends the money either for other securities or for goods for consumption. It is reasonable to suppose that the funds circulate from investor to investor until the entire amount is spent, either by corporations for industrial capital or by one person or another for consumption purposes, or at least for goods other than stock market securities. Meanwhile, each purchase of securities has tended to enhance their prices. It can easily be conceived that in a period characterized by only mild recessions, for example, 1922-29, such a process would go on cumulatively, requiring several short cycles to reach its limits at the point where prospective incomes were capitalized at such extravagant rates that a reaction became inevitable. According to this explanation of the boom, the irrational values set on future yields were not the results of an original speculative mania; rather the apparent mania was the result of an oversupply of funds seeking investment. Between these two rival explanations statistics afford no way of choosing which element was of more importance as an originating cause. Both were present, each reacted on the other, and the natural conclusion is that both were jointly responsible for the result.

Such a boom destroys one corrective for a lack of equilibrium in the economic order, on which economic theorists have relied in their descriptions of a 'static' state. According to these theories, when there is an over-supply of investment funds, yields

[100

should decline and this should reduce the incentive to further saving and investment. But these same low yields, taking shape as they do in ever increasing prices of existing securities, give rise to enormous speculative profits to the holders, quite apart from the earnings of the industrial properties which the securities represent. Thus the stimulus to increased purchase of securities, instead of being self-limiting, becomes cumulative within limits which the recent boom showed to be surprisingly wide.

Construction

With respect to construction, it seems probable that the principal factor in the early stages of the post-War boom was the shortage inherited from the World War. This was presumably larger than the aftermath of a typical short-cycle depression—accurate comparative measures are unfortunately lacking—and the work of making it good took longer to get under way, partly on account of post-War restrictions on rentals. Thus, once started, it persisted beyond the limits of one general business cycle, and acquired a momentum which invited speculative activity, and this in turn carried construction to the point of what appears to have been a rather unusually large over-supply, at least in certain fields. This may well have been a strong factor in the rising trend of the two cycles of 1921-24 and 1924-27, with effects which returned to help sustain the building boom itself.

A factor which undoubtedly assisted very greatly, and one which tied construction to the stock market to an increased extent, was the shift to the corporate form of financing, bringing with it broadened sources of funds and also the opportunity for construction motivated by profits of promotion rather than by expectation of returns from rentals. One general hypothesis suggested by this experience is that, in the field of durable goods, the duration of the rebound of any one considerable type of business may be a function of the extent to which the supply in existence has been limited as a result of the preceding depression or dislocation. For that reason different branches of production may have longer or shorter revival movements during any one revival of general business.

Banking

Bank loans (loans of Federal Reserve member banks) behave similarly to construction in that between 1922 and 1931 there is only one actual cyclical decline: the one beginning in November, 1929. In this field, however, this form of behavior is typical of previous experience. Bank loans have, since 1879, shown a strong secular uptrend and only a moderate cyclical movement, with the result that, on the average, the effect of a general business recession is approximately cancelled by the secular uptrend. In the average cycle pattern, bank loans rise strongly during the up-swing of general business and remain approximately stable during the down-swing. The period 1879-1908 includes eight general business cycles, but in only four of these do bank loans show any positive decline. These facts, as far as they go, suggest the existence of longer rhythms than those of the short cycle; or they may suggest a classification of cycles into major ones, which are serious enough to bring about a positive decline in bank loans, and lesser ones which are not.

Fixed Capital

Another striking feature of the period 1922-29 was a strong upward movement in the proportion of fixed capital to labor not only in industry but also in agriculture. Since adequate measures are lacking, it is not possible to make a fully conclusive comparison of the rate at which this change was going on during the post-War period and earlier periods, but its importance in the later period seems outstanding, and it was proceeding at an accelerating rate, as witnessed by the fact that the rate of growth in production of capital equipment was far greater than that of goods in general,[2] and greater also than in the pre-War period, 1899-1913. This movement was so pronounced as to create a sus-

2 See F. C. Mills, *op. cit.*, pp. 22, 280-1, 284.

picion that it was a concentration of growth rather than a true secular trend, and was greater than could be permanently maintained and absorbed, at least by our business system as it now operates.

This is corroborated by evidences of growing excess productive capacity in numerous industries. The evidence is overwhelming in some instances, though no adequate measure of real excess capacity exists. Figures of theoretical capacity as commonly given are subject to heavy deductions for the purpose in hand.[3] As to whether capital funds are really increasing faster than industry in general can absorb them, or are merely misdirected, there can hardly be any scientifically conclusive test; and it is especially difficult to see how the question could have been answered while the growth was going on.

The answer hinges not only on the increase in capital, but also on the effect it has had in increasing the productiveness of industry. And these later accretions of capital seem to have been more effective than those of preceding periods in increasing physical output. Professor Mills' figures indicate that the country's physical output increased faster from 1922 to 1929 than during the fourteen years preceding the World War, while the period from 1913 to 1922 witnessed a still smaller increase.[4] In manufacturing, the period of post-War prosperity clearly shows a

[3] This point will be amplified in Part V, see pp. 150-1.
[4] See *Economic Tendencies in the United States*, pp. 3, 189, 284.

higher rate of increase in product per worker, though the number of workers was increasing more slowly.

As to the relation of output to fixed capital, one attempt has been made to measure this ratio for the years 1899 to 1921.[5] The conclusion was that while product per worker increased, capital per worker increased from three to four times as much. In the period of post-War prosperity, the indications are that product much more nearly kept pace with capital; indeed, with economies in working capital, it is not certain that total capital has increased faster than product.

The 'law of diminishing productivity' would lead us to expect that product would increase at a rate intermediate between the increase of labor and that of capital. If it increased as fast as capital, that would mean that technical progress had entirely neutralized the effects of the principle of diminishing productivity, and in the long run that is probably too much to expect. Thus on *a priori* grounds one may conclude that in all probability product, relative to labor and capital, was increasing during the post-War period at a higher rate than one would expect to be maintained as a long-run normal rate of increase. Such conclusions, however, can never be more than provisional.

[5] See C. W. Cobb and Paul H. Douglas's A Theory of Productivity, *American Economic Review Supplement*, March, 1928, pp. 139-65. The study includes the construction of an index number of fixed capital.

Corporate Net Incomes

During the period 1922-29, profits as represented by corporate net incomes, increased faster than wages. In manufacturing, net incomes increased at an annual rate of 5.3 per cent, per capita earnings of wage earners at the rate of 1.6 per cent, and number of factory workers at 1 per cent.[6] The conclusion seems clear that there was an increase in the proportion of total income going to profits (including those left in the business) and a corresponding decrease in the relative proportion going to wages and salaries—this in spite of a very considerable increase in real wages, reckoned in terms of commodity buying power.[7] These are both changes of the type which characterizes the upward swings of the familiar short cycle; but they have persisted through two short cycles and the up-swing of a third, instead of being fully cancelled by the down-swing of each

[6] For corporate earnings, see *Economic Tendencies in the United States*, p. 482; for wages, *ibid.*, pp. 478-9, and for number of workers, *ibid.*, p. 417. Cf. also King's *The National Income and Its Purchasing Power* (National Bureau of Economic Research, 1930) pp. 196, 94, 108. In King's figures, interest and dividends appear as a growing percentage of the national income, but total entrepreneurial income *realized by individuals* about holds its relative position.

[7] Mr. M. C. Rorty suggests that this movement represents a lagging adjustment to a prior disturbance brought about by the changed price level following the World War. In his view, interest and dividends were less than a normal percentage of the national income in 1922, and rose to only a trifle above normal in 1929. The question remains whether this 'normal' represents a satisfactory state of long-run balance.

successive short cycle. It is as if we had superimposed on the three short cycles, one longer one whose up-swing lasted from 1921 to 1929 and whose down-swing would probably be found to coincide with the unusually long and deep down-swing of the last of the three short cycles. This last down-swing may be found to have fully cancelled the effects of the entire period 1921-29, with respect to the relative shares of income going to profits and to wages, wiping out the gains made by profits in this period.

Thus this ten-year period 1922-32 resembles the movements characterizing the shorter cycle in speculation, construction, growth of capital equipment and distribution of incomes. In two other factors of prime importance the movements of this period were far from characteristic of the shorter cyclical movements. Prices remained approximately stable but with a sagging tendency after 1925, culminating in a catastrophic fall. This may be interpreted as a long cycle superimposed on a downward secular trend; but such an analysis may not carry conviction. Nor is it wholly adequate to speak of it as a delayed post-War deflation, so far as that implies a return to what would have been normal had the War not occurred. If that has happened, it can only be by the merest chance, when the distribution of the world's gold, national budgets and balances of international trade and indebtedness are all racked by the strains of the post-War 'settlements'.

107]

Employment

With respect to employment, the figures for total factory employment for the ten-year period show simply three cycles, with little or no upward trend to match the growth of population. In the cases of railroads, mining and agriculture, numbers attached to these industries failed to keep pace with the growth of population.[8] Figures of actual unemployment are notoriously inadequate but if there was a ten-year cycle, its upward swing carried with it no clear decrease of unemployment, and possibly even an increase. The seemingly abnormal increase of capital equipment had not been employing many more workers, and may even have been displacing them, if allowance is made for the growth of population. Thus the heavy cyclical fall in employment, when it came, was all the more serious.

Durable Goods

Another feature of this ten-year period was a large increase in the proportion of our income going into durable goods, with all the consequences indicated in the earlier parts of this study. These types of expenditure are in a high degree optional, postponable and subject to intensified fluctuations, both because of the durability of the goods purchased and because of the luxury or semi-luxury character of

8 See King, *op. cit.,* pp. 56-7.

fresh additions to the community's supply. For both these reasons they represent types of goods in which the forces which operate toward the beginnings of a recovery might naturally be expected to be slower in their action in proportion both to the durability of the goods and to their luxury or semi-luxury character.[9] Thus elements of added sensitiveness have apparently been introduced into our economic system. This point will be developed in Part IV, dealing with this last cycle.

Conclusion

It is easier to record the changes occurring in such a period than to interpret their meaning. What are their causes? Are they the natural results of growing economic power, or only the natural results under certain conditions, for instance, of credit institutions and the distribution of incomes? Do they represent a state of balance or 'moving equilibrium' in the general sense of equality between supply and demand, adequate and unhampered use of existing productive powers and no obstacles to their future development and use? Or do they represent maladjustments in this large, but still limited, sense?

In dealing with the typical patterns of the short cycles, the *rationale* of different specific features was

[9] The importance of the increase of luxury goods, demand for which is highly sensitive, has been stressed by Mr. M. C. Rorty; see "How May Business Revival Be Forced?" *Harvard Business Review Supplement*, April, 1932, pp. 385-98.

examined as each came up for discussion. The nature of these longer swings is such an organic whole that this method seems hardly applicable; and the problem can better be treated as a unit. This will be attempted in Part VI, against the background of a study of the basic conditions of moving equilibrium in a growing society. An attempt will be made to judge at least tentatively the nature and meaning of the post-War movements.

PART FOUR

SPECIAL FEATURES OF THE

LAST CYCLE

Summary

MOST of the distinguishing features of the last cycle have already been indicated in the course of the discussion. There was the world-wide decline in prices, the beginnings of which were visible before the general decline in American business began, and which continued and grew serious hand in hand with the progress of the general business recession. There was the behavior of our export trade, which showed a strongly marked cycle in harmony with our own, and which took the lead on the decline—both features being peculiar to this cycle. There was the concentration of expansion upon securities rather than mainly upon goods, culminating in the mad boom in the stock market and the resulting violent collapse, together with the continuance of the boom past the peak of general business instead of taking the lead on the down-turn, as usual. There was the peculiar behavior of construction. There was the depression of agriculture which prevailed before the general business recession and became deeper. There was the attempt to sustain construction and capital expansion by the method of conference and voluntary action—an attempt which did not prevent heavy declines. There were the attempts to resist the decline of money wage rates and to sustain the prices of leading agricultural products by buying and holding the surplus. And there was the fiscal and monetary crisis in various foreign countries, coming to a head at a time when the depression had already gone deeper and lasted longer than usual. There was an unusual number of bank failures, becoming increasingly prevalent and alarming as the depression lengthened, and followed or accompanied by an unusual tightening of bank credit and a wave of withdrawal and hoarding of cash, against which a determined campaign was launched, first by methods similar to those first used in the attempt to sustain capital expenditures, and later by the Emergency Credit Corporation and other tangible means.[1]

Another feature of the current cycle was the piling up of unusually large stocks of several basic com-

[1] Since the above was written the situation has been brought to a head by the general banking suspension of March, 1933.

[112

modities, among which wheat and oil stood conspicuous but by no means alone. Ordinarily, literal over-production as evidenced by the actual piling up of stocks is a relatively small factor in the cycle, and only appears after recession has set in. In this case, there were some significant increases before the down-turn in general business; and the stocks of a number of basic materials ultimately accumulated appeared unusually and alarmingly large.

Another feature has been the unusually large part played by consumption goods in the decline; the decrease in their production has been great and began before that in other industries. Passenger automobiles were apparently the dominant factor in this movement, at least in the earlier stages. This suggests that we have an added problem to face in the relative increase of durable consumers' goods, new purchases of which at any given time are not in the class of necessities but are highly postponable or optional. Inventories in the hands of consumers thus come to be more and more important; and we must expect that an increasing length of time must elapse before these inventories will be worn down to a point at which new purchases will be required if the consumer is to go on consuming. Though sales of automobiles fell off enormously, it was not until 1931 that they fell clearly below what may be taken as a normal replacement basis; thus indicating an actual decrease in the number of normally effective cars in

113]

the hands of users; and even that did not mean that the gross number of cars of all ages was decreasing.

A cursory survey of conditions tends to the conclusion that practically all possible factors conspired to do their worst in the present depression; especially the non-cyclical factors which appear to have marked this as a phase of post-War dislocation even more than a cyclical decline. There are, it is true, some puzzles to confront in any such diagnosis. Construction, contrary to custom, was declining almost throughout the up-swing of general business; while stock exchange speculation, also contrary to custom, continued to rise until after the beginning of general recession. If one of these was an unfavorable condition, was the other favorable? And if both were unfavorable, how is this to be explained?

Probably the truth is that the particular timing of these movements was not of so much importance, especially as they tended to offset each other, as the fact that both had gone beyond the usual degree of expansion characterizing a typical cyclical up-swing. The impetus from the speeding-up of construction incident to making good the War-time shortage was not exhausted in one cycle, and was prolonged by the further stimulus of speculative building. And as to the stock market, the continued rise in paper values after the underlying productive processes had slowed up caused in itself an unusual and unbalanced condition, tending to make the final crash

[114

worse. It meant to a considerable extent that the usual adjustments to a slowing-up of production were not made at the usual time.

Stock prices during the great boom were capitalizing not current earnings but future increases of a sort which any systematic analysis should have revealed as beyond all human possibility. The only other justification for such values would have been a radical and enduring reduction of interest rates. But this should have affected stocks and bonds alike, and the rates on bonds and mortgages prevailing at the same time showed no such radical decline as would have been needed to rationalize the prices of stocks. What was happening was a relative shift of demand, in favor of speculative securities, out of all proportion to the magnitude of ordinary shifts of this sort, carrying values, relative to yields, to points far outside what could be called normal, unless on the basis of an expectation of future increase which no industrial system could maintain. A person who appreciated this fact might still have bought stocks in the hope that the craze would last long enough to enable him to sell out at a profit, leaving some other purchaser to bear the inevitable disillusionment; but this psychology of 'after us the deluge' was not the one which actually prevailed, and it could hardly have accounted for the extravagant lengths to which the boom was carried. Buyers who thought of the matter at all were typically convinced that the country had entered upon a 'new era' in which deluges were not to be permitted.

Non-Cyclical Factors: Post-War Conditions

The current depression is more than the end of a business cycle of unusual severity. On the basis of cyclical theory limited to the hypothesis of the type of cycle averaging in this country three and a third years, it is impossible fully to explain all its characteristics—its small rise, enormous decline and long-continued period of prostration. In part it may furnish evidence, of a provisional sort, of the combination of the shorter cycles with a longer cycle of about three times the average duration of the shorter ones. This longer cycle appears to rest in considerable part on the psychology of speculation, and on the related factors of expansion of fixed capital and of construction.

But these factors are themselves not unrelated to another set of factors which are not cyclical at all in any discoverable fashion: namely, the process of post-War reconstruction and the dislocated conditions of international finance and trade, which the War left behind it. One legacy of the War was a price structure which, even in 1921, had presumably not completed its destined deflation. In this country, prices were still well above the pre-War level, while the world at large had not returned to the gold basis. Along with this went a mal-distribution of the world's gold supply which left this country with ample gold to sustain the post-War price level without straining its credit machinery, while other countries lacked a gold basis adequate to the requirements that would be set up by resumption of specie payment. As country after country resumed specie payment, they took up the burden of sustaining a volume of media of exchange adequate to the current price level on a scant gold basis. Thus the price level rested on an insecure foundation, and what might be called the normal deflation was postponed. Any tendency to downward movements in prices was further blocked at numerous points by specific measures for sustaining the prices of numerous particular commodities. This entire situation meant weak currency and credit structures, which must be protected against large gold movements; while gold movements were called for by the War's legacy of economically abnormal debts and the impossibility of paying them in commodities. Palliatives such as short-time borrowing increased the instability.

The result would have been to strip Europe of gold completely, had it not been for a great flow of loans from this country—a movement which in the nature of the case could not go on forever. This we can now see, though no one could predict in advance when or how the end would come. The case was not like the former borrowings of the United

States from Europe: borrowings which furnished capital needed for the development of a virgin continent into the most productive area of the world. These new loans back to Europe were made to a weakened economy, in amounts beyond what was directly productive. They were made by a country unwilling to do what Europe had done when it was our creditor: namely, accept payment in goods. Thus there was doubt whether debtor economies would bear the aggregate debt charges in addition to their other burdens, and certainty that the creditor country would not accept real repayment if it could be made. The movement of European funds into the American stock market, lured by the boom, was an aggravating circumstance. Ultimately the price structure broke and a catastrophic fall in world prices followed. Later, credit structures also collapsed, having been further weakened by the piling up of perilously large volumes of international short-term obligations. Thus pressures accumulated through a period of years, and finally came to a head.

For the United States the post-War export of capital postponed for at least ten years the impact of the new position of a creditor country in which the War left us. To this new position we have not yet begun to adjust our economy, or manifested any real appreciation of the nature of the necessary adjustments or any willingness to make them. We continued apparently determined to go on selling goods abroad and unwilling to receive in return goods which competed with our own products. And now we stand helplessly contemplating the collapse of this system and unable to face in any new direction. Our tariff on competitive goods is nearly prohibitive, and two-thirds of our imports consist of those non-competitive goods which are left on the free list. Under these conditions Europe can manifestly not continue to take our products in the volume essential to our existing plan of prosperity; but with this fact we have not yet made our reckoning. This represents a non-cyclical factor of vast importance, both for the present and for the future.

Increase of Durable Goods

Another factor in the present situation, bearing not merely on the existing crisis but also on the probable character of future cycles, is the outcome of our rising standard of living and especially the increasing importance of durable consumers' goods. As we have already seen, these changes result in a great relative increase in the volume of purchases which are optional and to a high degree postponable, and hence peculiarly sensitive to changes in the flow of current incomes and in the general state of confidence.

A further complication is the fact that such purchases are largely made on credit—indeed, the volume of credit used to finance such purchases appears to have been increasing faster than the volume of this class of purchases, indicating an intensified increase in the resort to credit.[2] This credit is of a longer-term sort than retailers' current accounts, and is highly expansible because it is based on the specific security of the particular goods bought. And while credit may be more a passive and enabling force than an active and initiating one, it is still crucially important.

Any class of purchases made on this sort of credit is one in which it is possible for current purchases to move more or less independently of the volume of current income derived from past acts of production, and we have seen that durable goods are by their nature predisposed to just such movements. Such movements have a peculiar power to *initiate changes in the rate of production*. This they could not do if purchases must always equal income; income in turn being made up of the financial proceeds of *past acts of production*. Once initiated, changes in production return in the familiar cumulative fashion to cause further changes in purchases. Thus goods of this sort, bought in this way, are a peculiarly disturbing element in our economic life. And because this element is increasing, it may well

[2] This statement is based on a study of construction made for the National Bureau of Economic Research, in cooperation with the Committee on Recent Economic Changes, by W. C. Clark and Miss Victoria Pederson; and on the growth of installment selling as reported in unpublished studies made for the National Bureau.

be that, if no effective means of stabilization are found, business cycles in this country are destined to become progressively more severe in the future.

In this connection there is also the possibility that the increasing volume of durable goods may lengthen the time required for the using-up of inventories in the hands of consumers, and thus cause one of the forces of recovery to act more slowly. As a further result of longer periods of subnormal production, there may be more work to do, upon the revival of demand, to bring supplies up to a prosperity normal. The resulting expansion in these industries may be either more violent or more prolonged, depending on how rapidly they can expand their output. The outcome may take one of several forms: (1) more violent expansions of general business, (2) more prolonged expansions of general business, or (3) expansions in these special industries lasting over more than one short cycle of general business, as the post-War construction boom did, thus tending toward an alternation of mild and severe cycles. Possibly all three effects might appear at different times, according to the special conditions prevailing.

Conditions Bearing on Recovery

The study of the special features of the present depression seems to indicate that it may have extended past the point at which some of the usual forces of automatic recovery can be expected to come into operation, largely because consumers' reserves became exhausted, while there was still a large surplus of construction and capital equipment relative to the shrunken volume of purchasing power. As a result, the prospect of recovery through the usual automatic forces was no longer extremely hopeful, and a search for more powerful and positive measures was urgently indicated.

On the other hand, the trough of the depression witnessed widespread hoarding, an abnormal restriction of credit—abnormal even for a depression—and a condition approaching panic on the part of banks even before the general suspension of March, 1933.[3] All this gives some ground for hope that if these conditions can be overcome and an upward movement once started, it may have cumulative effects of the usual sort, and may even initiate the chain of causes leading to a recovery as complete as the new international conditions make possible. These new international conditions, however, act as a bar to the hope that we may quickly catch up with the trend of 1922-29 and continue on a prolongation of that upward movement. We cannot continue indefinitely to finance a large export surplus with loans

[3] This and the following paragraph were originally written before the inauguration of President Roosevelt and the general banking suspension of March, 1933. The final opportunity for revision comes as the Roosevelt recovery program is getting under way but too soon for any considered estimate of its results. Therefore the original statements have been allowed to remain.

over and above the debt payments due us, and thus maintain our industry in the happy state of working both for the foreign and the domestic markets. That particular vein of prosperity appears to be worked out. Hence it seems highly improbable that the next revival will reach the heights of 1928-29, whatever may ultimately happen.

One further consequence of serious moment follows. Improvements in technique have been installed, or stand ready to be installed, which will still further economize labor, and if total output does not reach the level of the former peak, the next revival cannot restore more than a part of the employment which the present depression took away. We shall have a large unemployment problem in the winter of 1933-34, and the following winter, even if revival follows upon the efforts of the Roosevelt administration and goes as far as any rational forecast can conceive. This means that, even while we face the immediate pressure to feed and shelter the needy, and relegate 'long-range planning' to an indefinite future, planning of an intermediate sort is pertinent, practical and almost necessary: planning for one, two and three years ahead. For example, a coordination and extension of present local and fragmentary schemes for enabling the otherwise unemployed to produce for their own and one another's needs under a system of barter or other interchange: this might be a most practical undertaking.

123]

PART FIVE

ANOTHER APPROACH: THE MEANING AND REQUIREMENTS OF BALANCE

Introduction

THE factual evidence on business cycles may be used in another way: to give a broader basis to the type of study which starts from the conditions of a theoretical equilibrium and explains business cycles by the absence of some of these conditions. Such theories are likely to rely on too simple and one-sided a picture of the conditions of equilibrium, and as a consequence to get too simple results. There is great power of simplification in substituting for the question: "How does business operate?" the question: "Why does it *not* operate according to the picture of ideal equilibrium?" To know how business operates requires many facts: to know that it does not follow the ideal picture requires very few. And

[124

the same is true of the task of explanation. To explain everything that happens is, needless to say, an
impossible task; but when the question is: "Why
does business *not* run smoothly?" one glaring gap
in the conditions of equilibrium is sufficient for an
answer which will carry conviction to many, however inadequate it may be to explain the full phenomenon of the actual cycle in all its complexity
and variety.

But after a real factual survey one can ask this
question with less danger of giving a naïvely simple
answer. One sees that there are many conditions
necessary to equilibrium, and many respects in which
they are not fulfilled. Thus a more adequate attempt
at the specification of the conditions of economic
stability might furnish the basis for a more valid
diagnosis of the causes of instability, while still sim-
plifying the picture enough to make it manageable.

One very important thing which this method does
is to afford a basis for an answer to the question
'why' instead of merely to the question 'how'. *Why*
do things act in the way they do instead of in some
other way? This we do not learn from a bare study
of the facts, which merely tells us *how* different
events succeed or accompany each other in the actual
system we possess. To get even a tentative answer
to the more searching question we need some basis
for judging what would be the results of a system
where certain crucial conditions were different; and

to answer it comprehensively we need a picture of a system in which there would be no business cycles.

One special service which such a method of study may render is to afford a basis for interpreting the meaning of trends operating over longer periods than the short cycles whose average length is forty months. Are these longer movements 'normal'? Are they evidence of lack of 'equilibrium'? Neither pure observation nor pure theory can give an absolute answer to such questions, but the two together can afford suggestions as to whether our economic system is such as to guarantee that such trends will be in a state of approximate equilibrium, or whether some of the necessary conditions are lacking. In the latter event, theory may indicate whether the results naturally to be expected are such as appear in the observed trends. These might then be provisionally diagnosed as representing lack of equilibrium: failure to balance the forces of supply and demand in the broadest sense. And if the concept of equilibrium is itself vague, such a study should help to make it more definite.

Of course, this picture of the requirements of stability would be an effort of the scientific imagination rather than a fact of observation; but a survey of the facts should vastly increase its realistic quality. And apparently the scientific imagination has to be called in at some stage or other of the process of

[126

interpreting and utilizing facts for the guidance of new policies; hence no apologies are called for.

The Meaning of 'Balance'

The whole process is strongly suggested by the use of the concept of 'balance' in an early report of the Committee on Recent Economic Changes. The present writer was set at once to wondering what 'balance' means in this connection. What can it mean in an economy expanding rapidly and at different rates in its various constituent parts? Can a condition be conceived and described which would deserve the name 'balance', in which population is increasing, capital increasing more rapidly, product per capita increasing at still a different rate, perhaps in the long run intermediate between the other two,[1] technical methods of production changing as they must to utilize the increasing supply of capital per worker, older methods being constantly rendered obsolete (though not constantly in every process at once), and new goods being developed as the consequence of increased spending power resulting from increased production. This is emphatically not a static condition, and it is one to which the conceptions of equilibrium and balance can be applied only in a special and limited sense.

The term 'balance' was used by the Committee on Recent Economic Changes only in the sense of a

[1] Cf. discussion in Part III, p. 105.

rough approximation, with the idea of a 'zone of tolerance' beyond which disproportions become serious. The question remains, however, approximation to what? Tolerable degree of departure from what? In the discussion that follows, whenever the conception of absolute balance appears, it is not used with the idea that no departures from this absolute balance are tolerable in a working system. Indeed it will appear that absolute balance, even as an ideal, involves mutually inconsistent requirements in a moving world. The concept will be used merely in an attempt to define the standards from which the tolerable degree of departure is to be gauged.

It is clear that business cycles in their very nature are departures from balance in the absolute sense. So also are seasonal fluctuations, though these are easier to allow for and to absorb into a reasonably predictable scheme of working and spending. For the present purpose we may leave seasonal fluctuations to one side, regarding them as in the main within the 'zone of tolerance', though that does not mean that nothing further should be done to minimize them. From one standpoint, they might be regarded as assimilated into a balanced scheme if idleness resulting were minimized and the unavoidable remainder made up for by higher rates of reward in the more seasonal trades sufficient to provide an annual income not clearly out of balance

[128

with those of other classes of workers or of property.[2]

As to business cycles, the question whether they are or are not within the 'zone of tolerance' is a question not of objective fact but of judgment. Such disturbances as the present are clearly outside such a zone, by any rational judgment. In this matter the chief service that can be rendered by a study of the conditions of balance is probably to show how movements in one feature of the economic system call for adjustments in other features; and how the condition we are accustomed to think of as balance in one field may imply lack of balance somewhere else, so that one or both will need to be revised in a synthesis that can fairly claim to be within the 'zone of tolerance' in all its features.

The idea of balance seems to have as its point of departure the idea of approximate equality of supply and demand, so far as this is consistent with movement and incentives for movement. But supply and demand for *goods* may reach momentary balance at very varying levels of price and of volume of production and employment. In that sense the present condition of depression might be said to be one of balance, though this is clearly true only in a most superficial sense. More fundamental is a balance between prices, costs and profits; meaning a state tending toward only such movements as can be sustained

[2] For fuller discussion, see the author's *Economics of Overhead Costs,* Chapter VIII.

without violent reversals. More fundamental still, perhaps, is a balance between supply and demand for *productive forces, especially labor;* in other words, freedom from undue amounts of unemployment. Millions of people with needs for goods, able and willing to work at producing things to satisfy these needs, and deprived of opportunity to do so, certainly represent an unbalanced condition between our productive powers and the need or potential demand for their employment.

The fact that supply and demand for goods can be balanced at present only at volumes of production that mean an intolerable amount of unemployment (lack of balance between supply and demand for labor) is evidence that the requirements of balance in the superficial and in the fundamental senses have not been harmonized, in our present system. It seems to indicate that the concept of balance is an incomplete concept, made up of elements which become to some extent incompatible under actual conditions. Perhaps the best we can hope for is a state in which the discrepancies between balance in different senses are compromised sufficiently to bring them all within the 'zone of tolerance'. This is what a piano-tuner does in adjusting the much smaller inconsistencies in the mathematical requirements governing the intervals of our musical scale. The result leaves differences in the character of compositions played in

[130

different keys, which a trained musician readily recognizes.

A fundamentally balanced economy would be one in which the business cycle as we know it would have ceased to exist, or would be limited to rather mild fluctuations. It would be a state in which productive powers and productive opportunities would be reasonably well matched, and there would be no great discrepancies between supply and demand, and no great wastes of productive powers for lack of opportunity to use them.

Labor and Employment

The things to be balanced are many; but first and foremost we may consider the supply of labor and the volume of employment, recognizing that they are dependent in turn upon a network of conditioning factors which will have to be separately considered. But before we can go on to consider them we are faced by the baffling fact that we cannot say offhand what percentage of complete employment should be taken as constituting balance in this one field. Even in this one matter, such concept of balance as we have is probably made up of incompatible elements. Industry is adjusted to an excess of unemployed labor in normal times; and in any dynamic economy based on free enterprise such a margin plays a considerable part in facilitating the starting of new enterprises and the expansion of existing

131]

ones. The role it plays may not be indispensable, but it is at least part of the provisional scheme of 'balance' to which we are accustomed; the balance between active and reserve workers. In another and probably more fundamental sense it represents a lack of balance.

This quota of unemployed is, in the necessities of the case, a shifting personnel—otherwise its members could hardly exist. Those who are occasionally or chronically among the number must, to that extent, be irregularly employed; and as the personnel is shifting, this means irregular employment for a larger number than is unemployed at any but an extraordinary time. Unless this reserve army can be kept down to smaller proportions than heretofore, we must accept the existence of irregular employment for a material fraction of the wage earners as part of our working approximation to 'balance', though not a satisfactory part. The underlying lack of balance which it represents will never be universally accepted as coming within the 'zone of tolerance' in the long run.

The state of employment in times of active business, while it never absorbs all the workers, absorbs too many for 'balance' from the standpoint of the employer's satisfaction with the quality of his working force. He expects to choose among the candidates and reject those who do not come up to standard. Super-active business involves a lowering of these standards, and discipline and the quality of work suffer. At other times, the worker's fear of losing the job is one of the forces helping the employer to restore discipline. From this standpoint, balance may mean sufficient unemployment to give the employer some benefit from the worker's fear of losing the job, and not so much as to breed dangerous unrest.

Possibly no employer formulates the matter in quite this cold-blooded way. Certainly the more progressive have advanced beyond this standard to the extent of taking active measures to reduce the amount of casual employment and to further the placing of handicapped workers. Many probably recognize unemployment as an evil and a waste, without fully realizing the extent to which their own systems of discipline and incentives are dependent on it. They may use disciplinary discharge only as a last resort, and still benefit unconsciously from the workers' fear of losing their jobs through layoffs occasioned by scarcity of work. As the issue comes more and more to be faced, employers must more and more revise and develop their systems of discipline and incentives in harmony with a greatly lessened volume of unemployment. Only so can a scheme of balance be developed deserving of the name, from the standpoint of the social scientist. And it may be that such a scheme, involving greatly increased regularity of employment, would for that very reason bring out the problem of the unemploy-

133]

able worker in a form which would make some effective community action necessary.

Thus balance in the labor market is hard to define, and harder still to visualize in terms of the concrete conditions necessary to bring it about. Fairly regular employment for all reasonably qualified workers seems, however, not a fantastic standard to set in the long run. Anything short of this leaves vast productive forces out of balance, as well as serious forces of social discontent. Our failure to achieve this standard is a result of causes which need investigating. Presumably it results from a lack of balance elsewhere in the system.

A balance between supply and demand for labor depends, among other things, on a reasonably steady rate of production in general. It is not proved that steady production would of itself guarantee the absorption of surplus labor, though the long-run forces of supply and demand would be working in that direction. But it seems clear that reasonably steady production is a necessary condition—that without it there will inevitably be chronically repeated periods of wide-spread unemployment.

Steady Production: the Individualist Prescription

Steady production is, from one standpoint, merely a corollary of the general assumption of balance between supply and demand, since the total supply of labor and capital is comparatively steady, and can

be in perfect balance with demand only when demand absorbs it all. This is theoretically possible,
because effective demand is itself the reflection of the
volume of production; and is potentially capable of
absorbing more goods than we have yet produced.
From the extreme individualistic standpoint, steady
production with full utilization of our productive
powers is merely a matter of producing the right
things, setting prices on them which will move them
off the markets, and adjusting the charges for the
productive factors at levels that will induce employers to make use of them.

In other words, if there is difficulty in maintaining full production, the logical individualist would
say: do not maintain prices. Slash them without
limit until full production is restored, for all except
the high-cost producers who may fall by the way-
side. If there is 'technological unemployment', do
not maintain wages. Slash them until the worker can
compete with the machine and the employer can
afford to hire him. Then the employer's own competition for labor and materials will put an end to the
slashing sooner than anyone expects, equilibrium
will be restored with full production instead of cur-
tailed production, and the people will be the richer.
If demand in some industries is so limited that full
employment can be had only at cut-throat wages,
the workers must offer their services elsewhere. It is
possible that a country in which such policies were

135]

actually followed would suffer less from depressions than does the United States in the twentieth century. It might produce more and consume more. But as to whether it could assure itself full and steady utilization of its productive powers by this method, there is room for doubt. The question is not simple.

If prices, wages and profits all fell in harmony, nothing might be accomplished. And if wages fell more than the other shares, might there not be a cutting-off of markets for consumers' goods which would defeat the purpose of the whole process? There is need of a balance between the portion of income spent for consumption and the portion saved, and this will be disturbed by any sudden shifting of incomes from wage and salaried workers, who spend most of their incomes, to profit-takers, from whom the bulk of the savings comes.

Savings and Capital Expenditures

If all savings were automatically and promptly spent for goods of some sort—capital equipment and raw materials—then the question might not be so urgent. The total demand for goods would be the same whether savings were large or small, and expenditures would equal production. But this does not automatically happen. There are a number of steps in the process, and they must maintain balance among themselves if the total volume of savings is to be always equal to the volume of net expenditures for capital goods. Original savings are supplemented at times by the expansive power of the credit system. Government may borrow a part, or may repay past borrowings. In the latter case, the volume of funds seeking productive investment is greater than the volume of original savings. Or if savings exceed the momentary requirements of business, they may flow into the stock market and send it upward, creating profits, some of which are spent for consumption, so that in effect part of the savings is diverted to consumptive expenditures, while the expansion of credit more than makes up the diversion. The savings that flow into a booming stock market are not obviously equal to the resulting expenditures on factories. Thus arise discrepancies between savings and expenditures for capital goods.

In the long run, perhaps, there must be a balance. If purchases of capital goods run ahead of savings, they must be liquidated out of future savings; and if savings are not put into capital goods of some sort they will not remain in existence. But the temporary discrepancies are enormously important; and it appears that they may endure over more than one short cycle. Since some discrepancy is very likely inseparable from any upward or downward inflection of the course of business, the problem is one of keeping them within reasonable bounds.

137]

A Stable Credit System versus Cumulative Movements

The chief conditions requisite in order that expenditures may equal incomes may perhaps be summed up in the formula of a non-fluctuating credit system. But that is not the same thing as saying that this condition can be brought about simply by the policies of banks and other credit institutions, still less by the agencies of central control which we now possess. They cannot force industry to absorb credit against its will, when there is no apparent profitable use to which the funds can be put. And to regulate the demand for credit, as well as the supply, is another way of stating the basic problem of regulating the expansion of industrial production.

One phase of this problem of stable credit and its effect on economic equilibrium is illustrated by the condition so often assumed in the type of economic theory which deals with conditions of equilibrium: namely, that if more is spent on one thing, there is just that much less left to spend on something else. If more is saved and invested, just that much less is left to be spent on consumption goods. If this condition were realized, movements in particular parts of the economic field would be more quickly self-limiting than they are in fact, while general disturbances of the whole volume of production and consumption could arise only from powerful outside

[138

forces. They could not be self-generating. Development would also probably be slower than it actually is.

As the system actually operates, spending more on one thing is quite likely to mean spending more on other things also, and *vice versa*. This is by reason of the combined action of two basic causes. One is an elastic credit system, which makes it possible to spend more for one thing without at the same time spending less for something else. The other is the fact that setting more people at work making any one thing gives them more spending power to use in buying other things so that the result is not less demand for other things, nor even the same amount as before, but actually more. If more is spent for capital equipment, more will also be spent for consumers' goods, not in spite of increased capital expenditures but because of them. A balanced economy must somehow get rid of this element of cumulative piling-up of impulses, or at least keep it within reasonable bounds, by controlling either its causes or its effects.

Long-Run Problems of Distribution of Incomes

When this condition is achieved, the worst instabilities in the demand for labor will have been removed. There will remain the question whether the rates of wages, and the relative costs of labor and capital, are such as to call into use the whole supply

139]

of labor. This depends on two factors. One is the total demand for goods, which is governed by the total volume of purchasing power currently spent, whether it comes from income or from credit. The second is the proportions in which it is economical for employers to use capital and labor, as governed by their relative costs at current rates of wages and of interest.

High wages have two effects, if carried to the point at which their increase exceeds that of the productiveness of industry. They tend to increase expenditures and decrease savings, by putting more of the nation's income in the hands of those who will spend a larger part of it for consumers' goods, and spend it more quickly. But they also tend to make labor more expensive, and so to increase the incentive of the employer to use more capital per worker: in other words, to replace some labor with machines.[3] Lower wages have the opposite effect in both these fields. In an economy where all savings were spent at once, low wages would not reduce total spendings, but would make labor more economical to hire, as compared with increased use of machinery. The resulting decrease in the effective demand for capital

[3] Theoretical objections have been raised to this proposition, but they do not appear sufficient to destroy its validity in the existing situation. The present writer has dealt with them briefly in Inductive Evidence on Marginal Productivity, *American Economic Review*, XVIII, 452, September, 1928. Full discussion at this point would lead the argument too far afield.

would reduce its price, until an equilibrium was reached.

In our actual economy, immediate expenditures on capital equipment depend more on the business man's demand for capital than on the supply of original savings, the elasticity of credit taking up any temporary discrepancies, while the price of capital is decidedly sluggish in its movements. In this situation, lower wages are likely to reduce the total amount of current spendings without greatly altering the price of capital or doing anything else to change materially the proportion of labor and capital which it is economical for the employer to use. These proportions are slow to change, being largely fixed by the character of capital equipment accumulated in the past. Thus it is possible that lower wages may in their immediate effect do more to decrease the effective demand for labor than to increase it. They may defeat their own end by reducing the immediate volume of spendings.

There is a real unsolved problem here; whether there is an incompatibility between the rates of wages which are necessary to make it profitable for employers to give labor full employment, and the high wages which are being commonly advocated as means of maintaining purchasing power. Can purchasing power be maintained only at rates of wages which are so high as to bring about 'technological unemployment'? The post-War trends in this country may be construed as evidence of failure to solve this dilemma. Possibly we shall not solve it until we reach a condition in which wage earners receive a larger share of the national income, in forms which do not constitute a wages-charge upon the employer's act of hiring them: in other words, until we achieve the goal of a capitalism in which everyone is a capitalist, or some other system which accomplishes the same result.

In the meantime, and with reference to the problem of cyclical fluctuations, stabilization of employment through stabilization of demand appears both more promising of success and more consistent with the long-run requirements of a stable economic order than attempted stabilization through unlimited slashing of wage rates. Particular wage rates may be too high for balance, and may need to come down. Others may be too low, enabling inefficient employers to survive whose business should be transferred to more competent ones, who could pay higher wages. And the automatic raising of real wage rates which sometimes occurs when prices fall during a business recession and money wages lag behind is clearly an unbalancing factor occurring at the wrong time and having nothing to do with the requirements of economic equilibrium. It tends to aggravate unemployment and thus to lower real earnings of labor as a whole, as distinct from hourly or weekly wage rates for those actually employed.

[142

New Goods

The absorption of available productive power may be a matter not merely of stimulating demand for existing goods, but also of developing new goods on which increased purchasing power may be spent. A rapidly advancing system cannot bring productive power and demand into balance without large and continual developments of this sort.

The characteristic history of new goods is that they are used first by the wealthy or well-to-do, serving to enlarge their consumption, and afterward spread to the lower income-groups as increased output and improved processes bring cheaper production, and as the expanding incomes of the members of the lower income-groups make it possible for them to enlarge their spendings. This whole process takes so much time that it cannot be crowded within one short cycle, though the last phase of it may make marked progress during any one expansion of business. Without this last phase, the process cannot have very large effects on business as a whole; and this final stage requires a widespread distribution of the gains resulting from increased productive power, not a concentration in the hands of the well-to-do minority. At any given time, the greatest possibilities for quick expansion lie in increasing the incomes of those who are just below the level which makes it possible for them to become large buyers of goods which have already been developed.

The basic problem here can be formulated as that of balance between expanding productive power and the rate at which the development of the corresponding expansion of our standard of living can go on. This expansion involves the development of new goods and of demand for them, and of such an amount and distribution of purchasing power as can make the demand effective and assimilate the new goods approximately as fast as we gain the power to produce them.

Hours of Labor

If we fail to develop consumption sufficiently to absorb our increased productive power, there is still another method of bringing about balance: namely, by reducing the hours of labor. But if this means forcing workers to accept a six-hour day and six hours' pay when they would rather work eight hours for eight hours' pay, it still leaves the length of the working day out of balance. Such a forcible reduction is essentially an emergency measure for distributing unemployment, not a permanent means of eliminating it. We may call this policy 'work-sharing'. It is quite different from the normal downward trend of the working day or working week which arises from the collective choice of the workers and has the effect of giving them part of the gains of increased production in the shape of more goods and part in the shape of more leisure. In this latter movement, a gradual shortening of the working week is accompanied by a gradual increase of real wages, not a decrease, as when men work part-time to distribute unemployment. We shall not have achieved true balance until these two standards come together; until the working week at which labor can find full employment is the same as the working week which the workers would freely choose in the course of their bargainings, and which carries with it as an ultimate effect an implied balancing of the value of more goods against the value of more leisure.[4]

Of course, if there are going to be industrial fluctuations, no given length of working week will solve the problem. In that event, there might be a system in which work-sharing is used to spread the effect of

[4] Mr. F. W. Thornton, who has read the manuscript of this study, comments to the effect that workers will commonly strive for shorter hours for the trade in general while at the same time trying to get longer hours for themselves as individuals. They feel that the ultimate adjustment of wages to a longer or shorter standard week is not the same as the effect of longer or shorter hours for an individual in a given setting of standard hours and wage rates. In the latter case it is obvious that more work means more pay; while in the former case shorter hours are not expected to mean proportionately decreased pay, nor even the foregoing of proportionate increases in pay which could otherwise be had. The discussion in the text refers to the fixing of standard hours: a choice in which the ultimate effects on consuming power are admittedly obscure in any given case, but which represents a dominant force to be reckoned with.

the fluctuations, so that they shall mean variations in hours worked by all who would normally be steady workers, while the average working week is itself normal. Or we might have a system in which the working week is rigid and all the fluctuations are taken care of by laying off workers so that the effect is concentrated on a minority—to pass over the danger some are contemplating, that the minority of unemployed may become the majority. Or we may have a system in which the buyers' market for labor is used as a lever to secure concessions from workers in various phases of working conditions, including longer hours, with the result that a given shrinkage of business leads to an even larger percentage of jobless workers. This is the worst system of all. It represents balance in one very limited respect, at a sacrifice of balance in more fundamental and important senses. It is clearly outside the 'zone of tolerance', yet in some measure this wrong course appears to have been followed during the current depression. In fact, the habitual and prevailing system might be characterized as mainly the second, or rigid-week system, with some admixture of the first and third; and a deal of advocacy of a fourth; namely, work-sharing that would be permanent rather than temporary.[5]

[5] Since the above was written, the national recovery program of 1933 has instituted a deliberate drive toward work-sharing without reduction of money wages, but in a setting of depreciating currency and expanding public works.

[146

As things stand, some cannot have all the goods they are willing to work for, because they cannot get full-time employment, and this in turn is because others are in the same position and therefore cannot spend. Or if some still have a normal income, they have not been offered the goods which will tempt them to spend a sufficient portion of it, while the amounts they save are not fully spent, or are spent on wasteful duplication of existing equipment, because industry has not developed either the technical forms of equipment or the new goods necessary to put the available productive power to work effectively. This seems to constitute a vicious circle, of which the unemployed are the victims.

Balance between Savings and Economic Exploration

If we are not ingenious enough to find what we wish to do with our new surplus of productive power, it may be wasted. If we try the wrong things, we have wildcat industries. If we do not try anything, we have 'technological unemployment'. 'Balance', under these conditions, involves the development of new standards of capital equipment adapted to changing proportions of capital to labor, and the direction of the increased productive power into making those commodities which are going to be desired by a population with more money to spend. The penalty for guessing wrong seems to be that, through the effects of unemployment, the popula-

147]

tion has less money to spend instead of more. In order to produce the happy state of 'balance' we must guess right, or find our way to the right answer by a process of trial and error that is not too wasteful. And it may well be that the voluntary savings of a rich nation tend to pile up faster than this process of trial and error can find how to make real use of them and that this condition may last for a considerable term of years. The post-War years in this country may very well be an example of this kind of a failure of balance.

We need, then, a balance between the rate of savings and the progress of economic exploration in the widest sense: exploration into more productive forms of capital and into new goods to make with it; into new standards of living, new levels of wages and new standards of leisure expressed in a shorter working week. All these are bound together in an interacting network, and all must be adjusted to one another before we can use all the productive power we have. At present we seem to be far short of that goal.

The amount of capital we can man is fixed only in terms of existing technical methods of production and types of equipment. In the long run it is indefinitely expansible, but only at a limited rate, because it requires new forms of capital, new goods and possibly other new adjustments. With a given labor supply, the forms of capital determine the

[148

amount of capital that can be manned. Some increase of capital can always be adapted for use by the existing labor supply through the employment of new forms that are already known; but any large increase involves much work for the engineers in developing new forms into which it can be fruitfully put, otherwise it would mean mere wasteful duplication of facilities which could be neither manned nor worked to capacity, and hence would be totally unproductive. It seems probable that a great deal of capital is consumed in this totally unproductive fashion, the fact being concealed because the resulting idleness of capital is distributed and does not all fall on the new capital.

The business cycle undoubtedly intensifies this effect, because the period of prosperity is a special stimulus to the building of surplus plants; moreover, capital construction is greatest at just the time when managers are paying less attention to the search for new and economic methods than they do in times of depression. The search for new methods, which goes on with extra intensity during a depression, prepares the way for a new wave of building, but only after an appreciable period. It seems clear that this wasteful duplication is not consistent with a state of balance; but the mere waste of capital may not in itself be as serious as the fact that it proceeds by spurts, resulting in irregularity which wastes labor power as well.

One requirement of balance, then, is a rate of development of new forms of equipment (and of new goods) sufficient to absorb a normal supply of savings without wasteful duplication of existing plants. A further requirement may be sufficiently low capital costs, especially interest charges, to make the use of these new forms of equipment economical. It is surely a lack of balance if interest rates are maintained around five or six per cent when new capital is being put to uses whose economic product for our economy as a whole is zero, or even less, while the facts of the case are masked in the way already indicated, by the ability of the new capital to capture some of the business which existing capital, equally efficient, is perfectly capable of handling. Balance would seem to require a lower rate of interest, low enough to make it economical to put capital to uses that frankly promise a low yield. Along with this condition goes the requirement of checks on wasteful duplication.

Over-equipment is to be judged on the basis of quality. Over-equipment in a serious sense exists when there is an over-supply of equipment of standard quality or sufficiently near standard to make its idleness for a considerable part of the time wasteful. On the other hand, much equipment that is too old and inefficient to be economical for continuous use may yet be economical to keep in reserve to handle occasional peak demands. Because of the high cost of operating such equipment a normal market is not demoralized by it, while, for purposes of occasional use only, this high operating cost is balanced by the fact that the equipment represents little or no capital value and can stand in reserve for long periods without piling up an unduly heavy burden of 'idle overhead'. Such reserves might be required in particular industries and to meet emergencies, breakdowns and seasonal fluctuations, even if industry in general were so stabilized as to remove cyclical fluctuations. For this reason business estimates of the amount of excess capacity must be taken with a grain of salt until some method is found of determining how much of the equipment is of the sort that can stand idle part of the time without real waste.

Over-Concentrations of Activity

One essential feature of balance is that no part of the economic system shall be working at a rate very much faster or slower than it can continue without outrunning or falling behind its proper proportion to the rest, as fixed by physical and economic forces. The rate of production of raw materials should equal the amount consumed in the production of finished goods (with allowance for the slow growth of stocks as total volume of production grows). And the rate of production of equipment should be such as the volume of savings and the development of technical methods indicate can be maintained. We have seen that there is no limit to the amount of capital that can ultimately be used, but that there are very narrow limits on the rate at which existing capital can be increased without wasteful duplication and a defeating of the end in view. If the industries producing capital goods are working at more than the rate which, if steadily maintained, would create all the capital permanent savings will finance, or all there are workers to man, or sufficient to produce all the goods the market can be geared to buy in the near future, then they are working at a rate which cannot, in the nature of the case, be permanently maintained.

The amount of consumers' goods the market can be geared to buy is elastic, and we have never reached its ultimate limits. But, like the amount of capital we can man, it can be increased only at a limited rate. The market will buy as much as it can produce if it produces just the commodities wanted by those among whom the income is divided, and if they spend for consumption all the funds not needed to finance a balanced supply of capital. But all this takes time to work out.

The market cannot permanently buy just the assortment of goods it is turning out in a period of booming business. At such times it is spending too much on capital goods and on durable goods in general to maintain the rate permanently, technical methods and knowledge being what they are. To maintain such a total rate of production, income

[152

should be so handled that expenditures would go more to consumption goods and less to capital expenditures. As a country, we should spend more and save less than we do at the height of a boom. This conclusion follows from the fact that we reach our highest rate of expenditures for consumption only when we are also diverting more of our productive power to capital goods than we can permanently use. Hence we never reach the rate of consumption that our productive power makes possible. If we were to produce capital equipment steadily at a rate we could absorb, and devoted all the rest of our productive energy to goods for consumption, our consuming power would be increased, possibly five per cent. But apparently the only way to make us voluntarily spend as much as this, and save as little (when we are prosperous), is to distribute our income more equally than it is now distributed, and that, as we have seen, raises many problems. Another factor which will affect the amount of capital that will be built up from savings out of a given social income is the development of social insurance. This means larger provision for future needs, but by a method which will in the long run build up less capital in proportion to the amount of provision made for the needs of the beneficiaries. This is because the beneficiary ultimately receives both interest and principal to spend, instead of keeping the principal permanently invested.

153]

If wages kept pace with total incomes in the upward swing of a business cycle, instead of falling behind as they typically do, more would be consumed. But would this mean a reduction of the unduly concentrated production of capital goods, by reason of a reduction of savings, or would it stimulate this concentrated production still further, because the increased demand for consumption goods enlarges the apparent field of profitable investment in instruments of production? Under such conditions the necessary financing could be furnished by an expansion of credit if original savings were insufficient. The latter result seems more than probable. And this points toward the conclusion that changes in the distribution of incomes are not alone sufficient; they can be effective only in connection with direct stabilization of those branches of production in which undue fluctuations are concentrated.

Movements of Prices, Money Values and Profits

In the realm of prices and money values generally a state of moving balance has its requirements. A fairly stable price level is one. Absolute stability is probably of no more than academic interest; but if there is not approximate stability, then there must be a condition in which all parts of the price system, and especially elements of cost of production, change harmoniously and promptly with changing prices and price levels, so that the interrelations of

[154

the parts of the price system shall always be those which balance requires. Rising general price levels should not in themselves produce general profits or falling prices cause general losses. Industries marked for relative decline should not show profits on account of a change in the value of money, which may lead to unsound expansion. Industries marked for more than average expansion should not experience losses due to falling general price levels, which may lead to unnecessary contraction.

The ideal condition is one in which expanding industries receive just sufficient profits to stimulate the growth that will bring productive capacity into balance with demand; no more and no less. And contracting industries should suffer just sufficient losses to bring about a contraction in the productive capacity engaged in them adequate to restore the balance in the other direction by causing the least efficient producers to drop out, and others to defer expansion or to contract by failing to make full replacements. This does not necessarily mean losses for all producers, if the least efficient respond quickly enough to their losses and retire while these are still moderate. But with the growing proportions of fixed capital and the corresponding proportion of overhead costs, a condition of general losses is more and more likely to occur before there is sufficient outflow of productive capacity to ease the situation.

And if business becomes hardened to living

through cyclical depressions, limiting output and holding on to await the revival, this habit interposes an added obstacle to prompt adjustment when long-run conditions call for a contraction. The meaning of losses becomes confused by the merging of the two kinds of movement, and appropriate action is obstructed. Thus the shorter cyclical fluctuations of industrial activity are not merely in themselves examples of lack of balance; they also tend further to obstruct the action of the longer-run forces. If prices are pegged—meaning always certain particular prices —this tends to perpetuate a state of over-equipment, as well as to prevent a recovery of demand, and keeps the price system at large unbalanced.

Other Points

One condition, helpful but probably not essential, is a reasonable balance between the effects of diminishing returns in agriculture, and the fact that, as per capita wealth increases, we do not expand our consumption of raw farm products as fast as our production and consumption of the utilities supplied by manufacturing, transportation, trade and professional and other services. If diminishing returns brought about at least a relative decline in the efficiency of human effort in agriculture as compared with other branches of production, at the same time that the products of agriculture made up a smaller and smaller fraction of the increasing national dividend, the result might be that something like a constant proportion of the population would be required in agricultural production. If agricultural efficiency increases as fast as the average of all economic operations, then there will naturally be a relative decline in the agricultural population. So long as this is only a relative and not an absolute decline, it may not constitute a very serious departure from balance, though even a relative decline may present some problems and difficulties. The expression that farming is a 'way of life' rather than a business indicates among other things a sluggishness of movement in response to economic incentives such that, if a large movement is called for, it is likely to lag until lack of balance becomes pronounced or even serious.

Some further specifications for the state of balance might be mentioned. The prices of securities should not fluctuate irrationally with respect to the long-run prospects of earnings, which in the nature of the case cannot fluctuate violently if the 'prospects' have any close relation to the facts. Foreign trade should rest on conditions of reasonable durability, not, for instance, on a basis of credit which is virtually certain to be rather quickly exhausted, or of tariffs which are morally certain to lead to reprisals. The war debts have thrown foreign trade out of balance. Temporary balance, apparent and not real, was secured by huge loans from this country. This was a paradox-

157]

ical proceeding: we loaned because our economy was not geared to accepting real payment on loans already made. Having come to the end of this particular road, we face the search for some other route toward a new and more genuine balance.

Conclusion

To sum up, it appears that balance in the full sense is an unattained ideal, equivalent among other things to economic stabilization. A tolerable working approximation to balance calls for a much greater degree of stability than we actually have. The requirements of such a system are not simple, and they afford numerous and varied suggestions as to the important causes, both of cyclical disturbances and of unbalanced conditions of a longer-run sort tending perhaps to become chronic. The observed trends of the post-War period in this country seem to afford some evidence of the kinds of unbalanced conditions which this theoretical study would lead us to expect.

In the concluding section the results of this approach and of the previous inductive study will be consolidated and tabulated in the form of lists of the most significant and responsible factors that have appeared in both approaches to the problem. If the reader will consider these in the light of the foregoing discussion, he will see that the two methods of approach have yielded practically the same lists

[158

of responsible factors. The chief difference is that the forces that tend to act progressively over longer periods than the forty-month cycle are emphasized in the second study, and their *rationale* investigated. This is natural, as the evidence on such matters plays a secondary part in the statistical records of the business cycle and contains within itself few hints as to the underlying causes at work. And on the other side of the picture, the abstract study of conditions essential to equilibrium frequently fails to yield clues to the time that various movements will need, whether falling within the limits of the short cycle or requiring a longer period. Hence this more purely theoretical study may be taken as corroborating the earlier conclusions, and supplementing them by more analysis of the longer-run trends and forces, thus giving them more nearly the emphasis that their importance deserves.

PART SIX

THE STRATEGIC FACTORS

Factors of Prediction versus Factors of Diagnosis

THE factors of strategic importance in the business cycle may be classified into those that may serve as means of prediction, those that may serve as means of prompt discovery and gauging of current conditions and of the stage of the cycle in which the country finds itself at any given moment, and those that may be susceptible to control and may thereby serve as means of controlling the course of business conditions. The first group is the one to which business men have hitherto paid most attention. The second and third groups are those on which the possibilities of long-run remedies really rest.

No one factor behaves with sufficient regularity in relation to the general business cycle to serve as

[160

an infallible index of prediction. And no group of factors can be so used with absolutely reliable results. Prediction-factors may be classified into those which represent some change of genuine initiatory influence and those which merely record the current phase of the cycle, from which the next phase may be expected to follow in about the usual time.

With regard to the first group, factors which normally take the lead cannot be counted on to do so in every case. There is probably always some initiatory factor or group of factors which could be picked out by sufficient study after the event; but the factor which plays this role in one instance may be replaced by different factors in another instance. And there is the ever-present possibility of some new and unique factors, or of some more or less familiar factors playing a new and unique role. Moreover, the minor fluctuations of the factors always leave considerable doubt as to whether a given factor has just reached its cyclical low point or high point, or whether it has merely experienced a brief interruption of a movement which will shortly be resumed. Few have a sufficient lead to make it possible to wait until their cyclical turning-point is surely determined, and still use them for predicting the corresponding cyclical turning-point of general business; and these few are too erratic in their behavior to make the prediction certain.

As to the type of prediction system which merely

records the current phase of the general cycle and allows the observer to infer that the next will follow in a normal time, the results are made highly uncertain by the large variations in the length of cycles and of their successive phases. And it is never safe to predict, for example, the extent of a coming expansion by the extent to which a current depression falls below 'normal', because such a 'normal' is always arbitrary or uncertain. Indeed a statistical trend line, projected forward to the date of the latest observations, has little claim to be regarded as normal with respect to current conditions. Non-cyclical changes and disturbances are always likely to vitiate it. Such a method might have succeeded fairly well in 1921, but would have failed utterly in 1929, or at any time during the succeeding three years. On this basis predictions of revival were repeatedly made and repeatedly followed by further contraction.

The hope that the technique of prediction will overcome these difficulties involves, paradoxically enough, not optimism but pessimism. For it carries with it the expectation that cycles of the present type will go on their uncontrolled course for some time to come; and that is precisely what must not be allowed to happen, in the view of the more liberal-minded of publicists and business men alike. Theoretically, predictions based on past experience should have a tendency to falsify themselves by leading to different conduct in the future; but so far there have

[162

been no very great evidences of such a tendency.

One reason why mere prediction will not put an end to business cycles is that business men will use the predictions to guide business policies of the same basic sort they now follow: expanding to take advantage of increasing demand and contracting to meet declining demand and building up excess capacity in the hope of increasing their proportionate shares of the existing business. If expansion is predicted, they will still take action which will tend to bring the expansion about and to intensify it, though perhaps more promptly than at present. If expansion is expected soon to turn into recession, they will then take the kind of action calculated to bring on the recession and to intensify it, though perhaps more promptly than they now do. As a result, they may not carry either the expansion or the recession quite so far as they now do; but to expect a greater change than this would be highly optimistic.

The theory that business cycles can be controlled as a result of successful prediction alone—if anyone holds this theory—rests on the implied assumption that cycles are due to the mistakes of judgment made by individual business men. For this theory the present study has yielded relatively little support, while it has indicated the very large importance of causes of a quite different sort; and the present writer believes this theory to be, in the main, false. The trouble seems to be not so much that business men mistake their interests—though that does happen, and aggravates some of the difficulties—as that their actual interests lie in doing the things which bring on the cycle, so long as they are acting as individual business men or representatives of individual business interests. A business man who refused to expand his sales on the up-swing would gain nothing, and one who refused to retrench on the down-swing would probably go bankrupt. One who stabilized his individual construction program would incur some risks by building ahead of demand or by being caught with inadequate reserve capacity in an expansion; and would not produce sufficient effect on the whole business situation to receive in return any substantial benefits in the way of stabilized demand for his own products—as he might hope to do if all business followed the same policy.

It seems to be a case in which the best policy for an individual to follow in adjusting himself to the existing bad conditions is not the same as the policy by which the business community as a whole may hope to get rid of the evil. It is only from a change in these customary reaction patterns that we may hope for real changes in the result. Something must happen to bring about a condition in which the response of business to a revival is not such as to make the revival over-run itself and make a recession inevitable. If that can be brought about, it may be that we shall not need infallible prediction; only

[164

prompt and reliable current diagnosis, to guide the neutralizing policies which business or government or both stand ready to put into effect.

The task of current diagnosis is far easier than that of prediction, though still not easy. There are plenty of indexes of general business activity which tell us well enough how fast business is going at any given moment. But this does not tell us our position relative to that elusive standard called 'normal', nor does it even dispose of the difficulty of determining in what precise phase of the business cycle we are at any time.

As to the first difficulty, the carrying of 'normal' or 'secular' trends down to the current moment is always a doubtful procedure, and hence the degree of departure from such normal trends is equally doubtful. Something may be accomplished, however, by better measures (and better mobilized information about them) of surplus capacity in construction, and keener analysis of the relation of prices of securities to possible prospective earnings. It was well known that stock prices during the great boom were capitalizing future increases rather than current earnings; but no systematic analysis appeared of the extent of future increase in earnings necessary to rationalize current prices. Had such an analysis been made, it must inevitably have revealed that such necessary future increases were beyond all human possibility.

As to the second difficulty—that of determining what stage of the cycle business has momentarily reached—a clear example is seen in the current depression, the duration and severity of which have gone so far beyond usual experience and expectation. Many persons thought we had reached the low point in January, 1930, and have thought so repeatedly since then, while we slipped down, with occasional abortive revivals, into deeper and deeper stagnation. And among persons who agree on the kind of rescue work that can be effectively employed there is still difference of opinion as to when it should have been undertaken in the present depression. Would it have been effective if employed promptly, or would it then have merely spent its force while the worst impact of the depression was still to come? Such chances as are implied in this uncertainty we shall doubtless have to take; and they will not be as great in the ordinary case as in the present one, since this is, after all, more than a mere business cycle.

And if measures of control are devised which have some degree of effect, the character of the problem will change. It will be neither the problem of prediction nor that of determining precisely where we are in the now-customary type of business cycle, but of determining when an approximately regularized economy has fallen below its normal trend of activity. And it will not be absolute activity that will count so much as activity relative to the full utilization of our existing working force. In short, the state of employment and unemployment will be a dominant index.

Causes: A Partial Theory of Business Cycles

If we group the factors into those having directly to do with production and those having directly to do with consumption, it appears that they interact so completely that it is impossible to say that one group is the active one and the other the passive. In this connection it may be worth while to break into the sequence in one of the late phases of an extreme depression like the present and follow it backward toward ultimate originating causes.

Let us start with a shrinkage of consumers' purchases because of hoarding, this being attributable in turn to the fear of losing one's job which arises after curtailment of production has already begun and further curtailments seem likely to follow. Curtailments of production in the winter of 1931-32, let us say, were made because normal bank credit was difficult to obtain; and the extreme niggardliness of the banks sprang from a state of fear engendered by a wave of bank failures, due in turn to the losses of the businesses that were the banks' debtors. These losses were caused by the combination of falling prices (mostly wholesale) and shrinking sales, both traceable to a decline of business buying and

167]

ultimately to a decline in consumers' purchases occurring earlier in the cycle than the particular decline in which our backward-tracing analysis started.

In the present instance there was added to this and compounded with it a world-wide collapse in basic commodity prices which was no part of an ordinary business cycle. Without this the more usual cyclical forces would have produced much milder results. Recognizing this fact, we may go on to deal with the typical cycle history.

The basic decline in consumers' purchases is a common feature of all cycles, and is mainly consequent upon an actual shrinkage in consumers' incomes, resulting in turn from a prior shortage of general employment and lessened production in industries at large. The earliest shrinkage in consumers' purchases can hardly be due in any significant degree to the fear of losing the job, since the cause for that fear has not yet made itself manifest to an extent sufficient to disturb the optimism that marks a time of active business. The general curtailment of employment and production which originates the decline of consumers' incomes includes a falling-off in physical production of consumers' goods prior to any similar definite falling-off in consumers' purchases. With this goes a much more intense falling-off in the work of producing durable goods (the reasons for which we have already

[168

traced), and which is preceded by a tapering-off of the rate of increase.

This is accompanied by a curtailment of credit of various sorts, and accordingly total expenditures fall off more than consumers' current expenditures out of current income. And while this curtailment may be intensified by any actual falling-off in consumers' incomes, the source from which its first manifestations arise may be no more than a cessation or slackening of expansion in the total amount of producers' equipment or durable consumers' goods, causing a positive decline in the rate of current production of these commodities. This may be merely because supplies of equipment or durable goods have caught up with demand. This in turn implies that demand expands irregularly, and that after an up-turn, production for a time expands faster than what we may call the original expansion of demand, and thus at a rate that cannot be permanently maintained.

These original expansions of demand may in their turn arise, first, from merely chance happenings; or, second, from the basic tendency which statisticians express in curves of normal growth, starting with something like a geometrical rate of increase, reaching a maximum rate of expansion, and then tapering off to a saturation-point. In such cases as we are concerned with, the saturation-point is best expressed as a uniform per capita rate of use or consumption, in a community with a growing population, or perhaps in some instances even a stronger upward trend representing normal per capita expenditure in a country with a gradually rising per capita income. The 'growth' in excess of this trend represents the process by which a new good or a new process makes its way to a fairly stable place relative to others, in an expanding economic system. If it is an absolutely new good the growth-curve may start from zero. If it is a case of a change enlarging the normal place held by an existing good, the growth-curve may be superimposed on a secular upward trend, or different growth-curves with different periods may be superimposed on each other.

These normal growth-curves we may regard as representing roughly certain causal forces which are ultimate for our present purpose. They may have to do with the development of new goods and of the conscious and active desire for them, or with new processes of production calling for increased investment in productive equipment. In either case there is no reason to suppose that either the curves of normal growth or the chance fluctuations which are combined with them have any inherent tendency, in their essential nature, to move in cycles of either three and one-third or of ten years. These inherent tendencies, be it remembered, are factors which are not to be observed unmodified in the statistics. The actual statistical changes record the results of the entire chain of cumulative sequences, returning on themselves endlessly, which have been indicated in a fragmentary way in the foregoing analysis. The inherent tendencies of what we have chosen to call the ultimate causal forces are so overlaid and transformed by these sequences of secondary and tertiary results that their original nature is buried, and can only be gotten at by other methods of inference than those of direct statistical tracing.

The development of new goods seems to reach maturity in varying periods of time. The automobile has required more than a generation, while miniature golf ran its course in a few months. In general, goods of large and enduring significance seem to require considerably more than a ten-year period for development. The same can be said of new productive processes, with modifications. The time required to develop the potentialities of a basic idea such as that of scientific management is as long or longer than has been required by the automobile, but single processes may be developed in a much shorter period. There may be an initial stage of experimental pioneering, followed by a putting of the method into actual production, this involving some small but appreciable demand for new equipment. If the method proves its economic worth, there may be virtually instant recognition of that fact, and a wave of imitation, sweeping over the entire field as fast as the character of the improvement admits and causing a very considerable demand for new equipment. Schumpeter's analysis of intermittent movements of pioneering followed by waves of imitation is pertinent on this point and is the outstanding theoretical treatment of it.[1]

As the work of overhauling production methods tends to be to some extent concentrated in the depression phase of the business cycle, the first applications of improved methods in actual production probably have some corresponding tendency to concentrate toward the later stages of depression. This would, as far as it went, tend to check a recession or initiate a revival; and the waves of imitation, occurring still later, would give a stronger impetus to revival. Thus this particular type of growth-curve may come to coincide with the general business cycle, to the extent that the timing of the initial pioneering is influenced by the cycle and is not a wholly independent fact. As to how far this actually happens, statistical measurement is well-nigh impossible. It is so much a matter of the kind of problem on which the regular executive staff focus their attention. The concentration of such developments may be relatively slight, after all. And even this can only be true of relatively minor developments; major changes require a much longer period. They could not be incubated, brought into successful applica-

---

[1] This theory, together with others, is summarized in W. C. Mitchell's *Business Cycles: The Problem and Its Setting*, Chapter I.

tion and widely imitated, all in the course of one depression and revival.

Whether this hypothesis be true or not, the actual bulk of the installation of machines, as well as of the actual growth of sales of new goods, is conditioned by effective demand and so follows the course of the general business cycle. The normal growth-curves of which we have been speaking express the underlying forces as they would develop if unmodified by these factors derived from the business cycle itself. In all probability they have a wide variety of natural periods. Many of them, representing the experimental development and subsequent general adoption of fairly specific and limited technical devices, may be prompt enough to be stimulated in their early stages by the spur of hard times, and to reach a considerable development during the subsequent expansion of general business. But few would be so short as to run their whole course in one business cycle. It is difficult to ascribe the length of the forty-month cycle to any natural periodicity of such growth-curves. The safer assumption is that the growth-curves have a chance distribution, modified by the business cycle in the ways already suggested.

The combined resultant of a number of these growth-curves superimposed on each other would naturally be a state of growth varying somewhat from decade to decade and with shorter and slighter fluctuations of an irregular sort. But there is still no

173]

reason to suppose that the combination of this composite growth-curve with purely chance fluctuations would show any natural tendency to run in cycles of the familiar observed lengths. There is every reason to suppose that these fundamental forces are, in point of timing with reference to the general business cycle, random forces.

If there is, as there certainly seems to be, a tendency to a qualified regularity in the ups and downs of business, its cause must be sought in the mechanism whereby business reacts to these original impulses. On the basis of the above analysis a theory of the business cycle can be constructed which would account for its salient features, as follows:

By way of starting-point we may take the impulse leading to an up-turn of business. This impulse may be one of a wide variety of possible sorts, or may represent a combination of more than one. It may be of the 'originating' type, or derived from a previous depression. It may affect output of producers' goods or output of consumers' goods, either directly or by way of the consumers' demand for them. 1. Production may take an up-turn without waiting for demand, owing to: (a) the removal of some specific obstruction—for example, a strike; (b) the need for replacement following a period when stocks in the hands of producers, dealers or consumers were allowed to decline, as may happen in a depression; (c) the development of a more optimistic (or less pessimistic) feeling among producers, whatever may be its source. 2. Demand for productive equipment may take an up-turn without waiting for increased demand for products, owing to: (a) changes in technical methods of production; (b) the development of new goods in anticipation of demand, or for which a potential demand appears to exist; (c) the need for resuming maintenance and replacement which has been temporarily postponed, as happens in a depression; (d) increased optimism, which may affect (a), (b) and (c). 3. A shifting in consumers' demand from one commodity to another may cause a demand for equipment to produce the new commodity without the possibility of an equivalent decrease, in the same space of time, for the equipment to produce the older and discarded commodity, thus giving rise to a net increase in the demand for equipment. 4. An upward inflection in the course of total consumers' demand may take place, from causes not dependent on prior increase of income (which would have to rest on increased production), as a result of: (a) the offering of attractive new goods; (b) the using up of 'consumers' inventories'; (c) a more optimistic mood, (d) selling effort, or (e) increased demand from abroad.

Except in the case of foreign purchases, an increase of demand, not derived from a prior increase of production, would necessarily carry with it at first either an increase of consumers' credit or a decrease of savings. The latter, be it noted, may not result in a decrease of funds available for purchase of productive equipment, since it may be more than offset by an expansion of producers' credit.

It will not be necessary to follow out the results of all these types of original impulse separately. If we start with this fourth group, we shall take in on the way all the essential features of the transmission and spreading of the other types of impulse. For an upward inflection in the course of 'original demand' has its most substantial result in the shape of an intensified upward swing in the output of means of production and of durable goods. And this is a condition to which all the other types of 'originating impulse' also lead.

If this resulting increase in production responded exactly and instantaneously to the original demand, and were not affected by any further secondary consequences, the derived curve would have the same period of swing as the original curve, though the timing of the peaks and troughs would be different, the derived curve appearing to lead.[2] But the derived curve does not respond exactly and instan-

[2] See Part II, Timing: Construction. See also Business Acceleration and the Law of Demand, *Journal of Political Economy*, XXV, 217-35, March, 1917; also *Economics of Overhead Costs*, Chapter XIX. Cf. also Capital Production and Consumer-Taking—a Reply, *Journal of Political Economy*, XXXIX, 814-6, December, 1931. This is a reply to Ragnar Frisch's The Interrelation Between Capital Production and Consumer-Taking: *Journal of Political Economy*, XXXIX, 646-54, October, 1931.

taneously to the original impulse, and it is reinforced
and modified by its own cumulative effects. It takes
time to produce the equipment and durable goods,
and meanwhile there is a shortage which sends prices
up. This in turn tends to cause an increase in speculative buying and buying for storage, which reacts
cumulatively to intensify the rise in prices. Guided
by the rising prices rather than by a statistical canvass
of demand and supply, competitive producers launch
upon the production of more goods and equipment
than necessary to meet the requirements of the
original expansion of demand.

The expansion of business at rising price-levels is
financed and made possible by expansion of credit,
moving in response to demand. At the same time
the increased productive activity results in increased
distribution of wages as soon as the expansion of
production begins and before the new durable goods,
or the products of the new equipment, are actually
on the markets. The effect is an increase of general
purchasing power which both intensifies the original
impulse and spreads its influence over commodities
in general, thus further stimulating the demand for
productive equipment. The competing producers,
who had started to produce too much, may even
find that their first program is not large enough for
this new state of demand, and further expansion
may ensue, with further diffused effects of the same
sort as before.

But equipment and stocks of durable goods are catching up with requirements, which will not expand indefinitely. Not all the increased income is spent, and some of what is 'saved' is probably temporarily absorbed in the speculative markets for securities without immediately taking effect in increased purchases of producers' or consumers' goods. By the time the market shows that requirements have been caught up with, there is an over-supply either in existence or in process of production. Production of equipment and durable goods now slackens, prices fall, the contraction in the basis of credit is intensified by forced sales and lack of confidence. With declining production, income distributions decline, the slackening is thus diffused and intensified, and the cycle is reversed.

The time required for all this to happen is quite independent of the time required for any 'originative' impulse to reach its natural saturation point, in case such an impulse played a part in starting this particular movement. If the original impulse were the development of an important new commodity, a generation might pass before it reached its saturation point if there were no interference from the spasmodic movements just described. Long before this, these secondary effects will have produced a cycle of expansion and contraction, interrupting the 'normal growth-curve'. There may, in fact, be several such cycles before this original impulse is ex-

[178

hausted. The railroad and the automobile has each played its part in a number of successive cycles.

On the downward course, consumption does not shrink as fast as production, while credit is contracting. Ultimately, such surplus stocks as may have accumulated are worked off and the need of replacement counteracts the temporary abnormal shrinkage of demand for productive equipment and durable goods. As a result demand begins to revive and the cumulative process starts once more, if not previously initiated by some random happening that affords an independent stimulus. At any point, in fact, this sequence may be altered, stimulated or dampened, speeded or retarded, by the interposition of some fresh outside factor. Or its character may be modified by variations in the behavior of the elements in the system of business responses, such as might arise from changes in the credit system or in the importance of durable consumers' goods, or the spread of the corporate form of financing of office and apartment buildings. But this system has sufficient momentum in and of itself to account for a considerable succession of cycles without constantly renewed stimulus from outside.

If this is a correct picture of the main determining features of the typical cycle, the average length is to be accounted for, not by any periodicity in the originating forces but by the time required for these reactions of the business system to run their course.

179]

If we were to draw a line depicting the original growth-curve of ultimate demand as it would be if unmodified, and a second line depicting the derived demand for durable goods as it would be if it moved in such a way as to satisfy the original demand instantly, the second line would, as already noted, have a period corresponding to that of the original line of growth of original demand, with an apparent lead of approximately a quarter-cycle owing to the fact that it reaches its peak at about the time the original curve is rising most rapidly. But the actual curve of derived productive activity does not behave in this way. It reacts on the original curve, modifying the latter in the direction of its own movements, including the tendency to an earlier peak. This reacts back on the derived curve, causing it to reach its peak earlier than it would otherwise. This effect is complicated by the fact that the derived productive activity does not at once rise to the full extent required to satisfy the increase in original demand, but lags at first, and then rises even more steeply in the effort to catch up, and finally is pushed beyond immediate requirements by the effects of speculation and of competitive duplication. The resulting recession reacts again on the demand for finished goods, and the natural curve of growth is interrupted by a decline.

Thus it is natural and logical that there should be several cycles of derived business activity during the course of one major growth-cycle of original demand. And the duration of these cycles is presumably governed largely by the time consumed in this process of lagging and subsequent catching-up and over-expansion, and in the subsequent process of clearing the markets and exhausting the excess of durable goods. This time-interval is dependent upon several factors, technical, commercial and psychological. Among these factors are those governing the time required to produce goods and to bring new equipment to the stage at which its products come on the market, including the time required to launch and finance projects of expansion. If the process of launching and financing projects and completing the first units of equipment or durable goods consumes on the average ten months, then it is logical that the expansion should involve considerably more time than this, and forty months becomes a rather natural average period for the entire cycle. A further conditioning factor is the growth of a general spirit of optimism, making business men more ready to build for the hope of future expansion, and by the subsequent evaporation of that spirit. The course of events is also affected by the continuation of production and prices on the basis of standing contracts made in the past. Another conditioning circumstance is the impossibility of developing new wants fast enough to make effective demand for consumers' goods expand as fast as income when income is expanding as rapidly as it does on the upgrade of the cycle.

It would naturally be expected, since all businesses are affected by the general cycle but not all are under the same degree of original stimulus, that some may have exhausted their original stimulus more completely than others by the time the general reaction comes. The original stimulus may be more persistent or less; the response may be prompter or slower. In fact, different industries may have different natural cyclical periods if left to themselves; and impulses of varying magnitudes in the same industry may tend toward diverse periods of oscillation. Thus some industries may be caught by the general decline because other industries have reached the point of reaction, though they themselves had not come to what would be their own natural period of recession. In such instances they may lag on the down-turn or lead on the next up-turn. In extreme instances an industry may fail to decline with general business, or it may remain prostrate through more than one full cycle. A few dominant industries subject to special conditions may lengthen or shorten one phase or the other of the cycle, affecting the length of the entire cycle in this way. Or the same result may be brought about by purely random forces.

This theoretical picture appears to harmonize with the observed facts of the cycle, including the approximate regularity with considerable variation

[182

both in the timing of the general cycle and in the behavior of the various specific series. It includes the intensified fluctuations of producers' goods and durable consumers' goods, the general behavior of prices, credit and security markets (though the particular relations of credit to security speculation were not gone into), and the behavior of incomes, expenditures and savings. Provisionally assuming it to be a fair picture, as far as it goes, we still have the problem of the various originating factors, and factors in the business system of responses to changing situations. To which, if to any, shall we attach peculiar strategic importance in controlling and determining the character of the result? And which, if any, may themselves be controlled by human action, and so used to control the outcome? This is, needless to say, the heart of the question.

Factors of Controlling Importance

For purposes of summary, we are almost forced to arrange the factors in lists, although this necessarily fails to do justice to their manifold organic interrelations. They fall rather naturally into three groups. The first consists of the 'originating causes', random or otherwise, which we may regard as ultimate for our purpose; the second consists of those elements in the reaction patterns of business which are directly concerned with bringing about the familiar forty-month business cycle. The third group

consists of factors responsible for longer trends and
the interrelations between them. Together with the
'originating causes', these may be among the forces
responsible for changes in the character and serious-
ness of the forty-month cycles, or they may possibly
be responsible for other cycles of a longer period,
or for progressive or chronic maladjustments in the
sense of inability to utilize the productive powers
we actually possess. In this third group conclusions
as to causal relationships are based more on theoretical analysis and less on inductive evidence, and
are more tentative in character; but if and when the
truth can be discovered about them, they may prove
to be no less important than the factors directly
responsible for the short cycles—possibly even more
so.

First Group: Originating Causes

In this first group belong such random factors as
weather in its effect on crops, wars and other chance
disturbances. These may have regularities of their
own, and they certainly have their own causes; but
their regularities are independent of those of the
business cycle, and their causes are either non-eco-
nomic or are outside the regular course of the business cycle. Here belong also such factors as the
origination (in contrast to the rate of development
and exploitation) of new wants, new goods and new
processes and methods of production. These have

[184

their own tendencies of progressive development and are characterized by certain irregularities which are, for all practical purposes, inescapable. These the business system seizes upon, intensifies and converts into cyclical movements whose lengths are presumably largely independent of the timing of the natural irregularities in these basic movements.

In this general class of forces also belong shifts in foreign trade arising from other causes than the state of the business cycle in our own country. So far as business cycles in foreign countries have different timing from our own, they may act as random and originative forces acting on the state of business in this country.

In this group, wars stand out for several reasons. They are particularly serious. They are definitely undesirable, and humanity is developing a definite ambition to control them. And they constitute the only item in the list which seems to be of such a nature as to be really subject to control that might ultimately succeed in removing it as a disturbing influence upon the economic system.

It is also true that the development of wants and the origination of new processes can be stimulated or retarded by the actions of a government or a people. On the other hand, the consumers' ultimate freedom of choice as to the kinds of goods he wants is one of the last things with which we shall attempt any general interference, at least in our dealings

185]

with this grade of economic problem. We are far from ready to begin dictating to him, as a measure for the stabilizing of business, when he shall, and when he shall not, adopt new goods and seek new kinds of gratification. And while we can pour larger or smaller funds into industrial research, we can never guarantee the exact results, how important any given invention will turn out to be, or whether it will come to fruition in 1935 or in 1937. In short, it seems that we may exercise some little control over the longer trends in these matters, if and when we gain sufficient wisdom to know what our welfare demands; but we can hardly hope to reduce the changes to perfect uniformity. There will always be irregularities, and if we have a business system that converts these irregularities into cycles of prosperity and depression, there will always be such cycles.

With the exceptions already indicated, the factors in this first group do not appear to be of great strategic importance for the purposes of humanity seeking to learn what it may do about this great problem. This is partly because there is so little that we can do about them, and partly because, in spite of their possible importance in initiating business movements, they do not seem to determine the character of the result which the business system, under the impact of these forces, brings to pass. To understand the length, timing and specific features of business

[186

cycles and kindred movements, we must turn to the second and third groups of factors.

Second Group: Business Responses Controlling the Short Cycle

Here the significant possibilities seem to include the following:

(1) The tendency to intensified fluctuations of derived demand for durable goods: both capital equipment and consumers' goods, with possible lesser tendencies of the same sort in the case of raw materials. In the case of capital equipment this includes the tendency to competitive duplication and excess building.

(2) Price movements and the lack of simultaneous and proportionate change in all parts of the price system, including wages and interest burdens. Price movements should be classified into cyclical movements, typically of moderate amplitude, and other movements due to special causes, such as the long decline from 1873 to 1896, the rise from 1897 to 1913, the War-time rise, the sharp deflation of 1920-21 and the second post-War deflation whose culmination marked the present depression. The cyclical movements are important causes of con-

187]

traction and expansion (or of more intense contraction and expansion than would otherwise occur), but they are not, like the other movements, 'originating causes'. Their regularity points clearly to the conclusion that they arise from other cyclical conditions. They are to be explained in terms of factors 1, 4 and 6-11.

(3) Intensified movements of profits derived from movements of money values and lagging interest and wage costs, and from changes in volume of production in connection with the existence of overhead costs which do not change proportionately with output.

(4) Movements of speculative demand for commodities.

(5) Speculation in securities.

(6) The effect of confidence or the lack of it on speculation, on expansion or contraction of business enterprise and on credit purchases generally, including those of consumers.

(7) The dependence of consumers' demand on the volume of income disbursed by businesses. This joins with the previous factors to form a vicious circle, reinforcing itself cumulatively. So much is certain, but the precise quantitative facts are as yet unknown: how closely the movements of these

two quantities correspond and the amount
and timing of any discrepancies. These depend in part on the movements of consumers' credit and plus and minus movements
in savings, and in part on the following
factor.

(8) Shifts in the proportionate distribution of
the national dividend between different
classes and income groups, taken in conjunction with the diverse habits and standards of consumption and savings of these
groups. The effect is instability in the proportions of the national income saved and
consumed, beyond what would arise in any
case from changes in per capita real income.

(9) The expansion and contraction of credit
granted to both producers and consumers,
making possible discrepancies between
total income and total spendings, or between savings and investment. This has
two types of effect. Firstly, it enables the
other forces mentioned to initiate changes
in rates of expenditures and production
with a freedom not otherwise possible.
Secondly, it acts at times as an independent
force to stimulate expansion or enforce
contraction.

(10) The time consumed in financial and physical

189]

preparation for increased production, and the resulting tendency to alternate lagging and hurrying to catch up, by which time an over-supply is in process of production.

(11) The time necessary to work off excess stocks and to develop the need for replacements and in that way to bring about a revival of demand (if not previously brought about by credit purchases or other means) from the excessively low point reached when durable goods are not being fully maintained and kept up to date.

This is a formidable list, though less formidable than the mass of statistical series which describe the whole course of successive cycles. Even this list omits several incidental factors such as the efficiency of labor and the concentration of managerial effort on economies and improvements during a depression, changes in the length of the working day and week and the development of what is called 'technological unemployment'.

Possibilities of Control as Guides to Strategic Importance

All of these eleven factors seem to be of importance, but some are hardly controllable. And they are all so interdependent that, of a group of two or more factors, for example, the demand for capital goods

[190

and the supply of capital funds, it may be that effective control of *either* might serve to control the others also, and to modify the entire course of the sequence.

Those least susceptible to control include those resting on the consumer's freedom to choose what he will do with his income, and those resting on the purely physical facts that govern the time taken by various processes. Business confidence, also, can hardly be controlled directly. Attempts to modify it must act through the more tangible conditions on which it depends. Among the remaining factors, presumably, are those which are of greatest strategic importance to us in our relation to this problem.

The tendency to intensified fluctuations of derived demand, including the demand for the work and materials involved in producing durable consumers' goods, as well as producers' goods, is of basic importance, in the judgment of the writer. If it could be controlled in all its manifestations, the primary result would be a great stabilization of the average rate of productive activity by cutting off those fluctuations of production which exceed the fluctuations of consumers' current expenditures. As a secondary result, consumers' expenditures would themselves be made far more stable than they now are. Thus the effects of stabilization would be cumulative, and the back of the business cycle would be broken. We have already seen that the magnitudes involved, with allowance for cumulative effects, are sufficient to justify this claim.

While any very close approach to complete stabilization is probably out of the range of possibility so long as we retain even the main elements of the present system of private enterprise, a great deal may still be accomplished if the task is approached with sufficient resolution and open-mindedness. The causes of intensified fluctuations are, in part at least, mechanical relationships as inescapable as the laws of physics: namely, the relation between changes in a total stock of durable goods which is increasing at a fluctuating rate, and changes in the rate of increase of the same stock. No magic of institutional formulae can make these two rates equal. If there is to be approximate stability, there must be some degree of control of the underlying fluctuations.

If there were no such thing as elasticity of credit the difficulty would be largely circumvented, but at a rather heavy price. The elasticity of credit undoubtedly facilitates and speeds the process of capital accumulation by enabling business to secure and spend at any time larger amounts of capital funds than have been furnished for the purpose by prior savings. The ultimate savings can, in a real sense, be furnished later, out of the increased productivity of the processes themselves.[3] To abandon all this

---

[3] It is not intended to imply that the banks have a magic power to create something out of nothing. They do have power to create addi-

would have a retarding effect on industrial progress; though whether it would be as serious as the retarding effect we now experience from depressions is something no one can prove. If there were no possibility of expanding credit, increased purchases of automobiles and residences would be limited to such current income as the consumer chose to divert from the fulfilment of other desires, and increased expenditures on capital equipment would be limited to that fraction of current income which the consumer chose not to spend, or which the business unit chose not to distribute. Short of this, a completely centralized banking system could, by rationing credit, accomplish virtually any desired degree of regularization. Unofficial private transactions might still transfer funds, but the funds would have to come out of income, not out of the resources of elastic expansion afforded by commercial banking.

tional purchasing power in the form of bank deposits placed at the disposal of borrowers. This purchasing power does not come out of anyone's *prior* abstinence; but it initiates a process of painless quasi-abstinence consisting simply in the fact that these depositors leave their accounts with the banks until they see fit to spend them, after which the recipients do the same. If the *only* effect of the expansion of deposits were to raise prices, there would be simultaneous involuntary abstinence of a different sort, forced on those who must pay the higher prices while their purchasing power is not increased. But the typical effect is only partly of this character, and is largely an increase in production, with the result that increases of capital goods do not require equivalent *prior* sacrifices in consumption. See H. G. Moulton, Commercial Banking and Capital Formation, *Journal of Political Economy*, XXVI, 849, 868-81, November, 1918.

Even this degree of control is too drastic to be seriously considered at present, but milder forms of control could accomplish much. The possibility of utilizing them effectively will be considered later.

Another line of attack is the attempt to control directly the volume of production of capital equipment and, if possible, of those durable consumers' goods whose fluctuations are governed by the same basic principle of intensification. As to the possibility of this type of control, it is of the utmost importance that these productive activities, at least in the field of capital equipment, are of such a sort that their timing is not immediately and exactly bound up with the movements of consumption or of consumers' purchases (which are the last items we shall probably think of controlling) but are connected with them by ties that admit an enormous amount of play within the business system itself.

This fact constitutes the reason for their intense fluctuations under existing conditions; and at the same time it affords a ground for hope that some of them at least might, under other conditions, be converted into stabilizing rather than unstabilizing influences. This would be difficult in the case of housing, and might prove impossible in that of passenger automobiles, especially so long as changes of style and model are as frequent and important in the trade as they are at present. And even in the field of capital equipment the difficulties are enor-

[194

mous. But it remains true that within this group are found the only industries in which efforts at regularization can with any promise at all be applied directly to the work of production; and that they are of sufficient importance to afford something approaching a cure if the difficulties involved can be successfully overcome.

The hope of control lies in the fact that, while the behavior of this group of industries is natural, under the operation of financial interests as seen by individual producers, it is, with some exceptions, optional and not compulsory to the extent that supplying consumers who come to buy goods, if the goods are on hand, may be regarded as compulsory; or as failing to supply them if they do *not* come to buy goods is compulsory. If producers learn to look at the matter collectively and see that their present behavior is contrary to their joint interests, as tending to produce booms and depressions, they can, if they care enough about it, regularize their purchases of permanent equipment and see that their inventories of goods do not move up and down in such a way as to intensify the fluctuations in ultimate consumers' demand. Even the production of durable consumers' goods can to some degree be regularized, if the problem is attacked with determination.

Even such a degree of control requires a broader and more collective view than is common in business. The steel industry can do little to stabilize the de-

195]

mand for steel; hence it is quite natural if the endeavors of steel producers, so long as they are acting by themselves, are directed to stabilizing prices at the expense of stabilizing demand and output. Action by the purchasers of steel is essential to the stabilization of the steel industry. And such action may not be beyond the reach of possibility when it is fully realized that to stabilize the demand for other commodities—for consumers' goods in general —it is necessary that production and payrolls in steel (taken as typical of producers' goods in general) shall be stabilized in order to remove the focus from which spread the really violent ups and downs in general purchasing power and in effective demand for commodities at large.

The primary method of procedure is to budget capital outlays on a regularized schedule which provides sufficient reserve capacity for all ordinary peaks of demand, and which refuses to be stampeded by the momentary state of the market into violent speedings-up or slowings-down. This is not an easy task. To bring about substantial results would almost certainly require not only cooperation between enterprises throughout a single industry but also affiliations between industries along lines of vertical integration. The steel industry, as already noted, cannot do much to stabilize itself because it cannot by itself stabilize the demand for steel. This has to be done, if at all, by the industries that consume

[196

steel. But as we have also seen, these industries, in turn, stand to gain through the general stabilization of purchasing power if the whole program is successfully carried out. Thus there is a mutual interest which should be strong enough to produce fairly adequate action, if industry can be organized in such a way as to make this interest effective. Whether this degree of organization can be brought about without going so far as to make the system of private enterprise impossible is a question which can be answered only by the process of experiment. At the least the change would be an evolutionary movement going a long way toward a system decidedly different from private enterprise as we now understand it. Not less than a generation would probably be required for business to make the necessary mental and material adjustments, and a delay of this length has its own element of danger. To assume that the economic system will give us unlimited time to find cures for its worst evils is not wise.

The same principle of regularization might, to some extent, be applied to residential construction, though under greater difficulties, since consumers can hardly be expected to organize to budget their collective expenditures on any such long-range program. The pressure would have to come from commercial builders, and would need to involve building ahead of demand to a considerable extent. In the case

197]

of automobiles, these methods offer little prospect of a stabilized production in the face of unstable demand. Here the control of credit extended to purchasers appears to afford the only effective hold.

Thus it appears that these factors are strategic in that they are potentially subject to control, and that through them something substantial may be accomplished. But this can be done only by difficult and far-reaching measures—measures which we do not seem to be prepared at present to take. This is quite natural, but it argues that we do not yet realize the full gravity of our situation.

If efforts to stabilize private activity in these fields fail, there is always the possibility of using public works to redress the balance. If private activity expands too intensely let public works contract, and if private activity contracts, let public works expand. This is not the place to discuss the whole theory and practice of the control of public works, or the obvious difficulties involved; we may merely note that public works are a section of this entire field in which the worst disturbances lie and from which they spread, and that they are a section of the field inherently susceptible to control, which could be used as far as it will go to neutralize the movements in the rest of the field. The amount of public works which could, within reason, be concentrated in dull times, does not appear from the figures as likely to be large enough, by itself, to counteract even a moderate depression.[4] Such a policy could succeed only as part of a much larger program.

If such a policy is undertaken, the method of financing is of vital importance, as affecting another vital factor: namely, the movements of total purchasing power. Financing by means of taxes which operate to decrease private expenditures will tend to neutralize the effect of expanding public works as a stimulus to total economic activity. Financing through the use of credit will tend to give it maximum effect, and the timing of repayment of the credit will also be of great importance. Repayment should be made so far as possible in times of active business when a brake rather than a spur is needed.

Passing on to price movements, and the corresponding changes in the other elements of the price system, here also we have forces of basic importance. The present system is a hybrid: neither free nor stabilized, but free in parts and resistant to change in other parts. This situation could be altered by more complete stabilization or by the attempt to bring about more consistent fluidity. Either might work better than the system now prevailing. And if instability of price levels is accepted, the attempt might still be made to stabilize the personal incomes of different classes, in the hope that this will result

[4] See Wolman, *Planning and Control of Public Works*, published by the National Bureau of Economic Research with the collaboration of the Committee on Recent Economic Changes, New York, 1930.

199]

in more stable expenditures and so tend to reduce indirectly the cyclical fluctuations of production and prices. At present we are not wise enough to choose with certainty between these possible courses. We do not know just what behavior of the price system is most desirable, just what system of regulation can best be used to bring it about, or just what adjustment of personal incomes will best promote the ends in view. Thus we are not mentally prepared for the effective control of the price factor. Nevertheless it must be classed among the major factors which are at least potentially, and to a considerable extent, controllable.

Stabilization of prices is not impossible. It may be approached through control of the currency system, or of credit, or of both. Or it may be approached, less usefully perhaps, by direct control of each separate part of the price system. Stabilization of the general level of prices would have the advantage that it would carry with it, without further need of control, stabilization of profits, of the distribution of income, and to some extent of the more damaging features of speculation in commodities and securities. If the prices of particular commodities were left free to move within a stable price structure, profits and losses would not be eliminated, but they would be freed from the perversions we have noted, which play so large a part in producing and intensifying undesirable general fluctuations. They might then

[200

perform their proper functions of stimulating the growth of efficient enterprises and the decline or elimination of inefficient ones, and of serving as a signal of shortages or surpluses of particular goods here or there in the economic system, and furnishing the impulse to make good the shortage or eliminate the surplus. The result would be a vast improvement over a system which gives the same signal indiscriminately for industry in general and so either stimulates further general expansion when industry is already over-stimulated, or further contraction when it is already depressed.

Passing on to the control of incomes within an unstable price system, we find that the apparent sources of instability in our hybrid system are of two different sorts, giving rise to two divergent policies. One apparent evil is the instability of incomes, the other the rigidity, or sluggishness of response, of the unit costs of labor and capital. Interest charges are largely fixed in money terms, and salaries and wage rates are relatively sluggish in their movements, while personal incomes from profits are partially stabilized in the case of dividends paid by those corporations which are strong enough to afford adequate reserves for this purpose. Thus we actually have a certain approach to a system of stabilized money incomes, but not a consistent approach. In particular, a sluggish movement of wage rates is not the same thing as stabilization of wage-

201]

earners' incomes. In fact, by rendering the unit cost of labor unresponsive, it may aggravate unemployment in dull times sufficiently to make the instability of wage-earners' incomes greater rather than less.

Thus certain features of the situation point toward the desirability of making personal incomes more stable than production, and thus breaking into the vicious circle whereby incomes fall because production has declined and production declines further because incomes have fallen. Other features of the situation point toward making the unit costs of labor and capital more responsive, and thus mitigating the intensified fluctuations of profits which, as we have seen, have such a disturbing effect. And of neither of these policies can it be said that we know with certainty what its full effects would be.

The first of these policies comes to grips with the problem of the dependence of consumers' demand on incomes and the dependence of incomes on the rate of production. This, as just noted, is one side of the vicious circle of depression—to borrow a figure of speech from Lewis Carroll's caterpillar, who assumed that a circle had two sides. At first sight the dependence of demand on income seems an inescapable fact; and indeed in its main outlines it is. But its action is susceptible to modification. There is every reason to suppose that the variation of consumers' expenditures is not identical with the variation of incomes, even now; and the discrep-

[202

ancies may be made to work in the right direction rather than in the wrong one by a well-considered use of the mechanisms of credit. Furthermore it seems certain that we can, if we wish, make the flow of income to consumers steadier, relative to the total national dividend, than it now is; for instance, by means of unemployment reserves. We must, however, watch the reactions of any such policy on the investment markets; and also make a wise choice of plans in order to put the burden in such form as to afford a maximum incentive to industries to stabilize, and a minimum inducement to workers to malinger.

We have already seen that the partial stabilization of dividends does not stabilize total purchasing power, but rather concentrates its fluctuations upon the element of corporate surplus and undivided profits, and upon the demand for the things on which these funds are spent. This fact has a moral for the many who are hoping that unemployment reserves may help to stabilize consumers' expenditures. They may be made to have this effect, but it will not follow automatically. The result will depend on the use made of the reserves, and on whether independent measures are taken to stabilize production in those fields into which the funds constituting reserves are likely to flow, in the process of being invested; and out of which they must come when the reserves are drawn down in an emergency.

Without stabilization of the production of capital equipment and other producers' goods, attempts to stabilize consumers' purchasing power by the setting aside of reserves, either for dividends (as is already done) or for wages (as is proposed) are likely to be baffled by the indirect effects of the uses to which the reserves are put while they are being held as reserves, and from which they must be withdrawn when they are paid out to beneficiaries.

If the reserves are put into securities, to be sold when benefits are to be paid, this means systematically buying in a dear market and selling in a cheap or demoralized one. Aside from the losses to the funds, such a policy might well aggravate business disturbances more than the distribution of benefits would mitigate them. A better plan would probably be some definite provision whereby such securities could be realized on by being used as a basis for loans which might serve to neutralize some of the shrinkage in bank credit which accompanies a depression. To be effective, this might require the provision in advance of emergency credit organizations, rather than setting them up after the emergency has become serious. For part of the funds, 'hoarding' during prosperous times may prove the safest and least disturbing form of investment.

The other policy we are considering—that of making unit costs more responsive—points toward the adjustment of wage and interest rates in terms of an index number of prices, so that the sluggishness of their adjustments may be, so far as possible, overcome. To be effective, this requires that interest on long-term loans be not fixed in money, but adjustable to a constant purchasing power. Wages and current interest rates may sometimes keep pace with prices, but fixed interest on standing loans never does. Such an adjustment would remove one chief cause of the misleading and perverted state of generally swollen profits. It would not, to be sure, eliminate the disproportionate variation of indirect labor and output which is based on mechanical facts about which there is presumably nothing to be done. What can be done, however, is to alter further the surrounding conditions of the wage contract so as to change the financial effect which this unequal variation has on the profits of the company and indirectly on the earnings of the wage earner. The most obvious measure of this sort is to lay a special charge on super-active employment to sustain out-of-work benefits in times of depression.

Clearly, the wage system will not cease to act as an aggravating factor in the business cycle until it ceases to be based on relatively stable money rates, measured in terms of a fluctuating standard of value, or on rates that lag in their adjustment. It may or may not be correct policy to maintain real wage rates in a time of depression. But it is certainly not correct policy to maintain uncompromisingly a system which causes real wage rates automatically to fall as profits rise and business over-expands, or to attempt to maintain rates which mean an actual rise of real wage rates as profits fall and depression spreads and intensifies. Yet this is—or would be—the result of sticking to fixed money wage rates at such a time. Any attempt to do this is probably bound to fail in its immediate objective, while if it succeeds, it cannot possibly result in stabilizing actual earnings.

This difficulty has been seen in an unusually intense form in the present depression, because it has occurred simultaneously with an enormous world-wide collapse of prices of a basically non-cyclical sort. It must be admitted that the average cyclical rise and fall of prices, and especially of costs of living, is so moderate that a system which should, for example, automatically adjust wage rates to a cost of living index, would have only a small effect either on the worker or on his employer. Its great usefulness would arise in precisely those instances in which the cycle is complicated by larger price movements of a non-cyclical character. Wage rates based on a wholesale price index would have more effect in stabilizing the real costs of business. To the wage-earner, they would mean that a standard week's labor would automatically yield increased purchasing power in the retail markets during business prosperity and decreased purchasing power during depression. The effect would probably be salutary, even from the standpoint of stability of real earnings for the workers, because it would remove one of the forces tending to aggravate instability of employment. If we had a clear choice between stable wage rates with unstable employment, and unstable wage rates with stable employment, there could be no doubt which is preferable.

All of which does not mean that business cycles are to be cured by such simple devices as a change in methods of wage payment. That would merely remove one aggravating factor, leaving other and more fundamental causes to be otherwise dealt with.

Speculation in securities is also difficult to control; indeed complete control and genuine speculation are contradictions in terms. And speculation may be affected by whatever is done in other fields, in unexpected and surprising ways. If restraining measures prevent funds from being used directly in business when they are searching for employment, the stock market is a natural substitute outlet. If unemployment reserves are accumulated in good times and drawn upon in times of depression, that may mean investing the funds in securities when the market is high and realizing on them when it is low, thus tending to aggravate both conditions. Such funds can probably be so handled as to avoid this danger, but it is a very real one, constituting a rather difficult problem to be met. In general, however, stabilization of production and of aggregate income should

207]

reduce the fluctuations of the free funds which find employment in the market, as well as increase the stability and certainty of earnings. Aside from setting limits on gambling types of transaction that make irresponsible use of other people's money and on the flow of other people's money into such uses (if possible), and setting higher standards for the securities themselves, it appears that putting the brakes on speculation must come, if at all, mainly as the result of action taken elsewhere for the stabilization of prices in general or of production in the critical fields. Speculation is an active factor, but our main power to control it is by indirect means.

The behavior of credit has already been mentioned in other connections as a factor of major importance. It is one of the most humbling factors to consider, for the reason that we have thought ourselves in a position to use it to some extent as a lever for control; and we find that we not only have not been able to make it do just what we wish, but also do not know precisely what we ought to try to make it do. And we entertain the suspicion that the organized machinery for controlling credit is not so all-powerful as we have often supposed. Certainly it is a mistake to expect the existing forms of credit organization to perform miracles in guiding the course of business.

The control of discount rates is probably not in itself sufficient, and there is not at present any ade-

[208

quately effective means of controlling the total
volume of credit directly; still less of discriminating
wisely between the different uses to which it is put.
So far as concerns the influencing of consumers'
expenses, credit in this field lies outside the scope
of our present institutions of control. But this does
not mean that stronger and more positive mechanisms cannot be devised, if the need seems sufficiently
urgent.

Here again we have the problem how far control
can go consistently with the continuance of private
enterprise and of the competitive principle. And
here again complete control and private competitive
enterprise are contradictions in terms. Nevertheless
this is perhaps the most all-pervasive agency conditioning the course of business, organized for control
to a limited extent, and with possibilities of controlling influence which go far beyond anything yet
demonstrated.

The reader need not be reminded that the purpose
of these excursions into the field of control is not to
frame a specific policy or to recommend particular
measures; but rather to shed light on the question
which factors among those responsible for business
cycles are of the greatest strategic importance. For
this purpose it is not necessary to select the best
possible devices, but only to show that some form
of effective control is possible. Factors we can control are for that reason of peculiar importance to us,

as human beings faced with a baffling and threatening problem. Such a canvassing of possibilities should, indeed, be a step toward the framing of a program; but the achieving of this final goal is a much longer and larger task, and one of a different sort.

From this standpoint, then, our study has revealed a number of factors as peculiarly strategic. Among these are: the intensified fluctuations of demand for productive equipment; and secondarily of demand for durable consumers' goods (which are less easily susceptible to control), price movements, movements of unit costs and of personal incomes, and the movement and distribution of credit. The all-important factor of profits is itself controlled, in its cyclical movements, by these other elements which condition it. Of secondary importance (still from the standpoint of control) is speculation in commodities and securities. This may, however, like profits, be influenced indirectly, via the factors which govern its movements. To all these causal forces the inherent possibility of control lends a commanding importance.

Third Group: Factors Responsible for Longer Trends

In this group belong the longer business trends, so far as they present problems of adjustment in the attempt to make full use of our powers of production. These longer trends are based on some of the originating forces already listed, such as inventions and the development of standards of living, and are modified by the business system of responses. Among their most important features are discrepancies between the rates of change of different economic factors, and the processes and problems of adjustment resulting from these discrepancies. Here are included the following factors:

(1) Long-run trends in the development of new productive processes, tending to increase productive power and to call for more capital per worker. Here we have the development of mechanization which, if not properly compensated by adjustments of hours and incomes and the development of new goods, may lead to 'technological unemployment'. Irregularities in this movement are among the causes of short cycles, as we have seen.

(2) The development of new goods into which to put our increased producing and consuming power. If this process lags, our producing power may not be fully utilized. Here we have also the increased development of durable goods and of 'optional purchases' incident to a rising standard of living, which, as we have seen, have their

211]

effect on the character of the short cycles.

(3) The balance between consumption and saving. A rapid increase in incomes may lead to 'over-saving' in the sense of a rate of saving too rapid for us to make the adjustments necessary to assimilate it, as our present system is geared to make them. This balance between consumption and saving is affected in turn by the following factor.

(4) The distribution of the national income among different income groups, which is at present mainly affected by the proportionate distribution between wages and property income.

(5) The relation between wages and interest in terms of their influence on the relative costs of labor and capital to employers, which in turn has an effect on mechanization and on the absorption of the supply of labor into productive employment. As we have seen, the requirement of labor costs low enough, relative to interest charges, to stimulate full employment, may be out of harmony with the requirement of labor incomes large enough to assure adequate consumption, unless changes are made in the system of distribution which

are more far-reaching than mere adjustments of wage rates.

(6) The apportionment of increased productive power between more goods and more leisure, as affected by the length of the standard working day and week. Here, as we have seen, there may be a discrepancy between the length of the working week necessary to absorb the existing labor supply, all the other factors being as they are, and the length which represents a desirable balance for the worker himself between more goods and more leisure. And as we have also seen, full use of our actual powers of production for the proper satisfaction of our wants for goods and for leisure requires an adjustment between all these factors, such as we have not yet learned to make.

(7) Among the forces of more enduring influence belong certain after-effects of the World War, especially the deflation of prices, the dislocation of international trade and indebtedness, and the weakening of foreign financial and economic structures. These are disturbing forces of the first magnitude, whose effects have come to a head only in 1929 and the subsequent depression. An incidental factor is the effect on our do-

213]

mestic capital markets of the repayment of our own domestic war debt.

(8) In this group belong perhaps those larger psychological swings from over-pessimism to over-optimism which seem to require more than the length of one short cycle to develop their full effects.

When we come to consider the possibility of control, as a guide to the strategic importance of these factors, we find truly interesting problems. As compared to the problems of control raised by the shorter business cycles, there are some increased difficulties and at least one rather pregnant new possibility. In general, of the factors listed here, those which can be controlled for one purpose can be controlled for the other, if we can only decide what they should be made to do.

The long-run trend toward more efficient productive processes, while not beyond all possibility of control, is not a thing which government will lightly undertake to limit or even to guide. Labor has some power to limit the introduction of labor-saving devices, but this is far from being a policy of collective control. It is possible also for government to take a hand in promoting the development and adoption of safety devices, as is done by the Bureau of Mines, which are not of a labor-saving character. But this again is not likely to lend itself to a deliberate con-

trol of the net rate at which labor-saving improvement proceeds, in the interests of a considered program of 'economic balance'. In the main, the course
of technical invention represents the force to which
other factors must adjust themselves.

Much the same could be said of the development
of new goods. The motive of profits is a powerful
stimulus to private business in precisely this direction; and while it may be strengthened or supplemented, it would be optimistic to expect very radical
changes to result from public efforts directed to this
end. And the psychological factors, as we have seen,
are mainly to be influenced by indirect means.

The after-effects of the World War form a special
group of problems. Among them price movements,
trade barriers and international debts are definitely
within the realm of international action. Such action
could go far toward restoring weakened financial
structures, and even toward mitigating underlying
economic weakness so far as it arises from the split-
ting-up of Europe into uneconomic national units.
Hours of labor and the distribution of the national
income are also clearly subject to control.

The balance between consumption and saving may
prove more difficult to deal with, even granting the
possibility of defining the desirable goal. The choice
of how much of one's personal income to spend and
how much to save is as definite a part of the realm of
personal liberty as the choice of what kind of goods

215]

to buy, and is almost, if not quite, as unlikely to be directly controlled. And whatever is done, within reason, to alter the distribution of income between wages and incomes from property, the mere upward movement of per capita income will tend to cause a larger percentage of the increased income to be saved. Workers of many grades contributed large amounts to the swollen flow of savings during the last boom, and granted resumption of progress they will do so again.

Yet there are possibilities of influencing the flow. Increasing amounts are saved by corporations; and if a reduction of the total is really desired, this portion could be reached by the taxing power or otherwise. And there is another series of measures which might have an effect in one direction or the other, in ways to which apparently little serious attention has yet been paid. These are the measures of institutionalized saving which are grouped under the general head of 'social insurance'. Would the general spread of such measures increase the total amount of savings or decrease it, over a period measured in decades? Some are rather casually taking for granted that the security provided by social insurance and especially by unemployment insurance will make workers more willing to spend their free incomes for consumption, since there will be less need to build up individual reserves against emergencies. But granting that there will be an effect of this sort, will it be sufficient to outweigh the huge reserves which the insurance systems will themselves require? The answer is far from clear. In the insurance reserves, all workers in the insured classes will be represented, whereas not all of them would save voluntarily as individuals. On the other hand, a given amount of saving will provide far more security if put in the form of social insurance. In particular, insurance reserves are calculated on the basis of spending principal as well as income before the transaction is closed, whereas individual savings are to a large extent made with at least the hope of spending only the income and maintaining the principal as a permanent asset. This is especially true in the United States, where the custom of buying annuities is far less widespread than in some European countries. Thus the substitution of insurance for private saving means installing a system under which there will be more spending in proportion to the capital funds accumulated than under the system of private saving in those cases where the saver succeeds in realizing his ambition to maintain his principal intact. Over against this stands the fact that the lower-paid wage-workers as a class do not typically succeed in realizing that ambition. The crises of their lives usually force them to spend their principal; and not much of their accumulation is permanent. Thus the extent to which insurance would substitute the ultimate spending of one's principal

217]

for the permanent maintenance of it remains in doubt, and may depend on how far the principle of social insurance is extended upward into the better-paid groups whose members have already achieved a moderate measure of security and economic stability. Another important factor will be the adequacy of the reserves accumulated: whether they are made sufficiently large to meet all demands, or whether serious emergencies will exhaust them and necessitate the use of public credit to maintain benefits. If the latter policy is followed an increase of capital accumulations may be avoided—at a price.

In short, one of the important features of the spread of social insurance is its effect on the balance between saving and spending. This effect cannot be definitely predicted, but can to some extent be governed, as the system develops, by changes in the extent, character and policy of the system itself.

Thus we see that a considerable number of the factors concerned with the longer trends have that grade of strategic importance which arises from our power to influence their action. The problems involved are subtle and difficult, and there is no likelihood of our reaching a quick solution of all of them, and guiding the forces of economic development into a regular course of unbroken and unmarred progress. But the potentiality exists and to that extent the forces we have dealt with are of especial strategic importance.

[218

Next Steps--the Place of Research

These, then, are the factors of most strategic importance in the business cycle and kindred illnesses of business, so far as this study has served to reveal them. They do not offer any easy and simple formula for the solution of these distressing problems. They indicate no panacea; they point rather to a deal of difficult experimenting with new methods of organization to accomplish new ends—difficult and perhaps not without danger. There is danger of going too far to turn back, on roads that lead to destinations we would not most of us consciously start out to reach. There is danger of setting up measures of control before we are wise enough to know just what to do with them and how to use them in the right way. And there is danger of doing nothing until it is too late, waiting to know just what to do—waiting perhaps for students to tell us things we can learn only from experience and to prove to us matters not susceptible of exact proof. We need more statistical information; we also need statistics not gathered merely to describe things but oriented to the provisional diagnoses which need to be tested, and to the needs of a program the main characteristics of which can be outlined with the knowledge already at hand.

It is clear from the foregoing study that a more adequate diagnosis of business cycles waits on a more fully-developed statistical picture of the main quantities in the interrelated network of factors that governs our economic life. More knowledge is wanted as to incomes, consumers' purchases, savings, investment and the purchase of productive equipment and of producers' goods in general, production and stocks of goods and credit. Rough approximations are useful as far as they go, but they fail to answer some of the crucial questions raised by existing theories. For this purpose the student will not find his material sufficient until the figures are accurate enough to reveal minor discrepancies between these very large totals; and until they are recorded at short enough intervals to enable him to detect short leads and lags. He needs to know whether consumers' expenses fluctuate more or less than consumers' incomes and whether either leads the other; and what discrepancies exist, if any, between savings and capital expenditures for producers' goods.

In the case of stocks of goods, we have seen that there is need not only of more complete figures, but of figures grouped according to the significance of these stocks in business cycles. As already indicated, some represent willingness to buy or to produce in anticipation of demand, and others represent inability to sell. Manufacturers' stocks of materials have a different significance from their stocks of finished goods. More important probably is the fact that an increase in some kinds of stocks indicates an increased amount of work done and paid for, compared to volume of sales; while the volume of agricultural products varies so much with weather and other natural conditions that they have very little significance of this sort.

In the case of credit, we have seen that there is need, not only of more accurate figures of consumers' credit, but also of a general segregation of loans according to the uses to which they are put: whether to finance consumption, production of consumers' goods, production of producers' goods, or speculation in commodities or securities. Volume of deposits and volume of loans also reveal different features of the credit situation. Volume of deposits, multiplied by rapidity of circulation, belongs in the estimate of the total flow of purchasing power, and under normal conditions constitutes over 90 per cent of this flow. Increases and decreases in the volume of loans going into any given use give an indication of the extent to which the volume of purchasing power available for that use exceeds or falls short of the amount received from current income.

One phase of this matter which presents an extremely knotty problem is the question what finally becomes of the funds (so largely derived from credit) which flow into the securities markets during a speculative boom. The proximate and ultimate effects of such a flow on expenditures for producers' and consumers' goods are very important to know, in attempting to diagnose the relation of movements in the securities markets to general business cycles.

If the stabilization of the work of installing capital equipment is of central importance, knowledge of the facts in this field is correspondingly vital. One of the first things which will be wanted is better evidence of the extent of excess capacity, present estimates being bafflingly inconclusive for the purpose in hand. The crux of the problem lies in the fact that a given amount of theoretical capacity does not mean that industry is actually equipped for continuous production under normal working shifts and normal operating conditions, at the rate which the theoretical capacity seems to indicate. This is true for four main reasons. One is the existence of seasonal peaks which cannot easily be removed. For example, mid-summer production of Portland cement is approximately double mid-winter production.[5] A second is the lack of uniform standards of normal working shifts.[6] A third is the fact that some reserves are necessary to provide against interruptions and the need of repairs. And a fourth is the fact that reserves even beyond this amount, when they consist of semi-obsolete equipment, still do not represent a real surplus for purposes of continuous

[5] See Robert F. Martin, Industrial Overcapacity, an analysis of figures compiled by the United States Bureau of Foreign and Domestic Commerce, *Bulletin of the Taylor Society*, June, 1932, p. 99.

[6] *Ibid.*, p. 94.

operation, because they are not economically suited to such use. There is, then, vital need for distinguishing between different grades of equipment on a basis which is pertinent to the practical needs of the case.

Semi-obsolete equipment has typically higher operating expense per unit of product than that which is up to date, but lower overhead costs, since it represents little or no investment. As a result, it may represent the cheapest way to handle occasional peaks or emergencies, as it would be too expensive to keep first-rate equipment idle most of the time for the sake of such occasional service; while at the same time the semi-obsolete units might be quite uneconomical for continuous service, on account of their high operating cost. Excess capacity in the primary sense exists only when there is a surplus of equipment of such quality as is economical to use for regular, as distinct from occasional, service; and this fact indicates the first and most important line of distinction to be drawn between equipment of standard and substandard quality.

The rate at which equipment is approaching and passing this dead-line, coupled with the normal growth of the industry, is the gauge of the effective demand for new units for replacements or enlargements; and this is the vital factor in any program of stabilized capital expenditures, involving as it would

223]

the drawing up of a budget looking some years ahead, if only as a goal to aim at.

Another obvious field for research lies in studies of the effects of policies which have been actually followed, in all the many areas of action which affect business cycles. It will not be easy to disentangle the effects of a given policy from those of the ever-varying conditions under which it is carried out; nevertheless the attempt should yield some useful results. One of the fields which should be covered consists of the efforts which have been made to put the otherwise unemployed to work producing goods for themselves and for each other, on a self-sufficing or a barter basis. These should be studied in the light of the possibility of linking up the widespread local experiments into a nation-wide network which would have a better prospect of efficiency through more adequate division of labor and operation on a larger scale.

Another way in which statistics can render service consists in studies looking to the setting of standards of possible achievement on a national scale. Business has developed the technique of standard-setting as one of its indispensable tools; and when the nation begins to think in terms of developing its national capacities, it also has need of standards as guides to its efforts. Estimates of this sort in the past have been one-sided and uncritical, drawing vague conclusions of vast unused capacities but without linking them up with the question of potential demand: of the concrete forms in which the results of such productive powers could be usefully put.

What is really needed is a serious canvass of the standard of living available to our people under reasonably full utilization of our powers of production; such canvass to be put into terms of housing space, bathtubs, refrigerators, central heating, clothing, automobiles and other goods, as well as improved education, medical service, recreational facilities and leisure. Such a survey would need to be based on the records which show how groups with different incomes actually direct their spendings. And it would need to take account of the effect of a slackening rate of growth of population, and of the stabilization of the production of capital equipment which is one prerequisite of the achievement of anything like full utilization of our powers of production.

A corollary of such a study would carry us into the problem of the distribution of spending power necessary to give effect to any given potential standard of living on a national scale. Another corollary would be a recognition of the likelihood of increased savings under the conditions contemplated (including the possible development of collective reserves for unemployment and old age), and a correlation of such savings with the volume of investment needed to equip the program at existing technical standards,

225]

and the possible field for further developments of capital investment, public and private. Such studies go far beyond the scope of mere statistical records of established facts, and are exposed to corresponding uncertainties; but there is no less need for making them, to the best of our ability, and revising them as new experience sheds new light.

When statistical studies have done all they can do, there will always remain the question of devising new policies and new instrumentalities for carrying them out. Here factual research can be of but limited usefulness. It may help to prevent the repetition of past mistakes; but the final verdict must be given by the process of experimentation, or of trial and error. The stabilization of capital expenditures, for example, requires the forming of new types of organization; and research in the ordinary sense cannot tell us how to do this. If experimentation waits for the completion of an adequate program of research, we shall make little progress. The two lines of attack on the problem must advance hand in hand.

AGGREGATE FLUCTUATIONS OF

PRODUCERS' GOODS, RESIDENTIAL

HOUSING AND AUTOMOBILES

THE aggregate movement of a group of such diverse series as here considered is not easy to estimate, in view of their differences of timing. The diversities of one series from cycle to cycle can be overcome by taking its average pattern through the successive stages of the cycle of general business. But this average pattern still differs in timing from one series to another. In meeting this difficulty, the fluctuations of these series will be presented in two ways; first, the fluctuations in the average general-cycle pattern of each series between the high and low points of its individual average movements; and second, an attempt will be made to estimate roughly the stages of the general business cycle which mark the high and low points of this group of series as an aggregate; and the fluctuation of each series between these points will be noted. These fluctuations will be stated as averages of the upward and downward movements, an upward movement of 60 per cent and a downward movement of 40 per cent appearing as an average movement of 50 per cent. The percentage is in each case a percentage of the average value of the series for the cycle in question.

The average cyclical movements of the series representing the groups in question are shown below, with the stages [1] of the general business cycle in which their high and low points occur and notes as to their general conformity. As already observed in the text, a pattern whose low point occurs in the eighth stage of the general cycle instead of the ninth is sufficiently typical of production series to be regarded as representing perfect conformity for series of this sort.

SERIES	STAGES OF GENERAL BUSINESS CYCLE MARKING HIGH AND LOW POINTS OF AVER-AGE-CYCLE PATTERN OF SPECIFIC SERIES	AVERAGE MOVE-MENT (PER CENT)	CONFORMITY TO TIMING OF GENERAL BUSINESS CYCLE
Producers' goods, physical production (Leong's study), 1919-27, 3 cycles..	5, 8	27	Virtually perfect; one-stage lead on upturn.
Manufacture of basic materials (Harvard series adjusted), 1919-27, 3 cycles	5, 8	28	Virtually perfect.

[1] See text, p. 9 for description of method of dividing the cycle into nine stages for purposes of comparing cycles of different length.

[228

Passenger cars, physical production, 1914-27, 4 cycles	4, 6	43	Three - stage lead on up-turn, one-stage lead on down-turn, some irregularity.
Trucks, physical production, 1914-27, 4 reference cycles, 3 specific cycles...	5, 8	58	Virtually perfect.
Construction contracts awarded, total 1912-24, 4 cycles	4, 7	52	Two - stage lead on up-turn, one-stage lead on down-turn. This series might reasonably be lagged one stage, resulting in more perfect conformity.

A selected list of producers' goods could be made up which would show far more than 27 per cent fluctuations, and might well account for the major part of the excess of this group above the average for all branches of production, at least in the 'industrial' class. Some of the items would be the following:

229]

SERIES	STAGES MARKING HIGH AND LOW POINTS OF AVERAGE-CYCLE PATTERN OF SERIES	AVERAGE MOVE-MENT (PER CENT)	CONFORMITY TO TIMING OF GENERAL BUSINESS CYCLE
Pig iron, 1885-1927, 13 cycles	5, 8	40	Virtually perfect.
Steel ingots, 1919-27, 3 cycles	5, 8	48	Extremely close.
Coke, 1912-27, 5 cycles..	5, 9	46	Perfect.
Machine-tool shipments (yearly basis), 1904-21, 5 reference cycles, 4 specific cycles	5, 9 (Stages 2, 4, 6 and 8 lacking)	52.5	Virtually perfect. Monthly figures would show larger fluctuations.
Fabricated structural steel sales, 1915-24, 3 cycles...	3, 7	80	Two-stage lead.

All but the last of these series conform so closely in their average pattern to the general business cycle and to one another, that their aggregate fluctuations, taken as a group, would be very nearly as great as that of a properly weighted average of their individual fluctuations for the same succession of cycles. Thus the aggregate impact of these products on the economic system is extremely heavy. For purposes of comparison, the following series might be used.

[230

APPENDIX

SERIES	STAGES MARKING HIGH AND LOW POINTS OF AVERAGE-CYCLE PATTERN	AVERAGE MOVE-MENT (PER CENT)	CONFORMITY TO TIMING OF GENERAL BUSINESS CYCLE
Physical production of consumers' goods excluding automobiles (Leong's study), 1919-27, 3 cycles..	4, 8	12	Lead, good conformity but some irregularities.
Industrial production, (Standard Statistics Company's index), 1912-27, 5 cycles	5, 9	24	Perfect.
Basic industries, (Federal Reserve Board index), 1919-27, 3 cycles	5, 8	23	Almost perfect.

It would be possible to determine the aggregate fluctuation of the group including producers' goods, construction and automobiles, by building up an inclusive series, properly weighted: but in this there would be one difficulty. What is the real meaning of the differences in timing between 'construction contracts awarded' and 'production of producers' goods'? Should the lead of the construction series be taken at its full face value? The one series records the completion of work, the other a preparatory stage in work which typically takes some months to complete. Thus it is reasonable to suppose that the timing of the actual work involved in construction might be better represented if the series were lagged, let us say, three months or even more.

231]

STRATEGIC FACTORS IN BUSINESS CYCLES

In dealing with series already divided into 'stages', it has seemed legitimate to lag the series of construction contracts by one stage, always recognizing that this is a very rough and ready procedure.

If this is done, it seems fairly clear that the high and low points of the aggregate movement of the group will occur in the fifth and eighth periods. If the average movement of each series, then, be taken between these two periods, the result will be a series of percentages which, if properly averaged, would give a fairly true measure of the aggregate movement of the group. Since the behavior of the construction series is regarded as abnormal for the last two cycles, and two of the other series go no further back than 1919, completely comparable series are available for only two cycles: 1919-24. Most of the series are available, however, for three cycles: 1915-24. The following evidence may, then, be used.

SERIES	AVERAGE MOVEMENT, STAGES 8-5-8 (PER CENT)	REMARKS
Producers' goods, physical production (Leong's study), 1919-24, 2 cycles	32	
Manufacture of basic materials (Harvard series adjusted), 1919-24, 2 cycles	34	
Passenger cars, physical production, 1915-24, 3 cycles	18	Peak in stage 4; sharp drop to stage 5.
Trucks, physical production, 1915-24, 3 cycles	69	

[232

APPENDIX

Further evidence afforded by these same series taken for
a longer period where available, together with other particular series of the same character (involving some over-
lapping) is as follows:

SERIES	AVERAGE MOVEMENT, STAGES 8-5-8 (PER CENT)	REMARKS
Producers' goods, physical production (Leong's study), 1919-27, 3 cycles	27	
Manufacture of basic materials (Harvard series adjusted), 1919-27, 3 cycles	28	
Passenger cars, physical production, 1915-27, 4 cycles	19	
Trucks, physical production, 1915-27, 4 cycles	58	
Construction contracts awarded, 1912-27, 5 cycles ...	32	
Same series, lagged one stage	52	
Pig iron, 1885-1927, 13 cycles	40	
Steel ingots, 1919-27, 3 cycles	48	

233]

Coke, 1912-27, 5 cycles   37

Machine-tool shipments(yearly basis, 1904-21, 5 reference cycles, 4 specific cycles	52.5	(Stage 8 lacking. Monthly figures would show larger fluctuations)
Fabricated structural steel, sales, 1915-24, 3 cycles	71.8	

One must allow for the fact that construction contracts are reported in money terms, thus exaggerating the actual physical movement, and for the further fact that the diffused effects of construction work are somewhat distributed in time. Taking these facts into consideration, it may very roughly be estimated that the aggregate fluctuation of this entire group in an average cycle could be not less than about 30 per cent.

INDEX

235]

INDEX

NATIONAL BUREAU PUBLICATIONS ON
BUSINESS CYCLES

I Books on Business Cycles

Business Cycles and Unemployment (1923)
Committee on Unemployment and Business Cycles of the
President's Conference on Unemployment, and a Special
Staff of the National Bureau
448 pp., $4.10

Employment, Hours and Earnings in Prosperity and Depression, United States, 1920-1922 (1923)
W. I. King
150 pp., 3.10

Business Annals (1926)
W. L. Thorp, with an introductory chapter, Business Cycles
as Revealed by Business Annals, by Wesley C. Mitchell
382 pp., 2.50

Migration and Business Cycles (1926)
Harry Jerome
258 pp., 2.50

Business Cycles: The Problem and Its Setting (1927)
Wesley C. Mitchell
514 pp., 5.00

Planning and Control of Public Works (1930)
Leo Wolman
292 pp., 2.50

The Smoothing of Time Series (1931)
F. R. Macaulay
174 pp., 2.00

Strategic Factors in Business Cycles (1934)
J. M. Clark
256 pp., 2.50

German Business Cycles, 1924-1933 (1934)
C. T. Schmidt
308 pp., 2.50

Public Works in Prosperity and Depression (1935)
A. D. Gayer
482 pp., 3.00

Prices in Recession and Recovery (1936)
Frederick C. Mills
602 pp., 4.00

*Some Theoretical Problems Suggested by the Movements of
Interest Rates, Bond Yields and Stock Prices in the United
States Since 1856* (1938)
F. R. Macaulay
612 pp., 5.00

Consumer Instalment Credit and Economic Fluctuations
(1942)
Gottfried Haberler
262 pp., 2.50

Measuring Business Cycles (1946)
A. F. Burns and Wesley C. Mitchell
592 pp., 5.00

Price-Quantity Interactions in Business Cycles (1946)
Frederick C. Mills
158 pp., 1.50

Changes in Income Distribution During the Great Depression (1946)
Horst Mendershausen
192 pp., 2.50

American Transportation in Prosperity and Depression
(1948)
Thor Hultgren
432 pp., 5.00

II Books Partly Concerned with Business Cycles

The Behavior of Prices (1927) 598 pp., 7.00
Frederick C. Mills

Recent Economic Changes in the United States (1929)
2 vol., 990 pp., 7.50
Committee on Recent Economic Changes of the President's
Conference on Unemployment, and a Special Staff of the
National Bureau

Seasonal Variations in Industry and Trade (1933) 480 pp., 4.00
Simon Kuznets

Production Trends in the United States Since 1870 (1934) 396 pp., 4.00
A. F. Burns

Industrial Profits in the United States (1934) 692 pp., 5.00
R. C. Epstein

Ebb and Flow in Trade Unionism (1936) 272 pp., 2.50
Leo Wolman

The International Gold Standard Reinterpreted, 1914-1934
(1940) 2 vol., 1474 pp., 12.00
William Adams Brown, Jr.

National Income and Its Composition, 1919-1938 (1941) 1012 pp., 5.00
Simon Kuznets

*Financing Small Corporations in Five Manufacturing In-
dustries, 1926-36* (1942) 192 pp., 1.50
C. L. Merwin

The Financing of Large Corporations, 1920-39 (1943) 160 pp., 1.50
Albert R. Koch

*Corporate Cash Balances, 1914-43: Manufacturing and
Trade* (1945) 148 pp., 2.00
Friedrich A. Lutz

National Income: A Summary of Findings (1946) 160 pp., 1.50
Simon Kuznets

Value of Commodity Output since 1869 (1947) 320 pp., 4.00
W. H. Shaw

Business Incorporations in the United States, 1800-1943
(1948) 196 pp., 6.00
G. Heberton Evans, Jr.

Out of print.

NATIONAL BUREAU OF ECONOMIC RESEARCH
1819 Broadway, New York 23, N. Y.

What Ends

A Novel

Andrew Ladd

New Issues Poetry & Prose

Western Michigan University
Kalamazoo, Michigan 49008

First American Edition, 2014.

ISBN-13: 978-1-936970-22-3

Library of Congress Cataloging-in-Publication Data:
Ladd, Andrew
What Ends: A Novel/Andrew Ladd
Library of Congress Control Number: 2013931585

Editor: William Olsen
Managing Editor: Kimberly Kolbe
Layout Editor: Elizabyth A. Hiscox
Editorial Intern: Allison Lee
Cover Design: Megan Lappe
Production Manager: Paul Sizer
The Design Center, Gwen Frostic School of Art
College of Fine Arts
Western Michigan University

This book is the winner of the Association of Writers & Writing Programs (AWP)
Award for the Novel. AWP is a national, nonprofit organization dedicated to
serving American letters, writers, and programs of writing.

Go to www.awpwriter.org for more information.

What Ends

A Novel

Andrew Ladd

NEW ISSUES

 WESTERN MICHIGAN UNIVERSITY

For Betty, Dwight, Leonas, and Maria—
I know you're reading somewhere.

1980

I.

The island's final child was born on a bleak, October evening: a boy, Trevor Alistair McCloud. At the time, of course, no one could know he'd be the last, and his birth was noted much as any other; even years later his brother and sister would remember less the event itself than the weeks before it, how their parents had shut the guesthouse early for the season, and the way the closing days of summer had left the island strangely muted. They'd reveled in the difference of those gravid afternoons, their father cooking all the meals, the pub downstairs completely empty, and their mother, usually so busy, spending her days on the sofa or in bed, exhausted but serene.

The family's first son, Barry, was seven, with coal-black hair and a splash of translucent freckles that stretched from ear to ear. He was a thoughtful boy, his manner unassuming, but to Flora—his sister, three years younger—he seemed practically omnipresent: a face behind her birthday candles, and the hand she held on walks, and the warm bundle by her side during their mother's stories on the couch. His laugh, as their father tickled them by the fire one evening, was the first memory she had.

They lived on Eilean Fìor, an island three miles long by one across, in a cluster of four others off Scotland's northwest coast. Of its twenty-eight inhabitants Barry and Flora were the only children, so from necessity if not fondness they were rarely far apart; they played together, and pooled their labor to get through chores, and with Trevor arriving had given up their separate rooms to make way for a nursery. Flora squeezed in with Barry now on a just-built set of bunk beds, and despite their endless bickering, about the dolls she left in his toy box, or the intricate wooden train tracks he set up across the floor, they found they liked the new arrangement. In the quiet after lights out they could whisper to each other for what felt like hours, until their breathing drifted into unison and they fell asleep contented.

Their room was on the second story in their family's sprawling, sandstone guesthouse—across the hall from their parents' bedroom and a bathroom, and flanked on either side by the new nursery and a study, where every weekend their father would curse his way through the accounting. All of it was hidden behind a wooden door off the main staircase, with *Do Not Enter* in crackled black letters across its middle. One floor up was an attic containing five small guestrooms, and one floor down was everything else: the kitchen, the pub; the lobby, the lounge; the heart of the community. The pub, especially, was always bustling, in summer with guests from upstairs and a steady stream of campers, and year-round with a dedicated group of local drinkers too, complaining about the weather, or trading gossip, or occasionally discussing the mainland's politics or football. And since most visitors found that atmosphere impossibly inviting, the lounge at the front of the house—ostensibly for public use as well—was for the most part a family living room, filled with photographs of relatives, and board games for the children, and the old, wood-cased wireless that once they'd kept upstairs. (There was no television, the children's father having inherited his own parents' stubborn suspicion of the things.)

The other islanders liked the atmosphere there, too, but that life revolved so completely around the guesthouse was mostly an accident of circumstance—they all knew it. The old general store was derelict; the granite chapel towards the jetty had been padlocked shut for years. So where else could they go? The ferry to the mainland took two hours, and even at the height of summer there was only one crossing a day—two on Fridays and Saturdays—so the nightlife in Mallaig, such as it was, was hardly worth it. (Doubly so in the winter, when the ferry ran just three days a week.) There were the other islands nearby, of course, but the smaller boats they used to hop between them, for visiting the post office or the doctor or the farmer's market, struggled when the sound was even moderately rough, and when a full-blown storm descended it was the ferry or nothing. Sometimes not that either.

For a long time, none of it had seemed to matter, to the McClouds or to the rest of Eilean Fìor. They always had enough food, spread across their vegetable plots and larders and sheep pens, to survive heartily even if the ferry never returned; they had enough water, tapped from a well near the center of the village, to last them far beyond what they'd ever need. They even had a school for the children, agreed to by the board of education when there were thirty students on the island and not just Barry. And most importantly they still had each other, and their livelihoods, and the guarantee at almost any time of day of a friendly visitor stopping by the pub.

Or, at least, they'd had all that, once. By the eve of Trevor's birth, though, that older way of life had begun to falter, and a skulking sense of the end, impending—however optimistically ignored, however strong their sentimental bonds—was slowly beginning to take hold.

*

The birth itself, that evening in October, was in the master bedroom at the guesthouse, attended only by Oonagh Kilgourie, a crofter's wife from the island's other side. It was an arrangement the children's mother, Maureen, had insisted on.

"I'm tired of going all the way to Fort William to get gawked at by teenage nurses," she'd told her husband one night, her hair bouncing defiantly. They were on the sofa, Flora at their feet and surrounded by crayons. "Oonagh and I can manage just fine on our own."

"But Reenie," he'd started to reply. "What if there are complications? At your age—"

"My age! I'm only thirty-nine, George, and it's not as if I haven't done this before. Anyway, people have been having weans here for hundreds of years without scurrying off to the mainland for someone to hold their hand."

Rubbing absent-mindedly at his bald spot and thinking he'd quite like some hand-holding, George had made some last-ditch point about the children being upset by the sight of her in labor.

"Oh, nonsense," she clucked, reaching down and patting Flora on the shoulder. "Poppet, will you be all right if your new brother or sister is born at home?"

Flora murmured yes, barely looking up.

"Hmph," said Maureen, and nodded in triumph.

The night of the birth, though, George called the region's doctor anyway, a plump, officious man from the largest island in the group, who arrived an hour later—relatively swift, given his small speedboat—and rushed up to the bedroom, shirt straining to come untucked beneath his belly. Almost immediately he was sent back downstairs.

"Everything seems to be in order," he said, as he reached the bottom landing. "The ladies are, ah...confident they have the situation in hand."

George nodded, unsurprised; he'd been scolded for even summoning the man. Instead, he suggested a whisky.

"Well," said the doctor, puffing out his chest. "I should stay, of course, in case I need to take charge." He glanced towards the ceiling, and his shoulders sank. "But perhaps I had better stick to tea."

"I'll put the kettle on," said George, and told the doctor to make himself comfortable in the living room. When he walked through with the tray a few minutes later, he found Barry cornering the man in an armchair and quizzing him on the finer points of childbirth.

"You see," the doctor was saying, "your mother...The baby can't come out until—your mother needs to be fully...prepared."

Barry leaned in. "But *how* did it get *inside* her in the first place?"

"Ach, wheesht," said George, setting down the tray on the center table. "Leave Dr. Nicol in peace. He's not an encyclopedia." He poured out a cup and carried it across the room. "There you are," he said, winking, while Barry returned to the board game he'd been playing with Flora. "Not a moment too soon, eh?"

The doctor chuckled nervously and thanked George, taking the teacup and a first, wincing sip. He swallowed. Sighed. "The McKinleys are moving away from Rum," he said. "I just heard."

George sat down in his own chair across the room. "Oh?"

"Aye, somewhere near Aviemore. The Post Office is relocating him."

"All change these days," said George, smiling gravely. "We've three more couples leaving here in the spring, too."

Carefully, the doctor set down his cup on the arm of his seat. "It's been worst on Fìor, hasn't it? How many in the past year?"

"More than two dozen." George sighed. "Six families. There's barely two dozen of us *left*."

"Such a pity," said the doctor, looking wistfully at the steam still rising off his tea.

Upstairs, Maureen let out a cry; the children both snapped to attention.

"Now, now, you two," said George, lowering himself from his chair to the floor. "There's no need to look so worried." He shuffled over to where they were sitting and put an arm around each of them. "She's okay. I promise."

The children nodded at him but still looked uneasy, so he pulled them both closer. "Listen," he began. "Have I ever told you what happened the night Barry was born?" He winked at the doctor over their shaking heads. "It's quite the tale." When their mother went into labor the first time, he explained, she'd been baking a birthday cake for Mrs. McKenzie, the woman who'd run the general store—and it was as she stood up from putting it in the oven that she felt the first contraction. But then, because she couldn't bear the thought of the food going to waste, she'd convinced herself it was nothing more than a spot of indigestion. "She ignored it for a full three hours!" George laughed. "It was only once the cake was iced, all three layers, and a pound of strawberries sliced and arranged on top, that she told me she thought the baby was coming."

"So he called me," said the doctor, cutting in, "and I hurried over to take them to the mainland. Except by then your father was in such a tizzy he tripped over his own feet when we got to the jetty and fell headfirst into the water."

"I think I swallowed some seaweed," said George, his voice plaintive but his face a giant grin. "It was about as tasty as your auntie Susan's Brussels sprouts."

Barry and Flora giggled, and the men waited for them to settle before they continued. Doctor Nicol told them how he'd taken off his jacket and used it to fish their father out; George told

12

them how Maureen had grown so impatient—afraid, after all the waiting, that she might end up having her first child right there in the doctor's speedboat—that she'd refused to let him go home and change. How he'd had to spend the crossing wrapped up in a blanket and shivering in the stern, instead.

"And when we finally got to Mallaig," said the doctor, "your dad was still so sopping wet the paramedics wouldn't let him into the ambulance. Didn't want him getting water everywhere."

George shook his head. "I had to spend an hour and a half waiting for a train to take me to Fort William, and when I got there I ended up walking to the hospital because no taxi would take me, either." He smiled. "I still made it, thank goodness."

He paused for a few seconds. Flora asked what had happened when she was born.

"Ach, you were easy," he said, with a dismissive wave. "We were both so traumatized by Barry we had everything planned to a T."

Her face fell. "Oh."

"But your first birthday," he continued, not missing a beat, "was a total mess." And then he was off again.

The children were used to their father telling stories like this, the way he'd start to talk and talk, each word, it seemed, giving him the energy to say another five. Mostly it happened on the walks they took on mild afternoons, once Barry was home from school; they'd set out along the village road and quickly veer off into the heather, hiking up hills to watch for boats across the water, or wading into sheltered dips and glens, to play hide and seek in the long grass or chase after mice and rabbits. The whole time their father told them his countless, gleeful stories, filling in his childhood on the island, and their family history, and a timeline of the place's ample past.

Fior's first inhabitants, he'd explained, were Picts, the only

13

signs of their existence a few wrecked foundations in the hills. Their most likely executioners, sailing through a few centuries later, were the Vikings, whose strange runes George had shown them once, carved into a cliff face down the coast. Then, another millennium after that, though the children could hardly conceive of so much time, there were the farm and fishing families who'd settled to serve their feudal laird, and finally came the village, after an eccentric new owner bought the island with the dream of making it a holiday resort. He was the one who'd built the guesthouse, in the late nineteenth century—and the newer cottages, and the jetty on the island's southern tip. He was the one who'd persuaded dozens of entrepreneurs, George's grandparents included, to move to the island with their families, and cater to the tourists he was sure would soon arrive.

And arrive they did, hundreds each summer—thousands in the best years—an endless stream of cruises up the coast. The ships would drop anchor early each morning and their genteel passengers would swarm ashore, spending the day buying woolen souvenirs at the village craft shops, and sending novelty postcards from the general store, and wrapping up the afternoon nibbling on scones and sandwiches in the guesthouse tearoom. (The pub came much later.) Then, in the evenings, they'd disappear just as quickly, back to their ferries and away to sea, leaving behind the island's few hundred inhabitants and any wealthier tourists who'd paid to spend some time ashore.

With the Great War things changed, of course—it simply wasn't safe to gad about the Atlantic anymore, even in the relatively sheltered sea around the Hebrides. *Your grandfather*, George had told them, sitting at the island's highest peak one day, *used to come up here and look for submarines*. He pointed out across the ocean. *You could see their shadows beneath the water, he said—like little black slugs, slithering along*. He put extra emphasis on *slithering* and leapt up towards the children as he did so, fingers wiggling. They laughed and shrieked, and scattered for the path.

After the war things started to pick up again, but then the thirties came, and the depression—and after that the tourists increasingly stayed away. The population shrank; the island's owner was forced to sell. And at that point their dad would always change the subject or gloss over the details, refusing to say more even when they asked him. It was only from Mr. Lewis, the island's schoolteacher, who'd been there for only eight years himself, that Barry learnt the truth: where the old owner loved the place for what it was, the new one was simply an investor, convinced the island would be a lucrative source of peat. When that came to nothing he raised the rents instead, and while the few who could bought their homes and land outright at that point—the McClouds and their guesthouse among them—the poorer families and the smaller croftholders had no choice but to leave. *And they never stopped leaving, Barry*, Mr. Lewis explained, sitting on the edge of his desk with his glasses sliding down his nose. *Even after the old crab died and his children donated the land to the wildlife trust, they didn't want to stay.* He pushed his glasses back up as Barry, leaning forward, asked: *why?* The teacher shrugged. *Who knows, Barry? Sixty people left in five years. It was half the island. Probably the rest of them just couldn't bear to see it.*

Barry later passed the story onto Flora, though in his retelling the details were inevitably smudged. The parts he'd failed to understand (rent, wildlife trusts, nostalgia) were left out altogether, while the landlord became a literal crab—a seven-foot-high one who'd chased the islanders away. His pincers cut people clean in two in Barry's version, and Flora hid beneath her blankets as she listened.

This was their habitual way of absorbing adults' stories: as jumping-off points for their own, inventing whole sagas around the tiniest of details. There was a Viking murderer, in their universe, who was exiled to the island as punishment for his crimes—he was the one who'd carved the runes along the coast—and a Pictish sorcerer who'd conjured the island from the sea. There were winds so dreadful, they imagined, they could blow children into the night, and thunderclaps so booming they left others briefly deaf. And then there were all the ships they imagined sunken just offshore, their contents washing up for days following a wreck: enormous jewels and treasure chests filled to burst, and strange, exotic animals, shaking their long fur dry as they lumbered up the beach.

Even lost in their imaginations, though, even with Barry's crab long gone, the two of them had still noticed the island's population trickling away; had grown accustomed to the procession of tearful goodbyes in the pub, the postcards from expatriates in mainland cities, and occasionally the strangers they'd see knocking on village doors. *Why are all those people going to the Leslies' house?* they asked at dinner one night. *They're thinking about buying it*, Maureen told them, with a snort. *I doubt they will.* And she was right—except for the old laird's manor, which sold to a Glaswegian woman the year before Trevor's birth, the rest of the village homes ended up abandoned.

The children weren't bothered by the constant departures, though; if anything they liked the island emptier, as it gave them more scope to play. There were fewer extra eyes to tell their parents if they were doing something wrong, now, and fewer spots off limits, so they could roam as they pleased around the silent houses, and the empty churchyard, and the musty old barns in the hills. Or else they could run off along the road, a mud track mixed with gravel and crushed shale that ran across the island, and follow it to the crofts on the north shore or, more often, to the jetty on the south. From there they could watch for seals around the distant skerries or carry on down the coast, searching for shells along the island's, seaweed-covered shores.

On a map, they knew, those shores followed an outline like the wing of a maple seed; their father had shown them one on a Christmas visit to their cousins' house in Perth. *Look*, he'd said, pointing to the seed compartment with his pinkie. *This is where the puffins nest.* He moved his finger towards the center of the wing. *And this is where we do.* The children nodded, picturing the map of the island their father displayed above the bar, acknowledging the similarity—but for some reason the image failed to resonate. Perhaps, with the island's only trees marooned in a plum orchard behind the old laird's house, the seed itself seemed too exotic to relate to home. Or perhaps the yellowing, dried out pod was too different from their own experience of scrabbling around the coast, over pea-green hills and concertinaed, basalt cliffs, and across the tiny burns breaking inland every few hundred feet.

Or perhaps it was the Stùc, the tiny spur on the island's north coast that ruined the maple seed outline anyway. Once upon a time it had been a natural harbor, their father had told them, one the Vikings would have used in the centuries before the jetty. *You see how it looks like an arm*, he explained, sticking his left hand out in front of him as they gazed down at the Stùc from a cliff—*ready to give someone a big hug?* He wrapped his outstretched arm around his right shoulder. *Well, that makes the water in the middle calmer, so boats could have docked there when it was too rough on the south shore.* He stuck his right hand in the crook formed by his awkward self-embrace, and waved his fingers at them. *See how comfortable they are in here?*

The children laughed at the analogy, though like the seed pod it wasn't perfect. The Stùc was an arm only when tides were low; the rest of the time it was connected to the main island by a wooden footbridge and nothing else. *The old laird built it*, George told them one afternoon, as they watched the wide, sandbar isthmus disappear beneath the water. *He wanted to have his house over there so he could holiday away from the riff raff—but he didn't want to have to wait for the tides to go in and out.* Barry frowned at that, and asked why, if the laird had wanted to be left alone so badly, he'd built the school on the Stùc as well. George grinned and ruffled the boy's hair. *Don't miss much, do you? It wasn't a school at first—it was the old servants' quarters.* Then it was Flora's turn to frown: *why did he need servants?* This time George only shook his head, chuckling to himself, and told her it was a long story that would have to wait for another time. *Now come on*, he'd said, turning towards home. *Let's go find some dinner.*

By eleven o'clock, the lounge's campfire atmosphere had vanished. The children were finished with their first board game and had already played another, and now Flora was back to her usual drawing while Barry struggled through a Roald Dahl book on the sofa, nodding off every few pages. Doctor Nicol, meanwhile, had given up the fight and was snoring softly in his chair, and George, chewing at the end of a pencil, was muddling through the *Scotsman*'s cryptic crossword.

Suddenly, there was a noise on the stairs, and George's head jerked up; by the time Mrs. Kilgourie reached the door he was already halfway across the room, and when she announced the baby boy's arrival Flora jumped to her feet, too. "Can we see him?" she squealed, jolting Barry and the doctor awake.

Mrs. Kilgourie nodded, and led them all upstairs to where Maureen lay, clutching the baby, her hair matted and a few streaks of red on her bedclothes. George approached her first, sitting down on the edge of the bed and planting a kiss on her cheek, and leaning in for a better look at the bundle in her arms.

"Another chip off the old block, eh?" He gave the blankets a gentle pat.

"I bloody well hope not," said Maureen, smiling.

"Are you okay, Mum?" asked Barry, stepping forward from where he stood with Flora and the other adults. His eyes flitted between her and the bloodstains.

"Aye," she said, looking away from George. "Just a wee bit tired."

With a look of relief the boy edged closer still, eventually reaching his mother and, with some encouragement, pulling back the edge of the baby's wrap. His eyes widened. "He's all purple, Mum!"

In the doorway the doctor cleared his throat. "That's normal, Barry." He glanced at Mrs. Kilgourie. "Sometimes being born can be as hard on the baby as it is on the mother."

At the sound of the doctor's voice Maureen looked in his direction, and then to his right, where Flora was fidgeting with a crayon she'd carried from downstairs. "Come on, dear," she said. "Come see your brother."

Nodding silently, Flora walked across the room, Barry moving aside to make room for her by the bed. And as she finally looked down at Trevor—at his tiny, puckered eyes, and his dab of a nose—she found herself reaching forward to stroke his cheek. The frown on her face softened.

"He looks nice," she said, glancing up, and Maureen smiled back in approval.

Mrs. Kilgourie bustled forward. "Right," she said, placing a hand on each of the children's backs. "That's enough. We've things to do." She ushered them to the door, where the doctor still stood looking gormless. "You too, Mr. Nicol," she said. "George will make up a guestroom for you."

"I—yes," said the doctor. "Thank you." He stepped into the

dark hallway with the children.

"And you bairns," Mrs. Kilgourie added, already closing the door behind them. "Get yourselves to bed. I'll want your help with breakfast." Behind her Maureen called out goodnight, but the door was shut before they could reply—leaving them to share a look of confusion with the doctor before brushing their teeth in silence and putting themselves to bed. It was the first night they could remember not having their mother tuck them in, and the first of many repercussions Trevor's birth would have. His arrival on the small, declining island was a pebble dropped in a pond; a dying stillness disturbed. But by the time the final ripples vanished, twenty-five years later, the boy born that evening in October would be the only one still there to see it.

II.

Nobody would ever know how the rats first made it to the island, or when exactly it had happened. For months after Barry first claimed to see one, his parents wouldn't even consider that it might be true, and once the situation had at last become impossible to ignore—once whole harvests sat ruined, once countless gnawed-through power lines had been replaced, once the seabirds that blanketed the island in normal years were gone—by then the only thing anyone could think to ask was: *how will we get rid of them?* Or, in bleaker moments: *will we?*

That came much later, though, after many more years of diaspora and disappointment, after Trevor's first steps and words—and after those early weeks following his birth, when his siblings realized that their lives, like that, had changed. Partly it was Mrs. Kilgourie: once she'd shooed the doctor out that first morning, after allowing him a hasty breakfast and a token examination of mother and child, she seemed to take up permanent residence. A small bag of her things appeared in one of the guestrooms upstairs; the dial on the living room radio moved to a classical station the children hated. She crowded visitations with their mother, and talked over them at dinners with their father, and at night, when they tried to take shelter from her in their room, she would appear at the door without warning (or cause, they thought), and mutter a stern *Hush! You'll wake the wean!* She imposed her fiats so completely that even the rats, when the children began to see them, would seem unobtrusive in comparison.

Just as present that first week, though less annoying, was Mr. Kilgourie, who arrived Saturday morning before the doctor had even left. He made little effort to disguise his motives—didn't even visit Maureen upstairs—just pulled off his green wellies in the hall and gave George a pat on the shoulder, and then padded toward the kitchen and the smell of sizzling bacon. Unlike his wife he brought no luggage, but he stayed for lunch and returned for dinner, and did the same the next day, too—and soon the faint whiff of his pipe smoke lingered in the living room, even when he wasn't there.

That first morning after Trevor's birth, Mr. Lewis also visited from the school on the Stùc. Better-mannered than Mr. Kilgourie, he at least stuck his head in the bedroom briefly to say congratulations and make a crack about his next paycheck being guaranteed—but after that, and a few quiet words with George, he spent the rest of the morning in the living room, trying to chat with Flora but being mostly monopolized by Barry. Over-stimulated from seeing his teacher outside the usual surroundings, the boy had developed a sudden exhibitionist streak, and bombarded Mr. Lewis with endless show-and-tells. *This is my favorite place to read! And this is a picture of my cousins in Perth! And—oh! Would you like to see my room?*

More exciting still was who turned up after Mr. Lewis: Bella, the Glaswegian woman who'd bought the laird's manor, and the Stùc's only other resident. That she was the first person to have moved to the island in the children's lifetime was fascinating enough, but in the year since then she'd kept mostly to herself, and had returned to the mainland for the winter months when the island's farms were dormant and the social scene at its peak—and so still none of the villagers knew anything about her. She was in her thirties, they knew that much, and was an artist, and apparently not a struggling one if the amount she'd spent on her house here was any indication. It wasn't just the building itself, and the orchard behind it—it was the renovations. They'd been hard to miss with the workmen going to and fro for weeks, and the steel beam she'd had shipped over, and the giant bags of masonry dust and other rubbish she'd then had shipped back out. She was a mystery—and now here she was, standing on their front step.

"Miss Fowkes," said George, opening the front door, while Barry and Flora hid just beyond the vestibule. "What a pleasant surprise."

"I heard congratulations were in order," she said stiffly, standing well away.

George nodded and thanked her, and asked if she'd like to come in.

"Oh no," she said. "Perhaps another time. I wouldn't want to intrude." She handed him a card, made of thick and grainy stock with an ink design of an angel on its front. "But please give this to your wife."

George took it, with more thanks, and then moved slightly to the side. "Are you sure you won't come in?" he asked. "It's really no bother." But she demurred again, mumbling goodbye and turning to walk home. Barry and Flora immediately galloped upstairs to watch her from their bedroom window, hypnotized by her long scarf, loose-knit and orange, whipping around her in the wind. Meanwhile, downstairs, George studied the card she'd left, bemused. It contained only five words, carved in loopy black calligraphy. *All the best*, it read. *Bella Fowkes.*

After that, the remaining visitors, arriving in a steady stream through Saturday evening and Sunday afternoon, were a bore, at least as far as the children were concerned. Each of the island's other households turned up bearing the usual array of gifts—pots of stew, jars of preserves—and with so little overlap it seemed as if they'd all sat down, upon hearing the news, and drawn up a plan. Their visits displayed that same military efficiency, too: they would arrive and troop up to the bedroom, cooing and fawning as appropriate, and then Mrs. Kilgourie would swiftly herd them back to the pub, where they'd sit and tell George what a splendid little boy he'd produced, and be on their way within an hour. It was eminently pleasant—but beneath that warmth there also seemed to lurk some deeper feeling of reproach. Of disappointment. As if, at the same meeting where they'd drawn up their schedule, they'd agreed as well that giving the island another child was a futile thing to do.

When Mrs. Kilgourie left at the end of Trevor's first week, the children entertained the brief hope that their lives might return to normal—but even in her absence the household's rhythms faltered. The occasional family storytelling nights ceased entirely; still, their mother wasn't tucking them into bed. And worst of all Trevor crowded out their meals each evening, perched in a battered plastic baby carrier at the table's head, the adults smiling and burbling at him as if Barry and Flora weren't even there. While in the past they'd often lingered to listen to their parents talk, now they ate in glum silence and asked as soon as they'd finished to be excused.

Other problems were slower to develop. Their father's afternoon walks with them, for instance, at first seemed unaffected. As October faded into November, though, they too began to taper off, George blaming the cold weather and the encroaching dark of winter, or his fatigue at being up with the baby in the middle of the night. After a few more weeks he wouldn't even be downstairs when Barry got home, and the boy would find Flora alone in their bedroom's early evening gloam. *Dad's taking a nap*, she'd say, and when he asked why she had no lights on she would look around, surprised, as if she hadn't noticed it was dark.

Meanwhile, with Barry at school during the days, Flora grew increasingly lethargic. For a while she tried spending the hours with her mother, as she'd done before Trevor's birth, but when Maureen wasn't tending to him now she didn't have the energy for much else—and when Flora attempted to play with him herself she was only left more frustrated. He wouldn't respond to her voice—wouldn't even turn his head at the sound, half the time!—and when she tried showing him her drawings he just grabbed at them with drool-slicked fingers and left them smudged or crumpled. She tried making faces at him, the way Barry sometimes had with her, or tickling him, or entertaining him with a toy, but still he'd only lie there gurgling. Having never seen another newborn, Flora took this lack of sentience personally, as if he were withholding some more meaningful response, and when she sometimes tried in desperation to coax more out of him—crushing his fingers around a crayon, or grabbing his head and turning it towards her when she spoke—her mother would quickly shoo her away to go help George with chores. Eventually she gave up leaving her room at all, and would sit and make up half-hearted worlds for her dolls or flip through the pictures in Barry's books, until three o'clock arrived and she moved to the window to watch for him walking home.

Then, at Christmas, another change. Rather than their usual visit to the mainland relatives, they stayed on the island, George and Maureen deciding that with Trevor still so young they didn't want to travel. For the first time since his birth the children perked up, enchanted by the prospect of decorating their own house, and of hanging stockings from their own mantel, and most of all, as their parents soon informed them, of their very first Christmas tree, ordered specially from the mainland. The day it was to be delivered they buzzed around the house all morning, and that afternoon Barry practically sprinted out the door to go collect it with their father and Mr. Kilgourie. (Flora, by this point, had started making paper chains to hang on it and couldn't be torn away.)

"I'm glad you stayed," said Maureen, settling on the sofa once the other two had left, Trevor in her arms, and making a show of admiring her daughter's glitter-covered handiwork. Then, after a few minutes, her voice turned sterner, and she told Flora there was something else they needed to discuss. The girl nodded absentmindedly, continuing to frantically cut and glue, until Maureen's voice hardened as she told Flora to pay attention and reluctantly the girl looked up. Maureen fixed her in a resolute stare, and began to explain that, given how much of their time the baby had been taking up, lately, and how unhappy Flora had seemed about it, they had decided that Flora would be starting school a few months early.

Flora, whose eyes had gradually been drifting back to her paper chains, now jerked to attention. "What!"

Trevor hiccupped.

"You're starting school early," Maureen repeated. "As soon as the Christmas break is over."

"But Mum!" Tears were filling her eyes now. "I don't *want* to go to school! I just want Barry to stay at home!" She glanced at Trevor, who hiccupped again. "It's not fair!"

"Flora—"

But the girl was standing up, now, and screaming at her mother that she hated her and hated the stupid baby, and was galloping upstairs just as Barry and George reappeared with the tree and Mr. Kilgourie.

"Where's young Flora off to?" the man asked, seeing her feet vanish over the top landing. He turned and began shuffling sideways down the narrow hallway, top of the tree in his hands. "She'll want to get a look at this fine specimen!"

"She's in one of her strops," said Maureen, standing to one side to let them into the living room.

"Well," Mr. Kilgourie said, huffing as they finally set the tree down and steadied it by the hearth. "This will bring her out of it!" He petted one of its branches; it sprung back eagerly.

Maureen dryly remarked that she rather doubted that, and indeed, when George went upstairs to try and reason with Flora he returned after barely five minutes. A door slammed upstairs. "She says"—he cleared his throat—"that she doesn't care if we decorate the whole stupid tree without her."

"Let's get started, then," said Maureen. "She can only sit up there stubbornly for so long."

So they did, Mr. Kilgourie making his excuses and his way out, and Maureen setting Trevor in his baby carrier while George fetched a box of decorations from the cupboard under the stairs. Only Barry seemed unsure what to do, rooted in the middle of the living room and glancing towards the ceiling at every stomp and bang.

"Don't worry," said Maureen, putting a hand on his shoulder. "She'll come around soon."

They were almost to the bottom of the decorations box, though, before Flora reappeared; Barry, hoisted up in his father's arms, was fumbling the angel into place on the bough when they heard the sniff behind them. They all turned, George lowering Barry to the ground again, and saw her standing in the doorway, eyes red and lashes still damp. Maureen took a deep breath.

"We saved your paper chains for you," she said, smiling.

She knelt down and picked up a string, still tangled on the floor.

Saying nothing, Flora sniffed again and stepped forward with her arm outstretched—and then, her mother holding it at the other end, she wrapped the chain around a few of the lower branches.

"Wonderful," said George. "Now, let's get a picture." He fetched his camera from upstairs and balanced it on a pile of books on the coffee table, and, setting the timer, took his place with the family in front of the tree: he and Maureen in the middle, the baby in her arms, and Barry and Flora standing one on either side—Barry's face slightly pink, still, from helping carry home the tree, and Flora with flecks of the paper chains' glitter in her hair.

"What happened?" Barry hissed at her, but George shushed them before she could respond, turning both their heads towards the camera. In the photograph the exchange was recorded as nothing but a quizzical stare across their parents' waist—the only, slight sign of anything the matter.

Despite her tantrum that night and several more to follow, Flora went to school in January as her mother had announced, walking there with Barry her first morning under a sky the color of lead. Barry tried his best to lift her mood as they walked, but the truth was he didn't want her there, either. The school had become his sanctuary over the past year, especially in the months since Trevor's birth, and even with his sister he didn't want to share it.

The school itself, the old servants' quarters on the Stùc, was stone and two floors high. (*That fellow didn't want for help!* their father liked to laugh.) Inside it was divided in half, with the "school" on the ground floor and the teacher's flat above, but with so few students in recent years, Mr. Lewis's space had begun to encroach downstairs. What was supposed to be his office, across the hallway from the single classroom, had now become a lounge, the old teacher's bureau shoved in a corner and covered with potted plants, and a sofa and several chairs moved in around the fireplace; what was supposed to be a storage closet for the pupils' coats was filled mostly with his own.

The classroom, meanwhile, had emptied. Most of its thirty desks were stacked against the rear wall these days with just four still facing the blackboard at the front, and even they were largely for show; for almost a year and a half, Barry had been the only student, and Mr. Lewis, of course, the only teacher—and as the two of them had grown to know each other they'd fallen, like an old married couple, into their own set of odd routines. At first Mr. Lewis had simply given up on standing by the board, pulling a chair to Barry's desk and demonstrating the day's lesson with pen and paper instead of chalk and slate. Before long they were wondering why they even bothered with that, and on an especially cold day during Barry's first February alone, they had moved to Mr. Lewis's sitting room to practice reading in the fire's flickering glow. Soon they were spending half the school day on the sofa, and after dropping his bag in the classroom every morning, Barry would wander across the hallway where Mr. Lewis would be waiting with a cup of tea and the morning's agenda.

It was that closeness Barry feared Flora would disrupt, and the worry was a prescient one: his sister was an intrusion, throwing off the balance in the classroom just as Trevor had at home. On that first, gloomy morning Mr. Lewis was waiting in the classroom when they arrived, a long-forgotten necktie looped underneath his collar. *Good morning*, he'd said, the phrase crisper than usual. *Please take your seats and we'll begin.* And though he still sat with Barry and explained things one-on-one as the day went on, their camaraderie seemed to dry up, somehow, turn brittle; when Barry faltered on a problem, now, or wondered how to spell a word, he was no longer guaranteed an instant response.

Instead, Mr. Lewis, hunched at Flora's desk, would say a quiet *I'll be there in a moment, Barry*, without even looking over.

Worst of all were the jotters. Barry's early workbooks—and the other children's, before they'd left—had always had the same magenta covers and blue-ruled pages, cool and smooth to the touch. His first term on his own, though, the maths textbook had called for charts and geometric shapes, and rather than hand out loose-leaf graph paper as he'd done in the past, Mr. Lewis on a whim ordered a new variety, the covers celadon green and the pages bigger, the baby-blue lines replaced by a grid of feathery grey squares. The change had so delighted Barry that Mr. Lewis began to order another new design each term, and soon the silly little things were overflowing from the classroom cupboards, their covers a blaze of different hues and their pages almost limitless in their shapes and sizes. The unveiling of the new jotters had become something they both looked forward to—but when they told Flora to pick the one she liked best that first morning, she only scowled, determined to dislike the place, and grabbed one from the pile that was closest. All of a sudden they felt sheepish for making such a fuss.

It didn't help, either, that Flora was so openly opposed to being there. It took twice as long as necessary to get her started on even basic tasks, and after five minutes she'd give up anyway and throw whatever it was to the floor. She butted into conversations and demanded almost hourly to be sent home, and sometimes, on particularly bad days, would ask to go to the bathroom and not return until someone went to find her. Usually she was hidden somewhere upstairs, drawing on a scrap of paper she'd filched on the way out, but as spring blew in she began to venture further: down to the beach, or climbing on the rocks around the water, or even, once, all the way home, where Maureen scolded her until the baby woke and then sent her to her room. After that, she took more care, vanishing altogether to a place Mr. Lewis could never find—at least, not until Bella returned in April that year and appeared at the school's front door one morning, gripping Flora firmly by the bicep. *Lose something?* she muttered, pushing the girl forward. *She walked right into my living room.*

Meanwhile, as spring opened into summer and two more couples fled the island, Barry saw the first of the rats. He was on his own, walking to the beach on a sunny weekend afternoon, when the thing scurried with no warning from the high grass beside the trail. Startled, he let out a cry and ran home.

"Dad!" he said, frantic, finding his father in the garden. "I've just seen something!"

George, tending to a row of carrots, didn't turn around. "Oh aye? What's that?"

When Barry told him, George laughed, and finally looked up. "Don't be daft, Barry—there aren't any rats here, only mice. You know that."

"No, Dad, no. It wasn't a mouse. It was much too big. And Mr. Lewis showed me a picture of a rat once. I'm sure that's what it was!"

"Barry," said George, standing up, "I've lived on this island all my life and not once have I seen a rat. It must have been something else."

"But—"

"Now go on, away with you. I think your mum wanted help in the kitchen."

Barry, confused, left his father among the carrots, trying to think of some way to prove what he'd seen. But the more he thought about it that afternoon the less clearly he could even picture what the thing had looked like, and by dinnertime he had more or less convinced himself it *had* been just a mouse.

A few weeks later, though, coming home from school, he

and Flora saw another one gnawing at something in the heather. Flora whimpered, grabbing at Barry's hand, and they hurried home, where, once again, George only scoffed, and tut-tutted, and told Barry he shouldn't be putting ideas in Flora's head.

Barry might have worried about it more, but once June arrived and the school year finished, he had something else on his mind: Flora's disappearances. Every few days she would casually announce after lunch that she was going out to play, and then for several hours was nowhere to be found. Their parents weren't worried; they were used to the children disappearing sometimes—had often disappeared themselves as kids—and in any case, although they weren't fully reopening until the following summer, when Trevor was older, they now had a steady stream of campers and day-hikers visiting the pub again, and were glad to have Flora out of their hair.

Barry, however, couldn't stop obsessing over where she might be going, and finally he followed her one day, along the road and onto the smaller path towards the Stùc. As he watched her stroll over the footbridge he stopped, frowning, knowing he'd be spotted if he went any farther—but in bed that night he confronted her, hooking his chin over his bunk's railing as soon as the lights were out.

"Why were you on the Stùc today?"

She rustled beneath him. "I wasn't."

"You were so!" He leaned even further over the side of the bed. "I saw you!"

She paused. "I don't have to tell you."

"Flora—"

"Leave me alone, Barry!" In the light from under the doorway he could see her duck beneath her covers, hissing that he was horrible and annoying. But when he threatened to tell their parents she reluctantly showed her face again and agreed to a compromise: she'd take him with her next time in exchange for his continued silence.

Once they left the next day, Flora seemed to have second thoughts. As soon as they were out of sight of the house she stopped and turned to him gravely. "You have to be really quiet when we get there, okay? Otherwise we'll get in trouble."

"I knew it!" said Barry. "I knew you were doing something bad!"

"It's not bad, really," she said, starting to walk again. "You'll see."

They wound down to the north shore and the bridge to the Stùc, but instead of the usual path to school, after they crossed, Flora led them along the shoreline and onto a rocky trail that ended at a steepish slope covered in thick gorse. They clambered up it, using the gnarled branches to steady themselves, and only once they reached the top did Barry realize where they were: behind Bella's orchard. Flora stared pointedly at him and motioned for quiet, and then crept forward to a crumbling, uneven section of the wall, climbing quickly up and over. On the other side she tiptoed ahead, leading him through the narrow gap between the trees—and finally, when the house came into sight, she stopped again, and beckoned him closer, and sat down on the ground.

As part of the renovations Bella had combined all the rooms along the back of the house into one, long space, and had knocked out some large chunks of the outer wall to make way for a row of giant windows, which filled the studio now with plentiful, peaceful daylight. It also put the inside on display to anyone in the orchard, and there she was, wearing only some running shorts and a stretched-out camisole, her chestnut brown hair pulled up in a ponytail. Barry sunk to the ground beside Flora and the two of them watched, instantly transfixed—Flora by the woman's arm moving across the canvas, and Barry by the faint shadow of a crease at the base of her shorts.

After what might have been an hour, he felt something brush up against his leg, and looked down to see one of the stony-brown rats sniffing around. He jumped to his feet, letting out an enormous yelp; when Flora turned to shush him she saw the rat and screamed too, and in the window, Bella, starting at the noise, joined in. She dropped her paintbrush and ran from the room, leaving Barry and Flora—and the rat—to scamper away.

They had barely reached the upstairs landing at the guesthouse when Bella stormed into the pub, shouting across the bar at George about *those little fucking monsters!* Cautiously, they peered over the banister—*I didn't realize this was the bloody Wicker Man!*—and saw their mother hurry into the pub just as a few other terrified customers hurried out—*aye, get back to the ferry before they start stalking you, too!* After a few more seconds both women had reappeared in the hallway, Bella wearing nothing but a flimsy housecoat and still roaring about how she'd call the police if this were Glasgow, and Maureen frantically shushing her.

"I'm sorry, Miss Fowkes," she said finally—firmly—once Bella began to quiet. "Obviously this is completely unacceptable. I can promise you it won't happen again."

Bella hmphed. "Thank you," she said, sighing and fixing her hair back into the ponytail that had apparently come undone on her dash from the Stùc. She kept winding it around her fingers, distracted, as the conversation went on. "I hate making a scene like this," she added, "but what would you do if you were alone in the house and noticed someone watching you through the window? They scared me half to death."

Maureen nodded, as if considering something. "This is really very unlike them, Miss Fowkes," she said, after a moment. "I'd hate for it to sour you on them permanently. Perhaps we could have you to dinner one night? Get everyone back on the right foot?"

Bella sighed again. "We'll see," she said. "For now just make sure they stay away—I've got a big show in the autumn and I don't need these distractions." Finally her hands fell from her hair and settled in the pockets of her housecoat. Her face twitched and she looked down, as if she'd forgotten it was all she was wearing; she coughed, and tightened the belt a little, and added, blushing: "I prefer *Ms.* Fowkes, by the way."

"Of course," said Maureen, her mouth suddenly a thin line, and showed the woman out before stomping upstairs to ground the children for the rest of the summer.

As autumn descended, and then winter, the rats seemed to retreat, but the reprieve was only temporary. When spring returned the infestation did too, and now in greater numbers. Barry and Flora saw them almost weekly on their walks to school, and Mr. Lewis, to Barry's relief, finally believed them and called their parents—and though George and Maureen never admitted that they'd perhaps been wrong, their incredulity at last began to falter. By the end of Flora's first full year of school their father had organized an emergency meeting for all the remaining islanders; traps were laid, holes plugged. Fingers crossed.

And then it was summer again, the guesthouse reopened and the days a frenzy. Trevor, not quite two, still required frequent attention, so Barry and Flora were enlisted to help wherever possible, emptying the bins, or tidying the kitchen after meals, or hoovering the public rooms at night. Their grounding from the previous year was not renewed, but to avoid any further accusations, the children mostly followed the road away from the Stùc whenever they ventured out. Instead they walked to the jetty, and followed the coast to a white quartzite beach on the island's south shore, whose sand gleamed in the sunlight and sang in the wind. There they'd watch the puffins and shearwaters circling overhead as raptly as they'd sat in Bella's orchard, as if the important part was simply some movement to hold their attention.

Occasionally, though, on midweek days when guests were sparse, one of them would sneak out alone and slip across the bridge, along that craggy trail and over the orchard's back wall. When Flora went, she crept back and forth beneath the studio's massive windows, peeking over the sills to admire the paintings added weekly to the walls; when Barry did, he simply found a shaded spot beneath a tree and watched the woman's every move while a helpless, unconscious love began to sprout. Throughout it all, neither child revealed their furtive stakeouts to the other, and if either one suspected then they never dared to ask—complicit in the silence of those first, seductive secrets.

III.

The years passed and Trevor grew, sloughing off successive sets of hand-me-downs without his siblings noticing a thing. It was only when he approached three, and Barry, himself almost eleven, recognized a beloved set of old pajamas at the breakfast table, that suddenly it struck him. In bed that night, he lay with his chin in its habitual place hooked over the bunk bed railing, and asked Flora, now seven-and-a-half, if she'd noticed the change too. Scooting sideways under her covers, she poked her head out from the bottom bunk.

"Yes!" she said. "And did you hear him at dinner? He said *I want more!*"

"No," Barry replied. "It was *I want Mum.*"

Flora snorted. "*I want Mum?* Why would he say that? She was right there!"

"It doesn't have to make sense," said Barry, flopping back onto his pillow. "He's only two-and-three-quarters."

"You're wrong," she told him, and before he could say anything more she'd hidden beneath her blanket.

It became a constant competition, seeing who could explain

their brother better. Every night they argued over what he'd said at dinner, and every afternoon they dashed through their homework, trying to beat the other one downstairs to steer his budding lexicon in their favor. Before long they were vying for nothing less than his complete devotion, and would sit on opposite sides of the room, wooing him with toys and sweets, as if the direction of his waddle proved some deeper understanding.

Those were Trevor's first memories, but soon he had amassed more: walking with his family the day a rat jumped at them from the heather; a springtime visit from Dr. Nicol to administer the shots, his arm tensing around the needle; and his first glimpse of fog, the anxious tingle in his stomach as the landscape was swallowed up by whiteness. He collected these small, impressionistic flashes—painstakingly, reverent, the way an adult might fill a shoebox with old postcards—and with each one the island felt more like it was *his*. When he tried to talk to Barry and Flora they only confirmed that belief, greeting descriptions of his most vivid memories with confused stares or shaking heads. Not until he was much older did he realize that the events most striking to a three-year-old were a matter of routine to others, and not until he had just turned four did something happen that seemed remarkable to all of them.

It was mid-afternoon on a Wednesday, and Trevor had come downstairs from a post-lunch nap to see if Barry and Flora had returned from school. They had not, but instead and to his great surprise the living room was full—with his parents, and Mr. Kilgourie, and a representative from each of the island's last households, the Pikes and the Thomases and the Mannings. And most bizarre: two strangers wearing suits.

Maureen noticed him in the doorway and waved him off, telling him to go play with his brother and sister.

"They're not home," he said, without moving. His eyes

turned to the strangers. "Who are they?"

Maureen gave a strained smile. "They're friends of ours," she said, and looked around the other people in the room, lingering on the two visitors. "Why don't you go get yourself a snack, love? Dinner won't be for a while."

Hesitant, Trevor did as he was told, but after fetching some oatcakes from the pantry, he tiptoed back to the hallway and began to listen, fascinated, despite understanding almost nothing.

"I'm afraid it's simply unacceptable, Mr. McCloud," said a voice he didn't recognize.

Mr. Kilgourie roared. "Unacceptable! And who are you to tell us what's acceptable and what's not? We're the ones who bloody live here!"

"Calm down, Jack," said someone else—Mr. Thomas, Trevor thought—and there was some scuffling as Mr. Kilgourie stalked across the room. Trevor wedged a few crumbs into his mouth, chewing as softly as he could.

"I'm not sure I see the issue," said his father.

Another unfamiliar voice responded. "The field mice on this island are an endangered species, Mr. McCloud, that's the issue. Are you familiar with Darwin's finches?"

"Good grief," muttered Mr. Kilgourie, the floor creaking as he began to move around again.

Just then Trevor felt something brush his elbow, and he let out a small shriek, spinning around to see Barry and Flora, returned from school. The adults, thankfully, seemed not to hear.

"What's going on?" whispered Flora.

"I don't know," said Trevor. "There are strangers here."

Barry and Flora shared a look, and then all three of them stood there listening. One of the unfamiliar voices was speaking again.

"The mice here have been isolated on the island for so

many years that they've diverged from the mainland species. Now they're unique to Eilean Fìor, and that means you can't go around laying poison all over the place. They need to be protected."

"I don't think you understand how bad it's become." Their mother was speaking now. "It's not just that they're getting into our homes—they're affecting the whole island. There are fewer plants, fewer birds...I've never seen the shearwaters so thin." She paused. "I find it hard to believe that's all a coinci—"

"My grazing area is completely ruined too," Mr. Kilgourie interrupted. "My sheep have nothing to bloody eat and neither do we."

"These are valid concerns, of course," said one of the visitors, "and we're not suggesting nothing be done. We're merely telling you that indiscriminately filling the island with rat poison is not an option the Trust is willing to consider."

Trevor put the last of the oatcakes in his mouth, now, a little too carelessly; a few pieces went down the wrong way and he began to cough. The two older children turned frantically to shush him, Flora clamping her hand over his mouth and Barry trying to shove them both around the corner, but it was too late. The conversation in the living room had stopped abruptly, and footsteps were moving towards the door.

"What on earth are you doing out here?" said Maureen, stepping into the hallway, eyes narrowed.

"Nothing, Mum," said Barry. "Me and Flora just got home, and—"

"I don't want to hear it," she snapped. "I taught you better than to eavesdrop on private conversations. Upstairs, now—all of you."

"But Mum," began Flora. "We weren't—"

"I told you, Flora, I'm not interested." She put her hands on her hips. "Now go on, all of you. Up to your rooms. We'll have words later."

"Sorry," mumbled Flora, and once the three of them had started up the stairs Maureen turned back to the living room, making her own apologies and leaving the children, bewildered, on the landing.

Soon enough they'd know everything they wanted about the strangers' plans. More, even, once the new year arrived, and a constant stream of consultants from the Trust. In the meantime, however, they found themselves distracted by other things: the end of the school term, and a Christmas trip to Perth, and, on the last night of the winter break, another mysterious conversation.

"You'll go to school alone tomorrow, dear," Maureen told Barry, as she passed him his second plate of dinner. All three children looked up at the announcement, but Flora, whose animosity towards school had inevitably faded over the years, reacted first.

"What?" she yelled, her fork clattering against her plate.

"Just for one day, love," said George. "You'll start again on Tuesday."

Barry and Trevor remained silent while Flora pressed on, voice shrill. "But *why*?"

"Because," said Maureen. "That's what Mr. Lewis wanted."

Flora crossed her arms and announced that it wasn't fair.

"Oh, wheesht," replied Maureen, rolling her eyes.

In bed that night, Barry and Flora speculated for close to an hour about what the announcement might mean. *Maybe he has a secret to tell me*, said Barry, trying not to hope too hard for the return of their former companionship. *Or maybe he's going to give me some special present.* Flora was more pessimistic. *Maybe you're in trouble*, she said—and after that Barry couldn't quite relax. Even at school the next day, when Mr. Lewis did greet him warmly, that glimmer of their past days only put Barry more on edge.

"So," the teacher began, leading Barry into the living room. "I suppose you're wondering why Flora's at home today."

Barry nodded.

"Well, not to worry," he smiled. "It's nothing sinister. Your parents and I just thought it might be an idea if I talked to you on your own about next year."

"Next year?"

"The thing is," said Mr. Lewis nodding, "unfortunately I'm not qualified to teach beyond primary school—and even if I were there certainly aren't the proper resources here on the island. So..."

"I've to start at boarding school," Barry explained to Flora later. She'd been sitting on the bottom landing waiting for him when he got home, legs crossed and chewing on a dark tangle of hair falling in her face. "What took you so long?" she said, jumping up and smacking him on the arm. "School finished ages ago."

He looked at his feet and told her he'd gone for a walk—and then they hurried upstairs, where he rattled through everything Mr. Lewis had said to him: that secondary school would be very different; that being in classes with other children would seem strange at first; and that even though the school where he'd be going, St. Fillan's, accepted mainland children, it catered specially to boarders from the islands—so he'd be in very good hands.

They'd heard of St. Fillan's before, of course; their parents had gone there, several years apart, and their father had often told them stories about it. He'd been so homesick his first few weeks, they knew, that one night he'd made an escape rope from his sheets—just like he'd seen in picture books—and broken his leg climbing out the window. For Halloween one year, when the school held its annual guising party, he'd dressed up as the headmaster and been given three weeks' detention, even as the teachers doling out sweets had smirked with ill-disguised amusement. And then there was the girl he'd escorted to the Leavers' Ball at the end of his final year: *she was so nervous*, he'd told them, winking, *that she threw up all over my kilt.*

Their mother was more reserved in her stories, hewing mainly to a few general observations about the poor quality of the food and ruing losing touch with several of her friends there. She also corroborated, when necessary, another of George's stories: the time he'd gone back to St. Fillan's, in Maureen's final year, to escort *her* to the Leavers' Ball. *All the other girls were so jealous*, she'd sigh, whenever he brought it up. *I had a strapping young university lad all my own, come to whisk me away.*

To Barry and Flora, though, St. Fillan's had never been more than a setting in their parents' past, its role in their own future never quite connecting. So the realization that Barry would soon be disappearing there felt like a rude awakening, never mind everything else that Mr. Lewis had told him to expect—a collection of words they'd barely understood. Cliques. Bullying. Peer pressure. As Barry related each successive detail, Flora's eyes bulged a little more. In the end, though, he left out the most unsettling thing of all.

"Now," Mr. Lewis had said, frowning very slightly as he leaned back in his armchair that afternoon. "St. Fillan's is a mixed school, Barry, which means there will be other girls there, as well as boys." He'd paused. "And so long as Flora's not here today, it seems like as good a time as any to go over some basic sex education—what do you say?"

He'd said nothing, in fact, had only nodded again, dazed, and followed Mr. Lewis to the classroom, where some new wall charts were secured to the blackboard with dusty scraps of tape. As the lesson wore on, he hadn't asked many questions, but his thoughts had raced away: he tried and failed to imagine the few

"They're going to take them to a zoo somewhere and keep them safe." He sighed. "That way when the rats are gone the mice can all come home again."

She made a sour face. "Why?"

"It's a long story." He filled his own bowl now and set it down in front of him. "But it's a very...sensible thing to do. So leave them be." He shifted in his seat and glanced at Barry and Trevor. "That goes for you, too."

Barry nodded, silent, while Trevor promised solemnly to behave—though in fact he didn't find the trappers that troublesome. Four-and-a-half, now, he spent his days dreaming up whole worlds for them while his siblings were at school: one day they were aliens—brain-eating, blood-sucking aliens!—to be avoided at all costs; others they were treasure hunters, or cowboys, or army special forces, and he, depending on his mood, their ally or their foe. He'd eavesdrop on their conversations in the pub each night, and watch them fan out from the village each morning, and sometimes would even follow them, at a distance, as they moved around the island. To him they were a symphony of avatars; a world's worth of souls.

And then, three weeks later, they were gone, as abruptly as they'd appeared. The older children arrived home from school to find the last of them, a middle-aged man with greying temples, standing with their mother in the hallway, bags at his feet and a rucksack on one shoulder.

"So, Mrs. McCloud," he was saying. "We're going to spend a few months making sure the mice are good and settled, and then we'll be back to start the rat hunt in earnest." With a grunt, he slipped his other shoulder through the rucksack's remaining strap. "We'll confirm closer to the time, but my guess would be early in the new year."

"Thank you, Mr. Cox," she said. "I hope you'll not take it

personally when I say I'm not much looking forward to it."

"Completely understandable." They shared a smile.

"Barry! Flora!" Trevor had appeared on the top landing and was now barreling down the stairs towards his siblings. "You have to come see what I found today!"

The rat catcher started at the noise, and so did Maureen. Her face darkening, she turned to Trevor as he reached the ground floor. "For goodness' sake, boy, calm yourself! We can't have you galloping around shouting your head off all the time—we open next week and our guests occasionally like some peace and quiet!"

Trevor froze. "But Mum—"

"But Mum nothing. You're old enough to learn some better manners."

The man cleared his throat. "Sorry," he said, as Maureen turned back to him. "I must be holding you up. Thank you again for your cooperation the past few weeks. I hope we haven't been too disruptive."

"No, no," she said, gazing at him with a strange, sad expression. She took a step backwards. "Have a safe journey, Mr. Cox."

"And you have a lovely evening, Mrs. McCloud." He picked up his bags and walked to the front door, nodding at the children as he passed. Once he was gone, Maureen turned to face them again. Trevor looked about to cry; Barry and Flora both had their arms around him.

She sighed. "Your dad would have said the same thing."

Barry and Flora exchanged glances.

"Ach, away with you," she said, stalking off towards the kitchen and muttering about needing to start dinner—while Trevor, a few tears sliding down his cheeks, gained yet another memory.

IV.

That summer came and went in a blur. In May, Barry was taken to visit St. Fillan's; in June he turned twelve; in July he spent his final day at school with Mr. Lewis; and finally, on a Wednesday night in August, the island gathered round to bid him farewell. Maureen had blacked out the date in the reservations' book almost a year in advance, so there were no guests upstairs that evening, no customers in the pub—just the islanders, and the heather glowing violet in the summer dusk, and the village, calm and settled.

The Kilgouries arrived first, around seven, a bottle of whisky in his arms and a casserole in hers. Barry greeted them at the door at his mother's instruction—*this is your party*, she'd said, when the bell rang, *now go be a good host*—and though his adolescent self-consciousness still clung to him as he did so, he also felt a certain sort of pride at being given such an adult job.

"Barry!" said Mr. Kilgourie, on the doorstep. "Can't wait to get out, eh? Soon enough, my lad! Soon enough!" He chuckled, mostly to himself.

"Mum's in the kitchen," Barry told them, "and Dad's setting up the lounge." He blushed. "Can I take that dish from you, Mrs. Kilgourie?"

She looked him up and down and seemed to satisfy herself that he could be trusted. "Aye, Barry," she said, passing it to him. "Tell your mother it needs twenty minutes in a hot oven." Her gaze shifted to Flora, who was lurking beyond the doorjamb. "And while he does that, young lady, you can take my coat."

As Barry disappeared down the hall Flora stepped forward with a dour stare, deliberately taking Mr. Kilgourie's coat first and folding it slowly over her arm before finally turning to his wife—but as the woman bent forward there was another knock at the door and Flora moved abruptly to answer it, smirking as Mrs. Kilgourie's things fell to the floor.

"Mr. Lewis!" she said, as Mrs. Kilgourie tutted behind her. "And..." She gasped—as if waking, suddenly, from a dream.

"Hello Flora," said Mr. Lewis, stepping into the vestibule. "You remember Bella, of course." He beckoned behind him, to where the artist stood on the front step.

Flora nodded dumbly and stepped aside to let them in, collecting everyone's things and telling them to make their way to the living room—while she, staggering beneath the heap of coats, started for the closet under the stairs. Stepping inside to hang everything up, she glanced back and forth down the hallway, and then quickly shut the door behind her. In the dark she fumbled for the light bulb dangling underneath the steps; the smell of must and canker filled her nostrils.

Bella was here. In the house.

Flora's fascination with the woman had changed over the years, perhaps, but never wavered; still she made her secret visits to the orchard every summer, and just as often, recently, had started sneaking over even when the place was empty. With Bella gone for the winter, she could stride boldly to the windows without fear of discovery or punishment, and study the older work left hanging on the walls year-round—and she took full advantage of that freedom, bringing a sketchpad of her own and climbing onto the windowsill to copy the paintings inside. Underneath her mattress she kept a growing sheaf of the illicit work: simple pencil drawings she did in the orchard while light and weather still permitted, and studies in paint or colored pencil from memory once winter had hunkered down. It was almost a disappointment, actually, when Bella had returned for the summer this year, as it forced Flora to once again conceal herself in the trees.

In the hallway closet now she stared at the woman's coat. It was flimsy, undyed linen, the color of baked clay—the sort of thing her mother would have scoffed at. *That'll keep her about as warm as a mothy dolly*, she'd say; Flora could hear it clearly as she reached forward to touch the fabric—to feel its soft stubble against her fingertips, to pull it to her face and breathe—

"What are you doing?"

She dropped the sleeve and turned to the door. Barry had opened it a crack and was peering in.

"Nothing," she said. "What are you doing?"

He pulled the door open further. "I saw the light on. I was going to turn it off." His eyes moved to Bella's coat; he stepped all the way into the closet, hunching to fit beneath the stairs. "Whose is that?"

Sighing, she told him.

"Bella?" He shut the door behind him. "*Bella?*"

"Yes, and I found it first, so go away."

"She's here?" His pupils were expanding in the dim light.

"She came with Mr. Lewis." Flora shifted, trying to move between him and the coat, when suddenly the stairs above them creaked. "Barry!" their mother called. "Flora! Where have you got to?"

They looked at each other for a moment, until reluctantly

Barry pushed the closet door open. "Sorry, Mum," he said, stepping out into the hallway. "We were hanging up the coats."

"Well hurry up," she harrumphed. "Honestly. Your guests are waiting."

The atmosphere in the living room felt thin, at first, unnatural. For one thing, there was the vague, lingering animosity between Bella and Maureen (who hadn't expected the woman to turn up, though Mr. Lewis had warned her she would), and by extension between Bella and Mrs. Kilgourie. And since the men—George, Mr. Kilgourie, and Mr. Lewis—seemed almost instantly to have fallen into their own group in the corner, that awkwardness between the women was all the more pronounced.

But the main problem was the guest of honor. It was Barry's send-off, after all, and so naturally, as the remaining islanders arrived—the Pikes and Thomases with more contributions of food, the Mannings with a hand-knit scarf as a parting gift—the attention was all on him. Yet he felt like he could barely remember his name that night, let alone make small talk: the sound of Bella's breathing at his side left him dizzy; the warmth that seemed to radiate from her prickled at his skin. Since his sex ed lesson at school that winter, and his failure to imagine himself—to imagine anyone—in the strange, invasive embrace of Mr. Lewis's wall charts, that initial hesitation had given way quite spectacularly to what felt like hours-long hallucinations: visions of Bella in such overwhelming nudity and anatomical detail that he would lie awake, taking deep breaths and trying to calm the bursts of adrenalin deep in his gut, while Flora snored softly in the bunk below him. And now, having her so close, it took all his effort to push those visions away again. *Are you excited about St. Fillan's, Barry?* someone would ask, and he'd respond in monosyllables, staring at the wisps of hair tucked behind her ears. *Do you know much about your bunkmate?* Her perfume, slowly stifling. *What will you miss most about the island?* He felt paralyzed by these sensations she was causing in him; terrified, by the sudden racing of his pulse and the warm patches of sweat beneath his arms.

At last the other guests began to tire of the silence, and as the food was brought out, the beer and whisky taking hold, the chatter in the room began to swell. People drifted in and out of Barry's circle, forming and reforming into smaller groups of two or three around the room: Mr. Pike and Mr. Manning discussed the day's paper and a plane crash in Japan, and marveled at why anyone would ever climb aboard such an airborne deathtrap; Mr. Thomas spoke to George about the summer's superlative weather; and while Maureen bustled to and fro refilling people's drinks, the other women held hushed summits in the corners, revealing sordid thoughts of leaving for the mainland soon themselves. By the fireplace, Mr. Lewis sat with the younger children, Flora monopolizing him the way Barry had after Trevor's birth, while Barry himself daydreamed through it all, watching Bella move from huddle to huddle.

"I say," said Mr. Kilgourie, loudly, as a post-dinner lull began to settle. A few heads turned at the noise. "Why don't we give Barry a wee drop of whisky, eh? What better occasion for his first taste?"

"Hardly his first taste," said George, as more guests fell quiet around the room. "He had such problems teething we could have opened a distillery." He laughed. "Still, it's a fine idea. What do you say, Reenie?"

She shrugged and gave a demure nod.

"Splendid!" said Mr. Kilgourie. He made his way to the sideboard to examine the malts there, and after letting his finger float from bottle top to bottle top for a few seconds, he picked one up by the neck. "Here we are, my lad, a nice MacAllan—aged twelve years, just like yourself!"

Barry smiled, anxious. He was still oppressively aware of Bella, standing a few feet behind him and to the left. She seemed to tug on that whole side of his body as he watched Mr. Kilgourie fill a glass with a generous dram and walk it across the room.

"Now," said the man, holding out the glass. "Normally you want to savor a whisky like this, take your time with it—but I always say your first time should be one big mouthful, straight down the gullet." He laughed. "It might catch you by surprise."

Everyone was watching as Barry took the tumbler and tilted it from side to side, considering the bronzy liquid. His nose wrinkled at the scent.

"Go on, son," said Mr. Kilgourie. "Tip it back."

Mr. Lewis stepped forward from his spot at the back of the room, reassuring Barry that he didn't need to gulp it all down at once if he didn't want to, but the boy was already moving the glass to his mouth, feeling its smoothness against his lips, his palate tingling as he inhaled. He took one, last, deep breath, and flung his head back—*Bravo!*—and his throat screamed instantly from the heat. Fingers still wrapped around the tumbler, he let his arm drop and began to cough.

Mr. Kilgourie cackled. "That's my boy!" he said, patting Barry on the shoulder. "What a show!" Behind him, George was grinning too. "Now," said Mr. Kilgourie, refilling his own glass as Barry continued to hack. "Time for the rest of us to lose a lung." He raised his arm and muttered *slainte*.

The attention began to shift away from Barry again, and Mr. Lewis moved towards him and asked if he was all right. Barry nodded, his eyes watering, and once Mr. Lewis had turned away Barry stumbled over to an armchair and slumped into it, surveying the room. His father and Mr. Kilgourie were cheersing in the corner, and as he watched them he began once more to feel that strange sense of pride he'd had while opening the front door. Suddenly, somehow, it seemed as if he'd crossed a threshold, had moved one step closer to adulthood, and, rubbing his jaw, mimicking his father and feeling for stubble that wasn't there, he glanced at Bella again. With a lopsided grin he stood up, and found his glass, and crossed the room to pour himself another drink.

This time he took a daintier sip, trying to copy Mr. Lewis, who was standing with a glass of his own and talking to Mr. Pike.

"Look at this, George!" Mr. Kilgourie laughed, noticing Barry by the sideboard. "We'll soon have him writing us tasting notes!"

George glanced over and smiled, and told Barry that ought to be his last, but the boy was hardly listening, still watching Bella as he emptied his glass. She was next to the hallway door and talking to Flora. Room swaying, he wove his way towards them.

"What are you doing?" he blurted out when he got close enough, perhaps a little too loudly. They both looked up, startled.

Flora scowled. "I was asking Ms. Fowkes if she wanted to see some of my drawings."

Barry turned to Bella, for a moment feeling brave enough to meet her gaze. "Do you?"

She gave them a polite smile. "I'm not sure it would be very nice to leave the party like that," she said, and Barry's heart sank.

Just then, however, his mother appeared. "Bella!" she said. "Glad to see the three of you have made up!" She was slurring slightly, hanging too long on her vowels. She motioned towards the children. "I told you they were good'uns, really."

Bella nodded, that polite smile still firmly on her face.

"We were asking her if she wanted to come upstairs," said Barry, adding quickly that it was because Flora wanted to show off her drawings.

"What a wonderful idea," said Maureen, her bleary eyes still fixed on Bella. "Our Flora's quite the artist, you know. Always scribbling away at something."

Flora blushed and whined for her mother to stop, but she was still staring hopefully at the other woman, who at last relented, sending the children bounding towards the stairs. With an uneasy look on her face, she followed them.

In their room, her eyes landed first on the bunk bed. "You share?"

Flora nodded, and started pointing out all the room's other features: where her dolls lived in the cupboard, and the spot by the window where she would sometimes sit and draw, and the pink and white beanbag she'd picked out from a catalogue—all by herself!—as a gift for her last birthday. With each excited detail Barry tuned out his sister's rambling and focused entirely on Bella, the walls still swimming behind her. *What if she were naked now?* he thought, as the increasingly familiar feeling of his erection began to press against his underwear; as he imagined her nipples, and her navel, and her thighs. Blushing, he sat down abruptly on Flora's beanbag, just as Bella put her drink on the dresser and sat down herself at the foot of the bottom bunk. "So," she said. "Let's have a look at these drawings."

Even in his hazy state, Barry registered some surprise as Flora lifted up the corner of her mattress and pulled out a bundle of paper. He'd had no idea she kept anything there; had no idea she'd done any drawings other than the ones she sometimes showed him.

"These are my really special ones," she was saying, as she handed them to Bella.

"I—" The woman's eyebrows shot up. "This is very good," she said, looking at the sheet on top of the pile. "Especially for someone so young." She motioned towards one of the corners. "You have a wonderful sense of perspective here. And it's a nicely muted palette. Very mature."

Flora beamed back at her.

As Bella set aside each subsequent drawing, though, a frown deepened across her face. Her cheeks began to redden; her commentary grew less substantial. When she reached the last one, her jaw now clenched, she handed it back to Flora in silence. Then, quietly, her hands clasped in her lap, she turned to the girl. "You've been coming to my studio again, haven't you?" (Across the room, Barry tensed.)

"Um..." said Flora. "Yes? But I didn't think you'd mind."

Bella opened her mouth to respond, but Flora cut her off. "I only did it because I want to be able to paint like you!"

That seemed to briefly disarm the woman, but her voice, when she eventually replied, was still icy. "Flattery will get you everywhere," she said. "But that doesn't make it okay to spy on people in their homes." She was standing up, now, and so was Barry, yanked back to reality and frantic to calm her down.

"Ms. Fowkes," he said, staggering a little as he got to his feet. "Wait."

"Oh ho!" She spun towards him. "And I suppose you came along for the show as well, did you?"

"No, I—"

"I don't believe this," she said.

And then she was gone, the door gliding shut in her wake.

"You idiot!" shouted Barry, and stalked across the room to where Flora was still cowering on the bottom bunk.

"I'm sorry," she said, beginning to cry, shuffling further back on her mattress. "I thought it would be okay!"

"How could you think it would be okay? How! You ruined everything!"

He was dashing into the hall, now, and down the stairs, but the living room was just a spinning fog of voices, and Bella nowhere to be seen. He blinked; tried to focus. Heard Mr. Lewis: *I'm sorry. I don't know what's suddenly got her so upset.*

The room lurched again. *Not to worry, Henry—I'd be in a hurry to get her home on her own, too!* Shoes were on his feet. The front door was opening. *It's not like that, Jack, honestly. We've just had dinner a few times.*

She was a few feet down the road.

She was by his side.

"Ms. Fowkes," he managed, just. The air was watery around them, the sky a mauve panel behind the hills.

She stopped and turned. "Go back inside."

"Please," he said. He took another step closer. "You can't leave."

Two birds flew overhead, squawks like chew toys.

"Oh? And why's that?"

He saw the two of them as if through a camera, composed side-by-side in the darkening valley. The birds overhead were gone. The guesthouse behind him was gone. He lifted an arm and put his hand, trembling, on her waist.

Her lip snarled. "*Get. Off. Me.*"

"But—"

She stepped backwards, out of his reach. "I knew it," she hissed. "Oh, they all tried to tell me it wasn't like that, that you didn't mean any harm, that you were too young to understand..."

"No," he started, "it wasn't—"

"But get a few whiskies in you and the truth comes out, eh?"

This wasn't right. She didn't understand.

"You're a pervy wee peeping tom," she said, looking as if she might be about to spit at him. "And you ought to be ashamed."

Her lips were red.

He lunged at her again, but she stepped out of the way with a shriek and he fell to the ground. The grass tickled his face.

"Barry!" His father was striding over, Mr. Lewis a few steps behind him. "What's going on?"

Rolling over and pushing himself up onto one elbow, he looked back in their direction.

"I told you," said Bella, behind him, and when he turned again to look at her she was already walking away. He clambered to his feet to chase after her, but his father was upon him, now, grabbing him by the shoulder and telling him to stay right where he was.

"Barry," said Mr. Lewis, catching up. "What happened?"

"Nothing," he said, squirming. He glowered at his father. "Let go of me."

George shook his head and started pushing him towards the house. "I think you need to go inside, young man."

Barry stopped struggling and looked up, his face whorled with frustration. "Fine," he said, wriggling free and starting unsteadily towards the house. When the guesthouse door slammed, it sent a muffled echo across the heather.

V.

A few days after Barry left for St. Fillan's, on a beautiful, late summer's morning, Trevor started at the primary school himself.

"Well," Mr. Lewis smiled, sitting on the building's front step as the boy skipped up that first morning, Flora straggling a few yards behind. "Isn't this a passing of the torch?" He extended his hand. "Welcome to Fìor Primary School, young man. Here's to many happy years." Trevor giggled, then reached out and shook.

The contrast with Flora's first day was remarkable. Partly it was Trevor's enthusiasm at finally joining his siblings' exclusive club; certainly he showed none of the combativeness that had marked his sister's early weeks in the classroom. But mainly it was Flora's behavior that once again controlled the mood. She seemed so lifeless, suddenly, that she might as well not have been there, and around that sluggishness the three of them slipped effortlessly into a new routine, Mr. Lewis flitting between them at his leisure, confident whoever he had his back to would behave.

The problem, of course, was Barry, his absence still conspicuous to Flora and his lack of contact worse. He had called twice since settling at St. Fillan's, but his conversations with his sister—with everyone, really—had been arduous, one-sided, and she had been able to glean little other than the very public location of the school's telephone. He'd told her nothing about what the place was like, nothing about the teachers, nothing about the other children...Nothing friendly or conciliatory at all, in fact, confirming the falling out she already feared they'd had, and still without her really knowing why. He hadn't apologized for shouting at her that night with Bella; had barely said another word to her before he'd left. Even when she'd asked if he was okay, when he eventually climbed into the top bunk that night, after an hour of hiding from their parents and one more still of scolding, he'd said nothing. Had said nothing to her at breakfast the next morning, either, even as Maureen, suddenly nostalgic, tried to give him a joyful, hero's send-off. And all he'd managed at the jetty, before he boarded the ferry with their father, was: *bye*. All because of one, honest mistake!

Then again, Flora was still brooding over the encounter with Bella herself. She had been so sure the woman would be thrilled to have an admirer that she'd never considered the possibility of a negative reaction. And now what was she supposed to do? She didn't dare return to the studio again, not with Bella so angry—and without that source of inspiration she found herself unable to do any drawing of her own. The few ideas she tried felt childish, silly, and thanks to the memory of Bella's furious expression that night she could barely concentrate when she sat down with a sketchpad, anyway.

As the months dragged on, her mood sank even further. The hours after school quickly grew too dark and cold to spend outside, and in the evenings, with her drawing at a standstill and Trevor in bed a full two hours ahead of her, Flora increasingly found herself slumped in her room with no company but her boredom. A few nights she'd tried asking her parents to play a game, as they'd done when Barry was around, but that only gave her another thing to miss about him—and besides, the games usually ended with her mother roping her into some pre-bedtime chore, and even staring vacantly at her bedroom carpeting seemed more appealing than that.

The beginning of November, though, a few weeks past Trevor's fifth birthday, she found herself wandering downstairs anyway, past the sounds of her mother's clattering in the kitchen and down the hallway to the pub. At that time of year the place was only marginally open—available, should some brave camper appear on the ferry, but in practice catering just to Mr. Kilgourie— and when she walked in that night all the lights were off except for a few bulbs around the bar. Most of the seating was turned up on the tables and draped with dust tarps for the winter, the giant stacks lurking at the edges of the room like giant, spectral jellyfish, and her father was perched on a stool on the customer side of the bar, hunched over a newspaper.

"Hi Dad," she said, walking over to him.

He looked up, surprised. "Hello, love. Is everything all right?"

She nodded, climbing onto the stool next to him. "What are you doing?"

"The crossword," he said, giving the paper a wistful glance. "It's not going very well."

Flora strained to see over his shoulder, to where a few lone letters had found their way into the grid amidst a cloud of eraser dust. She asked if she could help.

"Why not?" he smiled, and as she shuffled closer to him he launched into an explanation of cryptic crosswords' labyrinthine rules. "Okay," he started, tapping his pencil against the page. "Every clue here is divided into two halves: a cryptic half and a conventional half. The cryptic half shows you how to arrive at the answer through some sort of pun or wordplay, and the conventional half is a more straightforward clue. But the whole thing reads as a complete sentence, and you never know where one half ends and the other begins. Or which one comes first."

Flora stared at him blankly.

"Here," he said. "I'll give you an example." He scanned the page. "Okay: *SHARK*. The clue is *Beast told to be quiet on Noah's ship (5)*, so in this case the conventional part is *Beast*, which is just another way to describe a shark. Then the cryptic part works like this: if you told someone to be quiet, you'd say *Sh!*, which you add on to Noah's ship, the *ark*. Sh. Ark. Shark! See?"

Flora nodded, eyes fixed on where her fingers were fidgeting with the hem of her jumper. George sighed and put down his pen. "I'll tell you what," he said. "Let's start with something easier." He flipped through the paper until he found the normal crossword, and scanned the list of clues. "Ah. This one you should know: *berg dweller*. Two words."

Flora's eyes lit up. "Polar bear!" She'd done a report on the animals at school the year before.

"Well done!" said George. "Now, let's see what else there is..."

They ended up sitting there for over an hour working on that single puzzle, George coaxing Flora to most of the answers and stretching it out as long as he could, until a little after ten there were footsteps outside the door. "Have you seen Flora?" said Maureen, looking over her shoulder as she walked in. "It's past her bedtime and I can't find—" She turned to face them. "Oh."

George glanced at his watch. "Sorry, love. I didn't realize how late it was."

"We're doing a crossword, Mum!" added Flora, beaming.

"That's lovely, poppet." An emotionless smile formed on her face. "But it's time for bed. You'll have to come back to it in the morning."

Flora looked to her father; he shook his head. "She's right," he said. "Off you go." He leaned forward and gave her a kiss on the cheek. "We'll finish it tomorrow, I promise."

And so they did—and when they were through with that one they started immediately on another, until Maureen once again tore Flora away for bed. It was a strange thing, thought George, as he turned back to his own crossword that second night and listened to Flora clomp up the stairs: she'd never shown any interest in his puzzles before, or any word games, or even English, really. Her preference for the visual was always the overarching theme of their parents' evenings with Mr. Lewis. Stranger still, when he thought about it, was that he couldn't remember another time when he and Flora had spent time on their own like this. Barry had always been around, or Trevor, or else they'd all been doing something together as a family. It had never even occurred to him to invite just her to do something. And in the unexpected pleasure of her company these two nights, especially after her recent months of sullenness, he realized that he'd missed her lately almost as much as he'd missed Barry. Had missed the old, happy Flora, in any case. Crinkling his nose as he studied the page in front of him, he marveled at the difference.

If the mood at home was improving by Barry's winter break, his return seemed instantly to dampen it. He was a different boy than the one they'd sent away—taller, with a few mean patches of shadow on his jaw, and a remoteness none of them remembered—and it quickly became clear that there would be no happy reunion that Christmas. No possibility, as they'd all hoped, of pretending he'd never left.

His arrival, on a chill afternoon, was like a video played in reverse, as if as soon as the ferry had vanished over the horizon in August, somebody had flipped a switch and sent everything scrambling backwards: the ship reappeared; Maureen and the children reassumed their positions along the jetty; and Barry and his mop of black hair cruised effortlessly back to shore, stepping from the gangplank into a haze of hugs and kisses. Even in those first greetings, though, the change was clear; his sullenness the morning he'd left seemed warm in comparison.

"Welcome home, dear," said Maureen, wrapping her arms around him.

"Thanks," he mumbled, into her shoulder.

"Hi Barry!" squealed Trevor, running forward. "Is it brilliant to be back?"

Flora, watching from a few steps away, gave him a hopeful, tentative smile, but he only shrugged. "Yeah, I suppose."

As they walked towards home, Maureen and George fell into a quiet conversation of their own, while Barry hung back and Flora moved up by his side. It was only three in the afternoon, but the overcast sky was darkening already, the clouds absorbing the night like blotting paper.

"I missed you," said Flora.

"Yeah."

She pressed on. "It'll be nice having you home for a bit."

He made an odd noise, halfway between a grunt and a laugh.

"Mr. Lewis is looking forward to seeing you, too. He said you should go visit him tomorrow before he leaves for Christmas."

Barry barely reacted, still, and she reached towards him and touched his elbow, letting her voice grow softer. "What's wrong?"

He shook loose. "Nothing. I'm fine." And then he started walking faster again, leaving Flora to watch as the back of his neck bobbed farther ahead in silence.

It was like that for the rest of the evening, too, Barry stoic, moodier than Flora had been on even the worst nights in his absence, and the rest of the family trying to draw him out of it; after a heavy, wordless dinner, he slunk off to his bedroom and shut the door. "He's probably tired," said George, hopefully, and when Flora went upstairs later she found the lights in their room off and her brother unresponsive, so she assumed their father was right.

The next morning, though, it was the same again. After breakfast Barry disappeared immediately to his room, and when he emerged a few hours later it was only to shout a gruff goodbye as he hurried out the front door and down the road.

Out of force of habit, he started along the path to the Stùc, but after following that for a while he cut off along an even vaguer trail—a burn, really, after the recent weeks of rainfall—and into a shallow gully. There was a faint drizzle in the air, a fine spray, rolling around him as he sank further into his anorak and trudged on. A rat scurried past his feet.

Eventually the right wall of the gully leveled out enough that he could hike up it to a pair of boulders on a small rise. He strained his neck to make sure he was hidden from the path, then crouched down and shimmied backwards into a cleft between the rocks, and sat there not moving, feeling the damp seep into his trousers and watching a tiny patch of blue-grey sea between the hills in front of him. After several minutes, he sighed, then unzipped his coat and pulled out some cigarettes and a lighter.

He'd tried to follow Mr. Lewis's advice about avoiding trouble at the mainland school, but from his very first night, it seemed, he'd managed to bungle it. As soon as George had left, Barry's bunkmate, an older boy named Tam, had looked him up and down and asked: "Djou smoke?" And just as Mr. Lewis had told him to, Barry had uttered a decisive no; had told the other boy that he'd never even tried.

"Why not?" asked Tam, with a scowl. "Are you a saddo or something?"

Barry faltered. "I...No. They're bad for you. My teacher told me so."

"Is that a fact?" said Tam, smirking. "Well, fuck me. Thanks for the tip."

"You're welcome," said Barry, still uneasy.

Tam laughed and swaggered out the door, leaving Barry to sit there on his own for an hour, confused, before eventually shutting off the lights and going to bed early.

And then, in the playground during the next day's lunch break, he found himself surrounded.

"This is him," explained Tam, to a wall of other boys. "The new school nurse." The white light from the cloudy sky brought out the threatening lines in their faces; Barry noticed a gold stud glinting in one of their ears.

"Anyway, Baz," said Tam, turning to face him. "Since you're new, we thought we'd bring you a little welcome present." He reached into his pocket and took out the damp, contorted butt of a cigarette. "Thought maybe since you've never smoked before you'd want to try it." He held the butt forward. "Go on, big man. Take a drag."

Barry stared at him. "No thank you," he said, his voice quavering. "I...I...I'm not in the mood."

There was a roar of laughter from the other boys. "Not in the mood!" said Tam, eyebrows shooting up. "*Not in the mood!* Well that's a shame, see, because I've brought it just for you and my feelings'll be hurt if you don't take it." He took a step closer. "Don't you know it's rude to refuse a gift?"

Barry edged backwards. His body felt like a shell, and he a tiny, diminishing light inside. Not because of Tam, really—at least, not entirely—but because of all the other indignities of the past few days: Bella's angry rejection, and his parents' subsequent recriminations, and his stupid, stubborn tiff with Flora. He didn't know what he'd done to deserve any of it, but especially not this. The predatory speed with which Tam had turned on him seemed entirely unprovoked.

Instinctively he hugged his arms around his body as he continued to inch away—but by now the throng had seen enough, and pounced, pinning him to the ground. Tam knelt down beside him. "We were only trying to be friendly," he said, and with a look of horrifying concentration he pried open Barry's jaw and shoved the cigarette inside. The taste of mildew and smoky ash filled his mouth.

"Now swallow it," said Tam, leaning back.

Barry's eyes bulged. He tried not to wretch.

"I said swallow it!"

So Barry did as he was told, a few tears finally working their way out and down the sides of his face. The filter stuck in his throat on its way down, and he gulped back another wave of nausea. The wet streaks on his skin prickled in the breeze. He stuck out his tongue to prove the butt was gone, and with a satisfied nod Tam released him and stood up, the other boys following suit. Slowly, Barry began to sit up, but then his nausea surged again and this time he couldn't hold it. Leaning quickly to one side he threw up onto the asphalt. A few drops of bile splattered on his hand; the cigarette butt bounced once and came to a rest at the edge of the puddle. Still heaving, he wiped his mouth against his sleeve.

"Dearie me," said Tam, shaking his head. "It looks like you were right, Barry—they really are bad for you." And then he and the rest of his cronies had walked away laughing.

Once they were out of sight, Barry struggled to his feet. Recalling Mr. Lewis's brief lesson on bullying, he ran straight to the first teacher he could find, a short woman with a grey bun and half-moon spectacles, who looked as if she ran a tight ship. When she'd taken him to the headmaster's office, though, Tam was waiting outside, and when Barry pointed at him and tried to explain what had happened, the other boy just shook his head innocently.

"It's not true, Miss, I never touched him. We were trying to start a game of tig and he kicked me and ran away." He rolled up his trouser leg to reveal a smug, purple bruise.

"No," mewled Barry, but the teacher was already nodding.

"That'll be all, Thomas," she said, and ushered Barry into the office, where she explained the situation to the headmaster without Barry getting a word in. The man leaned back in his chair with an acid smile on his face. "I know you're new, young man, so I'll let you off this time. But we don't tolerate troublemakers here at St. Fillan's—one more incident like this and I'll be calling your parents."

Barry nodded, dazed, and left the office.

If it had been a simple case of bullying, perhaps things would have been different; perhaps Barry would have found the strength to resist the abuse, and the pranks, and the constant, braying taunts to try telling on them again. But having to return to the room he shared with Tam each evening, and lie awake with the slats above him bulging ominously: it broke him down. He lived in constant dread of whatever new cruelty Tam might dream up; his nerves were worn into brittle, twisted strands. It was only a few weeks before he asked the question from the bottom bunk one night, his voice quiet but every ounce of his will behind making it sound firm.

"Can I join your gang?" It was self-preservation—nothing more.

In the darkness he heard Tam shift above him. "Can you *what*?"

"I want to join your gang," he repeated. "What do I have to do?" What else could he do? If he told his parents they'd just talk to the headmaster, who'd tell them about the bruise on Tam's leg and Barry's alleged part in it, and how would that help? He could imagine his mother's voice cracking with disappointment. *Barry McCloud! You ought to know better!* At least this way he could leave his family out of it.

Tam had responded to Barry's request enthusiastically, no doubt for the fresh opportunities it presented to torment him—but if he'd been expecting Barry's resolve to crumble he wound up proven wrong. Whatever obstacles and initiations they threw in his path—stealing other kids' belongings, vandalizing the boys' toilets and spying in the girls', and trying cigarettes for real, of course—Barry did it all with grim determination and still emerged asking flatly to be admitted to the fold.

Sitting in his crook on the hillside, now, the damp beginning to soak through his coat, he finally put a cigarette between his lips and lit it. The smoke warmed him immediately.

He'd thought the habit, like all his other misdemeanors, would be just a necessary front, something he'd do while at school and then easily put aside during visits home; he hadn't even packed any cigarettes for the break. But by the end of the short train journey to Mallaig the cravings had already sunk their claws in, and after he'd greeted his dad at the train station he'd made up some excuse about wanting a snack and run off to the Co-op on the high street. He must have seemed particularly pathetic, out of breath and tears welling in his eyes, because the cashier didn't even ask for proof of age—just shook her head and handed them over, whispering to the woman who'd been queuing behind him as he hurried out the door. A few minutes later, crouching behind a boat ramp hidden from the road, he'd desperately sucked in the nicotine, hands shaking, and then rummaged through his bag for deodorant and chewing gum to mask the smell. That much, at least, he'd learned to do at school.

"Where did you get to for so long?" George had asked, when Barry finally jogged up beside him at the jetty. "I was beginning to think you'd hopped a train back!" He smiled, and patted the boy on the shoulder, and Barry's heart had crumpled.

The rain and wind were picking up now, and even sheltered between the rocks Barry's cigarette was struggling to stay lit. He sighed and stubbed it out on the ground beside him.

His victory, if that was the right word, had come on Halloween. The students had spent all day making costumes in class, and at night had roamed up and down the corridors, knocking on teachers' doors and doing tricks in exchange for sweets. When Barry had left his room to join the fun, in the ghost outfit he'd so carefully prepared, Tam—dressed as a vampire—had yanked him aside and led them instead to the playground, and the windows of the darkened staffroom. He handed Barry a rock.

"Throw this through the window," he said, "and you're in."

Barry took it from him and weighed it in his hand, not flinching even slightly at the command. The pangs of conscience he'd felt during Tam's first few challenges had grown easier and easier to ignore, even as the challenges themselves had grown each time more transgressive. It wasn't that he found them any less repugnant; he was just in too deep. What would be the point in refusing now, when his reward—his relief—was so tantalizingly close? He paused only for a few seconds before he closed his eyes and hefted the rock into the air.

"Fucking hell!" hissed Tam, as the window shattered above them. They both began to run, stopping only when they'd reached the junior common room and slipped into the crowd of other ghosts and ghouls. "You're a mad cunt, McCloud," Tam had said, a glimmer of respect, it seemed, creeping into his voice. "I didn't think you had it in you." He patted Barry on the back and disappeared to find the other boys, and that night Barry fell asleep easily for the first time in weeks.

He stood up from his nook between the rocks now and kicked some dirt over the butt of his cigarette, before making his way back down to the path and carrying on towards the beach.

Since then he'd seemed to have an uneasy truce with Tam. Certainly, the situation had improved: he was still sleeping better, and finding it easier to concentrate in class, and was even being spared from rule-breaking as often, with the impetus to prove himself removed. Every now and then, though, his old terror would return, Tam's mischievous smirks producing some Pavlovian response and convincing Barry the gang was about to turn on him once more. He doubted he would ever be able to shake the feeling completely.

He reached the shore at the end of the path and stared towards the Stùc, across the retreating tide. He avoided looking at Bella's house, farther back on the islet and fainter in the mist; though he'd often thought about her the past few months, his fantasies had mostly been replaced by his humiliating memory of that night, new details returning to him each time he recalled it: the disgust in her face, the feeling of her coat slipping from his fingers. Instead, now, he focused on the schoolhouse, where a few wisps of smoke were escaping from the chimney, and tried to picture Mr. Lewis inside, packing by himself. Occasionally glancing out the window, maybe, and wondering if Barry would show up.

And he wished he could go over there and tell Mr. Lewis everything, wished he could turn to the man for help and comfort as he'd done so many times before: the rats, and Trevor's birth— Flora's, too—and countless bad dreams that his parents, dealing with breakfast for guests, had been too busy to attend to. Even that night with Bella, Mr. Lewis had been the only one to look concerned instead of furious. But that was precisely why Barry couldn't confess to him now. Not after the man had tried so hard to prepare him for life at St. Fillan's, not after he'd explicitly warned Barry against everything he'd gone and done anyway. He couldn't bear admitting he'd been such a failure. Couldn't bear seeing any disappointment on the man's face. So finally, spitting a tarry glob into the sand, he turned and started home. At least he had a few weeks away from Tam.

VI.

Barry was due to return to St. Fillan's a week after Hogmanay, and though no one in the house would say it, they were counting down the days. His brooding from that first evening had lasted his entire visit, and while there had been a few signs of the old Barry reappearing—he'd gone for a walk with Flora and his father one morning, and spent the whole of Christmas Day outside his room—those victories, so hard-earned, had never seemed to stick. The decision to reunite on the island, instead of visiting the relatives in Perth as usual, seemed more foolish with each passing day.

Worse, it was a bitter winter, the wind monstrous and the rain icy. When the sky finally flickered to life, late each morning, fuzzy blotches of frost bloomed across the meadows, and the water in the island's inlets lay frozen and opaque. And at around ten on Barry's last morning at home, Trevor and Flora already gone for the year's first day at school, a brutal storm descended—a diluvial howl of rain, sleet, and gales, rattling the guesthouse windows so violently that Maureen, face pressed against one to peer outside, wondered if the glass might break.

"It's a bloody monsoon out there!" she said, turning to where George sat at the kitchen table, the previous day's paper in front of him. She had to shout to be heard over the rain's incessant drone. "I'm not sure you'll find much left of your veggies in the morning."

He frowned. "Aye, it does sound nasty." Holding up the paper, still open to a not-quite-finished crossword, he tapped the page with the back of his hand. "They didn't mention anything like it in the forecast—just said rain and a bit of wind."

She snorted. "The weatherman's usual mastery of understatement."

"I suppose this means we won't be seeing the ferry today," said George. "Is there anything we're running short on?"

Maureen shook her head, returning to her vigil at the window.

The storm blew on all morning, the noise outside at last growing softer as they sat down with Barry for lunch.

"Maybe you should go get them," said Maureen, after their plates were cleared, glancing first at the window and then to George. "Now that it's died down a bit."

"Oh, don't be silly, Reenie." He dabbed at his mouth with his napkin. "I'm sure if Henry thinks they need to come home early, he'll bring them back himself."

Maureen had been trying to tell herself the same thing, but hearing it from her husband didn't make it any more convincing. It seemed just as likely that Mr. Lewis was waiting for them, and they couldn't call to find out because he didn't have a phone; the two lines at the guesthouse—a private one for the business, and one in the pub for everyone else—were the island's lot. Even after the telecom company had appeared in the fifties, when the mainland economy was booming even as the island's withered, and installed an exchange on Fìor big enough to accommodate every household, nobody had really seen the point. The only people most of the islanders ever talked to were a few minutes' walk away, and the guesthouse phone was always there if anyone needed to call the mainland. (It had added an extra poignancy, for George and Maureen, to the recent years of emigration; they always knew when someone else was considering a move from the sudden hours they'd start spending in the pub.)

Maureen cleared her throat. "George," she said. "We don't know what Henry might be thinking, and we shouldn't force the decision on him anyway. I want you to go over there and collect them. Who knows how bad it might get again later?"

"But Reenie—"

"I'll go," said Barry.

Maureen swiveled on her chair. "Absolutely not! I don't want another one of you out in this."

"I'll be fine, Mum," he said, pushing back from the table. "It's died down, you said so yourself. And I haven't seen Mr. Lewis the whole time I've been home. If I don't go now I won't have another chance."

George nodded earnestly. "Yes, why not let Barry go?"

Maureen clenched her jaw and turned back to him. "George. Stop it."

"What? He's young and spry—he'll probably get over there faster than me, anyway."

"Yeah," said Barry, already heading for the door. "I can be there and back in less than an hour. Honest."

Maureen's shoulders tensed. "Fine," she said. "But get going. The sooner you're all back here the better." She glared at George as Barry left the room; he just shrugged, and stood up to start the dishes.

A few minutes after four, Maureen was standing at the kitchen window again, the remains of an anxious afternoon snack on the table behind her. By two, an hour already since Barry had left, there had still been no sign of him; by three, night had started to fall. And now, past even the normal time when Flora and Trevor should have been home, the sky was black, and all three of them were missing. Outside the hail had intensified, hammering against the window in marble-sized chunks. There was a lone flash, somewhere far over the sea, and a single, echoing thunderclap. The walls creaked in the wind.

Suddenly she let out a shriek, slamming her palm against the edge of the sink and sending a bar of soap flying towards the drain, where it came to rest beside a piece of decomposing lettuce. Taking a deep breath and trying to hold on to some composure, she left the room and walked towards the lounge. George, sitting in his armchair reading, glanced up as she entered.

"Still no sign?"

"Of course there's still no bloody sign!" she snapped. "Look at it out there!" She threw up one arm in the direction of the window. "Look at it!"

Quietly, he closed his book.

"It's after four, George. They should be back by now. They should have been back hours ago."

He stood up and joined her where she'd moved by the window. "Henry never would have let them out in this, Reenie. They're fine. He'll be keeping them there with him 'til it's safe." He tried to put a hand on her shoulder, but she wriggled loose.

"And what about Barry? We don't even know if he made it there in the first place! Anything could have happened to him."

George hesitated, wetting the inside of his mouth. "It was still calm when he left. I'm sure he got there safely." He tilted his head in sympathy. "It's not as if he's some clueless tourist. He knows how to handle himself."

"He's only twelve, George! He doesn't know anything." Her voice was shaking. "You should have gone yourself. You know you should have."

He pursed his lips. "You're right," he said. "I should have. I just—it looked like it was clearing up, and it was so nice to see him enthusiastic about something..." He reached for her shoulder again, more firmly this time, and pulled her around to look at him. "I'm sorry, Reenie. I am."

"Well," she muttered. "Apologies aren't what we need right now, are they?"

He gave her a withering look. "You don't still expect me to go over there, do you? Even if I can get across in one piece, what am I meant to do then? It's far too dangerous for any of them to be out in it."

"George, I need to know he's okay. And as you very astutely pointed out, this is all your bloody fault—the least you can do is get out there and fix it."

"Reenie..." They stared at each other for a few seconds. Finally, he shook his head in resignation. "All right," he said. "I'll go now."

It was fifteen minutes before he left, though, after fortifying himself against the elements, and twenty again before he made it to the path, unable to even see his feet without the torch pointed straight at them. Coughing and wiping water from his face, he tramped down towards the beach, at last making it to the messy slop of sand almost forty-five minutes after leaving the house. He stopped, to catch his breath and shine his light ahead towards the bridge.

It wasn't there.

He swung the torch from side to side, certain he must be looking in the wrong place; took a few panicked steps forward. Rain was pooling in his philtrum, and forming thick clumps in his eyelashes, and trickling down the back of his neck—and then, at last, he spotted it. In the wind it had been wrenched free of its steps to the main island, and now, boardwalk half-ripped away, it was writhing in the swell like some giant, dying insect, still tethered, just, to its foundation on the Stùc.

For several minutes—he wasn't sure how long—he simply stood there staring, the beam from his flashlight still pointed straight ahead. He tried to think of some way he could get over. Tried not to wonder what had become of Barry, who had surely tried to cross; after all, if the bridge had been gone already when he reached the shore himself, he would have simply turned around and come home. And surely, George told himself, the chances were tiny of it having broken in those short moments Barry was on it. Surely he had made it. But then again, what if he had, and the bridge had given way as all three of them had been crossing back?

Teeth chattering and skin blistering in the wind, George snapped himself out of it, accepting that there was nothing he could do for the time being, and started moving towards the path—pulling his hat tighter around his face and wondering how he would break it to Maureen.

In the end, he opted for straightforward.

"The bridge is gone," he said, as he closed the front door behind him.

"Gone?" she repeated, staring at him from the hallway. "What do you mean, gone?"

"I mean it's gone," he said. "Not there. Blown away." He tossed his soaking hat to the ground.

"My God." Her face had turned grey. "I—What are we going to do?"

He grimaced, shaking the water from his sleeves. "Nothing."

"Nothing? We can't do nothing!"

He pulled off one boot, and with the other still on his foot looked up at her, lopsided. "We can't do *anything*, Reenie! Not without the bridge. Not until it dies down. We have to wait."

There was a crackle of hail against the transom, as if to emphasize the point, and Maureen, with a groan, turned and left George standing in the vestibule.

At first she returned to her pacing in front of the living room window, dreaming up worst-case scenarios and listening to George skulk around upstairs and eventually retreat to the pub. After an hour of that, desperate for some distraction, she stomped to the kitchen, glaring at the light around the pub door as she passed it, and began to cook—anything she could think of, just stirring and chopping and frying and baking in a helpless, mechanical frenzy. Before long, two different soups simmered on the stove, and the flapjacks cooling on the table filled the whole ground floor with the smell of oats and toffee. She stood in the center of the room for a few moments, surveying it all, her gaze coming to rest on the door to the hallway. George still hadn't emerged from his hiding place. Hadn't spoken another word to her since he'd returned.

Against her better judgment, she started towards the pub.

"I'm just here to get a drink," she said, barging through the door.

He nodded at the empty glasses beside him. "Why do you think I've been here all night?"

She grunted and bustled behind the bar, where she poured a liberal slug of gin into a tumbler and, after a few seconds scanning the array of bottles fixed to the wall, a splash of vermouth. (During their courtship she'd hated martinis but had choked them down to appear sophisticated; these days they'd become her nip of choice.) She turned and looked beneath the counter. "Where are the olives?"

"We're out," he said, still frowning at his crossword. "I wasn't going to re-order until we opened."

Letting out an irritated sigh, she set the tumbler down on the bar and stirred it with her finger.

"Olives!" George exclaimed, suddenly. He scribbled something into the crossword. "*Oil supplier turned evil in the bones at first!*"

Rolling her eyes, she asked him how he could be doing a crossword at a time like this; he crossed out the successfully cracked clue and looked up, raising an eyebrow. "How can you be cooking?"

She took another sip of her drink and swished it around her mouth for a few moments before swallowing. "Fair enough." She sighed. "I'm sorry, George. I know you're upset too." She slipped out from behind the bar and took a seat next to him. "I'm just at my wit's end."

He laid down his paper and shuffled sideways on his stool so he could put an arm around her. "I know, Reenie." He pulled her closer. "But I'm sure they're fine."

For several minutes they sat like that, saying nothing, eyes closed, beating back the day's tension. He stroked her hair; she squeezed his knee. The windows kept on crackling in the rain. Finally she lifted her head, slightly, and turned to stare at him for what felt like the fiftieth time that day—and then, to her surprise, they kissed. Not the usual goodnight kiss they exchanged in the evenings, or even the more protracted sort they sometimes allowed themselves at Hogmanay. Not even the sort they shared on the rare occasions when they had sex, really, which these days felt largely ceremonial. No, this was something else, borne of the high emotions of the past few hours; more like the closer, deeper-felt kisses of their earliest years. It seemed almost alien to her, the pressing and prodding of his stubble against her chin after so long, his tongue swishing over hers. To her embarrassment, she found herself reminded of her last trip to the dentist.

Yet the sensation was still comforting, she realized, as her hand found his. It must have been a decade since they'd sought each other out like this, and longer still since those winter mornings when they would lie in bed for hours, giggling as George's parents clomped around pointedly outside the door. That suddenly such fondness had reappeared seemed like proof, somehow, that they had made at least one good decision in the past, no matter what had happened since or what might happen today. And at last that thought forced out Maureen's memories of the dentist, and her visions of the bridge and of her children, and focused her mind instead on the increasingly natural feeling of kissing her husband, and their gradual undressing, and their slow sink to the pub's cool floor.

It was much later, another hour or two, when the phone began to ring, and by then Maureen was in the kitchen again, spooning cooled soup into storage containers. She looked up. The clock showed a few minutes past ten, and instinctively she feared the worst—even as, dropping her ladle and running to answer, she struggled to think of any scenario in which the call could be about the children.

"Maureen?" The voice on the line was faint. "It's Henry Lewis."

"Henry!" She gripped the handset tighter. Had they been airlifted to the mainland, somehow? In this weather? "How are you calling? Where are you?"

"I'm at Bella's," the tinny voice replied. "I don't know why I didn't think of it sooner—I should have known she'd keep a working phone year round."

She shut her eyes tight. "Is everyone okay? Is Barry with you?"

Down the hallway she heard George emerge from the pub.

"Everyone's fine," said Mr. Lewis, hesitant. "Barry's here."

Maureen felt her knees go weak. "Thank God."

"I'm worried about him, though." Lowering his voice, he explained what had happened that afternoon: Barry's appearance at the school's door, babbling about how the bridge had come apart behind him; how he'd seemed to relax as the hours had passed, chatting to Mr. Lewis while Flora and Trevor worked at their desks. But then, too: how the generator had died as the four of them read aloud together on the sofa, plunging them into darkness; how, as Mr. Lewis had bundled them up and taken them instead to Bella's empty house, Barry had scowled and lagged behind, his good mood just as suddenly evaporating. "And then he broke down, Maureen." A sheepish pause. "Bella and I have started seeing each other, and when he realized he started screaming at me. Completely lost the plot. Said I'd betrayed him, or something like that." His voice dropped even further. "I couldn't really follow him, to be honest—it was all very emotional and incoherent and teenagerish. Goodness knows what must have been going on at St. Fillan's the past few months."

Maureen wrapped her cardigan more tightly around her. "He hasn't been himself," she murmured.

"Anyway," Mr. Lewis said. "I've put him to bed in Bella's guestroom, but maybe we should sit him down tomorrow for a chat. Find out what's bothering him."

Maureen grimaced, predicting—correctly—that they'd get no further than the few attempts she'd already made. But she told Mr. Lewis that sounded like a good idea and thanked him before finally hanging up. She turned to George, who had moved up beside her, and smiled with relief. "They're okay," she said. "Barry's okay."

He smiled back, and hugged her.

On the Stùc, though, Barry was not okay; he had just

listened to Mr. Lewis's side of the entire conversation, crouched outside the box room where Bella kept her telephone, and was seething. Had already been seething when he'd heard Mr. Lewis go in there, and had crept from the guestroom where he'd been lying wide awake. Had already been seething, even, when Mr. Lewis had dragged him to bed in the first place and wrestled him under the covers, pleading with him to calm down and patiently enduring Barry's alternating silence and profanity.

The most frustrating thing was how cannily Mr. Lewis had summarized the situation. Barry *had* relaxed that afternoon, *had* found being back with his old teacher infinitely more soothing than his past weeks at home; had begun, even, to contemplate confiding in him after all. And Mr. Lewis had been right, too, that Barry's mood had soured again as soon as the man had produced his spare key and opened Bella's front door. It simply hadn't squared with Barry's social map of the island, no matter how he'd tried to convince himself there was some more innocent explanation. And when they'd stepped inside—into the inner chamber he'd so long dreamt of—and immediately Barry had spotted one of Mr. Lewis's scarves hanging on the coat rack, well: that was it. He'd exploded, unable to believe that the man could even fathom pursuing Bella when Barry had already made his own feelings for her so spectacularly clear. Had let months of frustration pour out against his teacher while his siblings edged backwards, agog.

And though years later he would remember this night and be forced to admit that Mr. Lewis had also been right to call his reaction incoherent and emotional and teenagerish, hearing it described that way with his wounds so fresh only enraged him further. So with Mr. Lewis putting down the phone now and standing up, Barry turned and ran, not stopping when the man entered the hallway and called for him to wait. He leapt down the stairs two at a time, sprinting through the kitchen and into Bella's giant studio; hurried to the corner of the room and through a small back door into the orchard. Ran until he reached his old hiding spot beneath one of the trees, then looked back towards the studio windows to see the light click on and Mr. Lewis's mouth moving as he called out Barry's name. And then he let his head fall back against the tree, defeated.

There wasn't any point in running any further, he realized; Mr. Lewis would catch him soon enough and march him back upstairs, and resisting would only get him wetter. But he also knew he wouldn't budge, now, wouldn't tell the man any more than he'd told his parents, no matter how earnest a chat he tried to sit him down for. Wouldn't grant that fucking traitor one more piece of his trust. And he told himself, too—screamed it in his head—that he was finished with the island. That he couldn't come back, not permanently, not after this and his past few miserable weeks at home. What else was left here for him?

He asked himself that question again as Mr. Lewis finally found him, teeth chattering beneath his tree, and led him back inside. Asked it again as he peeled off his sodden clothes, and again as he lay in Bella's guest bed, listening to the softening patter of rain against the windows, and watching the shadows make patterns on the ceiling. Each time, he found himself equally at a loss for an answer—and his last thoughts before he fell asleep, sometime past midnight, were of his family growing old without him, and all the places he could live instead, and a desperate plan to escape as soon as possible.

1995

VII.

May, and the start of another tourist season. As if in preparation, the weather had been warm and dry that spring, and an unusually large flock of puffins had returned, swooping overhead from nest to sea and back—their beaks luminous even silhouetted against the sky. And though it was probably mere fancy, it sounded to the few remaining islanders, the ones who had lived through the drama of the rats, long past—George and Maureen, and Flora, and Bella and no one else—as if there were an extra liveliness to the puffins' cries this year; a feeling of triumph at the reclamation of their home.

Flora had been back on the island for almost a year now, after finishing her final term at St. Fillan's. In the face of so many other islanders departing, her homecoming had felt like a milestone, of sorts—especially since Barry had never returned— but it had passed without much fanfare, at least on her part: she simply stepped from the ferry that afternoon with a reserved smile, no bigger than if this were just another visit. Each summer since she'd left for St. Fillan's, after all, she'd hauled her bulging trunk home with her father; each summer her spirits had leapt at the first glimpse of the village; and each summer she'd practically skipped around her room the morning after her arrival, replacing belongings in the gaps on her shelves with a haphazard kind of joy.

But it was precisely during her unpacking this time when she'd had the first, hazy realization that she wouldn't be disappearing again in August. That she had no idea, actually, when she might ever disappear anywhere again. And suddenly her room felt as if it were shrinking all around her, the ugly pink beanbag she'd picked out for her birthday years ago, worn down to its threads, creeping ominously in her direction, and the bunk beds she'd once shared with Barry towering in the corner. Dropping the jumper she was holding, she hurried downstairs to see if her mother needed help in the kitchen.

After breakfast the feeling weakened, thankfully, and once she was thrown into her duties at the guesthouse it seemed to pass altogether, tidied up or forgotten in the everyday bustle. Occasionally she even enjoyed being back, taking a nostalgic pleasure in her daily chores: pouring pints with the same precision as her father, or fluffing guestroom pillows with the ferocity she'd always seen in her mother. When the season finished that first summer she'd started to discover the other perks of adult life on the island, too. Compared to her final year at St. Fillan's, a whirlwind of straight A's and prefecture and the hockey squad and the art club, the calm of the off-season was luxurious. She slept late and spent as many hours as she liked hunched over her sketchbook, and took lazy walks almost every afternoon—either around the hills with her father or on her own, to the Stùc and a visit with Bella.

Bella's animosity following Barry's going-away party had given way, a year or so later, to after-school art lessons, arranged by Mr. Lewis through methods Flora had never been able to discern. Though initially Flora had met with her for just an hour every Wednesday, Bella had quickly warmed to her and their time had expanded to two hours twice a week; by the time Flora left for St. Fillan's the art lessons were little more than joint studio sessions, the two of them chatting while they painted, with Bella offering pointers occasionally, if at all. While Flora was away at school or Bella on the mainland for the winter, they kept up a healthy correspondence, Flora sending photographs of her recent work and Bella replying with her critique—and before long other details began to seep into their letters, too: worries about exams and other teenage drama from Flora, and news of professional success and a deepening love with Mr. Lewis from Bella (whose eventual wedding, naturally, Flora had attended). And even with Mr. Lewis reassigned to Edinburgh nowadays, and Bella spending less and less time on the island, she and Flora remained fast friends, regularly meeting for afternoon tea whenever the woman was around.

Flora's visits with Bella were the only thing, actually, that let her forget her fears about the future, even if she was doing her best to transform the guesthouse into someplace she could picture living again, long-term and contented. Small things, at first: two of the preset stations on the living room radio were quietly changed; her ratty beanbag covered tactfully with a throw. But as the months passed, larger differences also started to accumulate, her stacks of old books and drawings packed away in a closet, a small CD player purchased for her bedside table, and her home improvements encroaching beyond the confines of her bedroom. She hung a few of her pictures in the hallway, and put her desk lamp from St. Fillan's on the downstairs telephone table, and after Christmas—spent on the island, as had become their custom since Barry left for St. Fillan's, despite that first year's disasters—she arranged for a subscription to the *Guardian*, a hipper newspaper to supplement her father's stodgy *Scotsman*. (They tried one of its crosswords one night, but George couldn't get his head around the different style of the other paper's clues.)

The biggest change—the biggest drama—came at the start of spring, when Flora suggested they replace the bunk beds. To her the issue seemed relatively innocuous, and so she'd broached it flippantly over breakfast one day: *why don't we finally chuck the bunks, eh?* But her parents were so aggrieved by the suggestion, her mother in particular, that it took weeks of smoothing things over before she could bring it up again. Even then she'd had to propose a compromise: they'd detach the top bunk and move it to one of the single rooms upstairs. That way they'd have an extra bed to offer when the season started, *and of course*, she'd added, though she found it somewhat ridiculous, *whenever Barry wants to come back we can always move it down again.* As if he ever would; it had been almost two years since they'd even *heard* from him and three since he'd last visited—and five, already, since he'd left for the oil job. Before that he'd shown no desire to spend any more time on the island than absolutely necessary, either, and Flora, at least, had given up on him ever coming back. Frankly, after his alternating apathy and mean-spiritedness his last few years at home, she didn't particularly want him to, and couldn't quite understand why her parents did. (Only when Trevor returned for the Easter holidays and was livid to find his brother's bed moved—*you can't just go around changing things like that!*—did she wonder if perhaps she'd been a little heartless.)

In any case, as the season started again for her first full summer home, her new life on the island—or rather, her old life, made over—had started to take shape. And while that suffocating feeling of the first few days still found her from time to time, when it did, she ignored it as best she could. Because she couldn't leave now, she knew that. Couldn't even consider it. Her parents were both approaching sixty, and it was increasingly difficult for them to run the guesthouse on their own: her mother's hands, riddled with arthritic knots, made her former chores impossible, and her father's legs would ache and swell whenever he manned the bar too long. Hiring help was also out of the question; the one time Flora suggested it, George laughed and told her they were barely making a profit as it was. *Besides, what are we supposed to do?* he'd added. *Put a notice in the local paper?*

So with Trevor still at school and Barry long since vanished, the filial duty clearly fell on Flora. She had to be the one to stay, the one to make the sacrifice—and with the same studiousness she'd shown at school she threw herself into it, willfully forgetting how effusive the careers officer at St. Fillan's had been as he'd looked over her exam results; willfully forgetting the awards her artwork had won at local competitions in Fort William, the certificates of achievement now packed away in her bedroom closet. Willfully forgetting, at least for the time being, her thoughts of anything else.

The season's first week felt brisk, as it always did. Flora was constantly rushing from the guestrooms to the kitchen, from the laundry to the pub, from the house to the jetty—even with only four guests out of a possible eight!—and at night she would slump into bed and exhale deeply, every muscle like lead, and stare at the ceiling for half an hour until the day's buzz subsided and she gradually fell asleep.

But as it always did, too, that perpetual weariness soon began to feel normal, and by the end of the second week it no longer even felt like weariness. Instead it became just another layer in her life's daily rhythm, and one she could easily gloss over while she focused on the things she found more pleasant. In particular she started to enjoy her shifts in the pub, and more and more found herself unwinding there as the evening tapered away, doodling absentminded caricatures of customers on her waiter's pad, or fiddling with new cocktail recipes, or simply listening, moony and enchanted, to the stories people told her about life elsewhere. She was even amused by the clumsy flirting she drew from middle-aged husbands on vacation with their wives, and flattered on the few occasions when it happened with the men closer to her age—usually campers who wanted a night cap before bundling up for the evening. She was never tempted to reciprocate, though; such encounters were only a game, she firmly told herself, another harmless way to pass the time. Any sign of real attraction would only create another shortcoming the island couldn't possibly resolve.

And then, in August, he appeared.

It was a golden summer evening, the sun well above the horizon even at seven o'clock, and casting long, inviting shadows as the week's guests, two couples, looked over their menus. When he walked in she was mixing aperitifs at the bar, and she looked up, startled, at the creak of the door; her mother had checked him in that morning and he'd been out walking all day, so she'd more or less forgotten he existed. This was the first time she'd even set eyes on him.

He seemed an unusual sort to be staying, she thought, as he surveyed the room's tables and made his way to one by the window. His crisp, cropped hair, for a start, and his equally crisp shirt—he looked more like a businessman than the salt-of-the-earth vacationers who usually took rooms. He was younger, too, and people his age usually roughed it in tents; she wondered what had inspired him to stay in a stuffy old B&B like this. (Then again, she mused, maybe the crisp shirt answered that question.)

"Nice night," she said, walking over to him with a menu. He turned from the window and looked at her, dumbstruck, as if he'd forgotten for a moment that he was sitting in a pub. She straightened her shirt in the awkward silence. "Can I get you something?"

"Um, yes," he said, seeming to snap out of his trance. "I'll have a pint."

"Of...?"

This flummoxed him again. "I don't know. Something local. Some good Scottish beer."

With a cynical laugh she told him she'd see what she could do, and returned to the bar. She was disconcerted, somehow, by the way he'd stared at her so intently, and was mostly quiet as she went about the rest of the evening, taking his order and delivering his food with a minimum of small talk. He lingered, though, 'til long past eight, the other customers gone and the kitchen closed for the night, and as she returned to take his last, empty glass, he did it again: gave her that searching look. Smiled.

"That was delicious," he said.

She muttered thanks and hurried back to the bar. To her dismay, he followed.

"I'm Michael," he said, taking a seat on one of the stools. The sun had dropped below the hills, finally, but the sky in the windows behind him was still smeared with pastel pinks and blues. She let out a small, resigned sigh.

"Flora."

There wasn't any difference, she tried to reassure herself, between him and the other young men who usually took an interest in her. If anything he had less appeal: lacked the athletic physique of the hikers and the ruggedness of the campers, and on careful scrutiny wasn't any more than moderately attractive, his hairline in the first stages of receding and his nose a little crooked. And yet there was still that something, tightening up her stomach. A feeling normally not there.

She picked up a fresh pint glass and tipped it towards him;

he nodded and asked for another of whatever he'd had with dinner, and she nodded back, glad to have something else to focus on. As she poured the beer she frowned in concentration, making tiny adjustments to the glass's tilt as a line of thin bubbles began to bloom across the surface. When she was done she pulled it away from the tap and set it down on the counter with a flourish, announcing the price; he smiled and glanced down to where he'd already put the money in front of her. She blushed.

"So," he said, as she gathered up the coins. "You live here?"

"Aye," she replied. "Always have done."

He raised an eyebrow. "You've never left?"

"Don't be daft," she said. She picked up a cloth from next to the glass-washing sink and began to wipe down the bar. "I went to boarding school near Fort William."

He leaned backwards, still perched on his stool. "But you haven't been to Glasgow, even? Or Edinburgh?"

She shook her head, and asked him where he was from. London, he told her; he worked at an investment bank.

"And what brings you here?" She dropped the cloth by the sink again, and began searching for some other task to fill her hands.

"I'd never been to Scotland," he shrugged. "And I had a long weekend so I thought I'd give it a look. Felt like a holiday."

She laughed. "You felt like a holiday and you came to *Scotland*?"

He smiled sheepishly. "I read about this place a few years ago—when you were having your rat problems. I've been curious ever since. Is that strange?"

Flora shook her head. "Happens all the time. I'm not sure what it is about vermin, but they're a real crowd pleaser." She motioned for him to look above the bar, where her father had blown up and framed a series of news clippings about the infestation. "I hope you're not too disappointed that we're rid of them these days."

"Oh no," he said. "It's so beautiful up here. And I can't tell you how amazing it is to get out of the city. This is exactly what I needed."

She laughed again and told him he was a funny one, and after that she began to feel a little less on guard. He told her about his childhood in a village in southern England—*not too different from this one*, he said, winking, *though we had one or two more people*—and she told him about the history of the guesthouse, and the island, and, unwittingly, about its slow, unwavering decline. He asked her about her time on the mainland, and whether she ever considered going back, and when she hesitated, then, he quickly changed the subject. Instead he began to talk about what he'd done that day, how he'd walked to the bluffs on the island's north coast and seen another, smaller islet a short ways off; how he'd seen buildings on it and yet no obvious way to get across.

"I spent fifteen minutes staring at it," he told her, "trying to work it out. There's no bridge, no dock—nothing! I'm still completely baffled."

"Oh, it's easy," she said, inexplicably glad to know the answer.

"Well then," he said, banging his hand against the counter with a laugh. "Put me out of my misery!"

Before she could, though, the door to the pub swung open and George strolled in. "Evening love," he said to Flora. "Evening, Mr... Talbot, is it?"

"Michael," he said. "Please."

"Michael then." George leaned sideways against the bar. "I hate to ask, but a couple of people over walking for the day have managed to miss the last ferry—thought it left at seven, not six." He rolled his eyes. "They've been waiting at the jetty for the last two hours wondering what was taking so long."

Michael nodded. "Is there no schedule down there?"

"I—Well...No." He shook his head. "Anyway. If it wouldn't be too much trouble I was hoping we could move you to another room so that we can squeeze them in for the evening. We'll offer you a discount, of course."

Waving him off, Michael insisted a discount wasn't necessary.

"Splendid." George turned to his daughter. "And if you don't mind, love, they'd like some supper. Could you whip something up for them?"

She scowled, about to ask why her mother couldn't do it, but his expression told her not to bother; probably Maureen was already in bed. "Ach, fine," she said, glancing wistfully at Michael, who had drained his glass and was standing up.

"You'll have to tell me later," he said, smiling, and then he and George went to move his things—leaving Flora, alone in the pub, mind racing.

"Sounds like you fancy him," Bella told her, two days later, both of them sipping tea in the woman's studio. Flora was describing what she'd done the day before: how she'd woken early and dragged Michael down to the beach; how she'd waltzed him across the wet sand of the land bridge, barely recognizing herself, leaping and bobbing between puddles and rust-colored seaweed; and how she'd taken him to the schoolhouse, and its chilly, bluish bareness. In the classroom the blackboard had been wiped clean into chalky circles, and an old projector sat next to it on the floor, power cord wrapped around its neck as if it had strangled itself in desperation; several bundles of jotters were stacked in one corner, collecting dust. And though that desolation seemed sad as she explained it to Bella now, in the moment she'd been too distracted to notice, by the intoxicating feeling of telling Michael all the island's stories, and by the stories about London he told her in return: the deafening march of City commuters on the Tube each morning; early evening pub crawls home, through grand-sounding places like Threadneedle Street and Bishopsgate and Hoxton; and his frantic report writing marathons 'til three a.m., leaving time only for a few hours sleep beneath his desk while the sun rose over the Thames. Mostly, though, she loved how captivated he was by the island itself, and how his interest seemed to imbue new value in her life there. Made it feel like something she could be proud of. After their visit to the school they'd walked back to the guesthouse together, and that evening spent several more hours in the pub— and then Flora had been late getting to the Stùc today, too, because she'd lost track of time while talking to him over lunch.

But she still assured Bella, now, that romance was the last thing on her mind.

"I don't see why you're so opposed to the idea," the woman replied, stirring at her tea. "You're nineteen. Occasionally nineteen-year-olds are attracted to the opposite sex."

"I'm not opposed to the idea, it's just—"

"You're stuck wasting away on this island and don't want to get too attached to anyone?" She leaned back with a smug look.

Bella's bluntness had ceased to surprise Flora, after so many years of being at its mercy; from their earliest art lessons the woman hadn't shied from candor. *Don't be so derivative*, she'd said of an ambitious watercolor of a sunset; *twee*, she'd dismissed a sketch of Trevor sleeping. *Monet might have got away with it, but Monet could do convincing foreshortening.* Such comments had often sent Flora home in tears, but that had only made her try twice as hard the next time. Besides, part of the reason the barbs hurt so much was that most of the time they tapped doubts she'd already had herself.

Bella was wrong about Michael though, Flora thought

now, taking a bite of scone. It wasn't that simple. Yes, okay, she was stuck on the island for the time being, and yes, she was often conscious of that when rebuffing advances in the pub. But she still doubted she had any serious interest in Michael, because never, not once, not in a year of charming customers or nearly five at school, had she ever, as Bella put it, "fancied" anyone. And why, of all people, would this stiff English twit have changed that?

St. Fillan's had given her plenty of experience with the mechanics of lust, of course, thanks mainly to the irresistible concupiscence of her friend Maisie. On Flora's very first night, after George had left for the ferry, Maisie had somehow engineered a game of Spin the Bottle with a gaggle of other first-years, and those early, curious kisses had developed over the years into countless fumbling embraces after school dances and stolen moments in dark corners of the playground. In a pleasing sort of symmetry, Maisie had also engineered, after the Leavers' Ball on their *last* night, a very compromising situation between Flora and a member of the school rugby team. But all of it, the slobbery kissing, and the awkward mutual undressing, and the repeated attempts to guide hands beneath waistbands—it ultimately struck her as rather pointless. (Even the poor rugby player she sent away after barely twenty minutes.)

It wasn't that she failed to grasp the potential for excitement in such things, and certainly she was no more interested in other girls, despite the sweatiest requests and fantasies of the boys' dorm over the years. She simply failed to actually find that excitement with anyone who cared to try. Not since the incident with Tam.

It had started in the dining hall one lunchtime: she'd been sitting with her bunkmate Judith, and Maisie, two tables over from Barry and the rest of his posse, when she'd heard her name and looked over to several of the boys laughing. *Don't look!* Maisie had hissed, but despite Flora's best, self-conscious efforts to ignore them, she couldn't help but steal a few more glances—and the boys had continued to whoop and holler about something for the rest of lunch, until finally, as they were standing up and leaving, Tam had looked right at her, and winked.

"*Did you see that?*" Maisie whispered, nudging Flora as soon as they were out of earshot. "Tam McLaren just winked at you!"

Judith leaned in. "Do you know him, or something?"

Flora assured them she did not.

"It must be because he's friends with your brother," said Maisie, relishing the speculation. "He probably put in a good word for you."

Flora doubted it, and told her friends as much—she and Barry hadn't been on good enough terms to do each other any favors since he'd started at St. Fillan's, never mind the screaming match they'd had the night before *she'd* started, a few weeks earlier. But they wouldn't listen.

"You should definitely ask him out," said Maisie, nodding. "I bet he'd well do it."

"But he's a fifth year!" shrieked Judith. "Fifth years don't go out with first years!"

"This is different," said Maisie. "He knows her brother. Besides," she narrowed her eyes and added, in a conspiratorial whisper, "I hear he has a massive willy."

Looking back, Flora couldn't quite tell if her attraction to Tam had started then or later, or when exactly she'd realized what it was—but somewhere between that wink and her friends' encouragement, it took hold. When she saw him in the corridor or the playground her palms would sweat and tingle, her insides spiraling around themselves; at night she'd lie awake and imagine being with him on her own, replaying the few kisses she'd had on that first night of Spin the Bottle, with Tam in the place of the spotty, nervous first-years—and then imagining doing all the other things Maisie always described in such gleeful, lurid detail. He took her over, engulfed her, and when a few weeks later she was in the library studying by herself and he abruptly appeared at her side, she couldn't do anything except stare up at him.

"How'd you like to take a wee walk?" he'd said.

Nodding helplessly, she'd followed. "Are we going to your room?" she asked, struggling to keep up as he strode out of the library and ahead of her down the hallway.

He grinned down at her. "You'll see."

But suddenly there had been a commotion behind them; a shout, and the frantic clap-clap of footsteps on stone floor.

"Lay one more fucking finger on her, Tam, and you're dead!"

Flora turned and saw Barry running towards them, two of his other friends in pursuit. Tam saw it too, and grabbing Flora by the hand he tried to run himself—but still she couldn't keep up, and Barry was drawing ever nearer.

"Barry!" she'd screamed at him, over her shoulder. "What are you *doing*? Leave us alone!"

Tam skipped to a stop at that, and turned around. "Hear that, Baz? She wants you to leave us alone!" He was still squeezing her hand. "Looks like she knows what she's doing after all, eh?"

And then it was all over: Barry, still hurtling forward, reached where they were standing, and with one last shout of *You're fucking dead!* he smashed his forehead into Tam's face. The boy's grip on Flora loosened instantly, and as the brawl intensified she slipped away, the cries of approaching teachers echoing behind her.

Furious, she returned, sobbing, to her room, where Judith quickly summoned Maisie and the three of them picked the incident apart. Judith told her that she might still have a chance with Tam; Maisie theorized at some length as to what combinations of protuberance and orifice might have occurred without Barry's interruption. Before long, however, there was a frantic knock at the door, and Barry, blood caked down his shirt, was pushing his way in. Tam had claimed that Flora lured him to the hallway deliberately for an ambush, Barry told them, and the headmaster was already threatening both of them with expulsion—but Flora would be fine, he assured her, looking pointedly at each of the three girls, if they did exactly what he said. *Just tell them she's been here all afternoon.*

Still angry, Flora had screamed at him to get out; probably she would have stewed all evening had the deputy headmistress not shown up twenty minutes later and asked exactly the same questions Barry said she would. At that she numbly acquiesced, lying stony-faced about where she'd spent the afternoon, her longing for Tam evaporating—too shocked someone would deceive her like that, unprovoked, to muster any other response. It was little wonder, really, that romance had since failed to interest her.

Out of embarrassment she'd never confided any of this to Bella, however, and now simply told her that Michael wasn't anything special. "He's clumsy," she said, "and he's balding and...he's *gauche*. I'd rather have that enthusiastic groper from the rugby team."

"Ha!" Bella set her teacup down. "*Gauche*, is he? Glad to see you've spent some time with the thesaurus since you've been home."

"I—"

"And if he's so unremarkable, why do you seem congenitally unable to stop talking about him?"

Flora set her own cup down, and crossed her arms. "You asked."

"Anyway," said Bella, clearing her throat. "If you can bear to change the subject I have something else I want to talk about." She leaned back in her chair. "I'd like you to have my studio." Flora gawked at her. "I mean, I'm not giving it to you for good—I'll still want to use it from time to time, and one of these days I might even try and sell it again. But now that Henry and I are living in marital bliss there's not much point in me spending six months a year on my own here, not when I have perfectly good studio space in Edinburgh. And meanwhile it seems a shame to have you struggling away in that cramped bedroom of yours. Besides," she smirked, never passing up a chance to tease Flora about her childhood spying. "I know how much you enjoy lurking around this place."

"I don't know what to say," said Flora.

"Say thank you," Bella replied. "And then have some fantastic work to show for it the next time I'm here."

Flora took a deep breath. "Okay," she said. "Thank you."

"You're more than welcome." She looked at her watch and smirked again. "Now, you'd best be making your way home—the tide'll be in soon and you wouldn't want to get stuck over here on Prince Charming's last night."

Glancing at her own watch, Flora was surprised at how late it was—so she did as Bella had suggested and hurried out, all the while insisting that Michael had nothing to do with it. Indeed, determined to prove Bella wrong, she told her father she had a splitting headache when she got home and begged off her pub shift for the night, instead spending the evening locked up in her room, not seeking Michael out or even going downstairs for dinner lest she accidentally run into him. Not that she needed to avoid him, she reminded herself, because he *was* awkward and he was a little plain, and whatever she might have thought she felt was a passing madness—a side effect of spending so much time with him the past few days—and nothing else.

But as Maisie had done with Tam years earlier, Bella's hand in the situation had changed things, somehow, the outside suggestion of attraction carving relief into Flora's inner, conflicted feelings. Even as she continued with her hopeless rationalizations that night, she was already hatching a plan for the next morning: she would talk her way out of serving and instead help her mother in the kitchen, so that when it came time to meet the ferry for the morning delivery she could innocently volunteer, and make her way to the jetty as Michael did too. *What a coincidence!*, she'd say, pulling on her shoes at the bottom landing while he clomped down behind her with his backpack and gaudy bright red anorak, and they would make the walk together. And then, at the jetty, ferry ready to depart, they would look at each other, and she would step forward, and finally she would kiss him—still telling herself, probably, that it meant nothing—hoping as she did so that it would purge any trace of her infatuation, unload it onto him, and that once the ferry glided away she would never have to think of him again.

Which was how it happened, mostly, up until the final moment. But for some reason, instead of kissing him, she couldn't quite bring herself to do anything but grip him in a hug. "It's been really nice getting to know you," she said, pulling away, shouting over the roar of the ferry's engine.

He fished his ticket from his pocket. "You too, Flora," he said, and made his way up the gangplank. The bitter smell of petrol rushed to fill the space where he'd been standing, and without even a single, remorseful look behind him, he was gone.

VIII.

Towards the end of that October, George sat working on a crossword in the pub, the house quiet and empty: Flora was on the Stùc again (she never seemed to be anywhere else, these days), and Maureen had gone to the mainland to visit Trevor for his half-term break and birthday.

Flora had suggested that George go along for the trip too, but he'd demurred. Even now, with the season weeks past, the phone still rang frequently with enquiries, which often turned into bookings for the next year—and precisely because Flora was on the Stùc so much recently he felt he couldn't leave the place unmanned. Somebody had to worry about the business.

He frowned, reading over one of the crossword clues. *Annoyed expressions a cow might make? (5)*

It wasn't really fair to say the women didn't also worry about the business, he knew that. But they sometimes seemed to shuffle through their guesthouse duties solely from some stoic sense of duty. In spite of all the years they'd given to the place, and all his efforts to make them care, they never seemed that invested in whether the guesthouse flopped or flourished. And that stung.

Or perhaps, alone in the house again, as lately he increasingly was, he simply felt sorry for himself.

Annoyed expressions a cow might make? Was *might make* a clue for an anagram, he wondered? He tried rearranging *a cow* in his head a few times—*Ocaw? Cwao? Awoc?*—but he was too distracted to picture the letters dancing around as he normally did. He looked up at the clock above the bar. Where was Flora, anyway?

When she'd first told them that Bella was giving her free rein of the studio, he hadn't known what to think. Hadn't known what to think, either, that Flora was so thrilled by the idea. Of course, she'd always been fond of her drawing and painting, and she'd always been fascinated with Bella and the old manor, too—but it had caught him quite off guard the way she'd latched onto the place, growing more and more excited with each passing day before the handover, and wasting not a single second when the end of summer arrived and Bella finally left. Flora had skipped back and forth across the isthmus as much as the tide allowed that day, carrying armfuls of her things—sketchpads, paintbrushes, old jumpers, books—and that night she'd even slept there, as if suddenly she had no need for home at all.

Waco? Wacos? Could that be an annoyed expression? Some reference to that bust-up in Texas a few years back? He'd followed the siege closely in the paper at the time, fascinated not by the gruesome voyeurism but by the fact that even in a country as big as America, people couldn't seem to live without getting in each other's way. He'd always supposed that all the conflict on the island in his lifetime—the clashes between the crofters and entrepreneurs in his childhood, and between him and the Trust as he'd grown older, and of course between Maureen and Bella—had been down to the tininess of the place. But reading about Waco made him wonder if such territorial disagreements were simply a part of life. Without a doubt that was why Reenie had been livid when she'd learned about the studio—even if, sensing perhaps that a more objective tack would have more luck, she'd dressed up her objections as something else. *You know I get nervous about the Stùc now that the bridge is gone*, she'd said. *I won't have you over there a second more than necessary—what if you get stranded in a storm again?* Flora hadn't bought it, pointing out all the reasons why the studio was actually an excellent idea—no more paint stains on her room's carpet, no more of Reenie's kitchen implements going missing for still lifes—and had reminded them, in any case, that it wasn't any safer being stranded in the guesthouse during a storm. (She'd stared at her mother, then, as if willing her to bring up Bella, but Reenie had reluctantly backed down.)

He stared at the crossword some more. It probably wasn't an anagram after all, he told himself. *Annoyed expressions*: frowns? Growls?

Maybe, he supposed, he was wrong about Reenie's motives—or at least was oversimplifying. Yes, she and Bella had a history of animosity, and no, the line about storms hadn't been terribly convincing. But perhaps his wife was upset simply because Flora had taken the studio without even consulting them. Maybe she was upset because yet another child was drifting away from her. Indeed, with Barry vanished into the North Sea and Trevor still at school, to have Flora suddenly decamp was a particularly cruel desertion. Even he'd been a little hurt.

Scowls? That had *cow* in it, at least—but it was too many letters.

Once he might have tried to talk to Reenie, to find out exactly what was bothering her, but now it hardly seemed worth the effort. The past few years she had ceased discussing much of anything with him other than the dull, day-to-day matters around the guesthouse. He shook his head faintly. When they'd been young she had always been so expressive, too. Right from their very first conversation, her openness had startled him.

She had been sixteen at the time, and he twenty, spending the last weeks of summer on the island before returning for his final year at Glasgow. He hadn't expected to be at home at all that year; he'd planned a pilgrim's progress around Europe to mark his final summer as a student. But then his older brother, James, had died while on deployment in Cyprus, and after seeing his mother's awful state at the funeral he hadn't wanted to leave her alone. So he'd cancelled his trip and returned home instead, and had been strolling down to the jetty that morning to fetch the messages when, out of nowhere, Maureen had appeared next to him as if blooming from the gorse.

"George McCloud," she'd said, and he turned with a start.

"Oh." He squinted at her. "Hello. It's Maureen, isn't it?"

They'd overlapped for a few years at the primary school, so he was vaguely aware of her existence, but other than that they'd never had much to do with each other. Her parents were fishers, and the fishers spurned anyone who catered to the island's tourists. Respectable jobs involved hard labor, as far as they were concerned, not hawking souvenirs or entertaining rich Englishmen or selling up the island's secret spots. (No doubt the Calvinist homilies delivered by the island's pastor each week only further confirmed that prejudice.)

"My friends call me Reenie," she said, beginning to skip alongside him. "You can too, if you like."

He swallowed. "And how can I help you today, Reenie?"

And that was when, quite matter-of-factly, she'd replied she was going to marry him.

"Marry me?" he said, laughing off the suggestion. "But I'm not even going to be here after this summer! I'm going back to uni! And once I'm finished there my uncle's arranging an internship for me with the *Scotsman* in Edinburgh."

"I'll come with you," she said, without blinking. "It won't matter where you go if I'm your wife." She smiled coyly. "Anyway, Edinburgh doesn't sound so bad."

He'd laughed again, more uneasily this time. "Aye, well. We'll have to wait and see." He cleared his throat. "Now go on, away with you. I'm not your babysitter."

"Whatever you say, George McCloud," she'd replied, and bounded away down the hill, as naturally as if they'd been discussing the weather.

He'd put her out of his head after that, and returned to Glasgow without seeing her again; by the time he visited at Christmas he had mostly forgotten about her. But there she was, now seventeen, and unofficially permitted in the pub—where she turned up every evening to try and snatch a few minutes of his time. He pretended to find it awkward, assuring his curious parents he had no idea why she kept hanging about, and yet something about her determination stoked his ego; this time when he returned to Glasgow he didn't as successfully forget about her, and as his Easter break drew near he began to wonder if she'd be waiting for him again. Hoping even, if he was honest, that she would be. To his surprise he found he liked the notion of a willing woman standing by for his return—and return he would, he knew that. Going off to Edinburgh for a few years was a fine thing for a young man to do, but he couldn't stay there forever, not with James gone. He was the only son left now; it was up to him to take over from his parents when they could no longer manage the guesthouse on their own. And if he had a prospective wife there, with hardly any effort, well: so much the better.

Maureen always was waiting for him, too, and if the gossip his parents picked up was accurate she had rejected several other suitors from among the island's young men. After that he unabashedly began to miss her, to count the days until his brief visits home, and during those weeks he savored every moment. In the evenings they'd sit in the lounge well past midnight, Reenie giggling at his jokes or stroking his arm in admiration, and in the afternoons they went on walks along the beach, sharing passionate embraces in a small cove near the Stùc. And of course he'd gone to St. Fillan's in her final year to take her to the Leavers' Ball.

He never suggested she visit him, though, in Glasgow or in Edinburgh. The whole point of his time on the mainland was to go out and experience the world, after all, to be a carefree young man, not to start a family with the girl from back home. Besides—and this is what he told her when she asked—he was staying at his uncle's house in Edinburgh; bringing her along with him would have been too much of an imposition. She'd tried not to show her disappointment.

Instead they'd exchanged letters for the years he was abroad, and after that, at twenty-four, he'd returned to the island ready to settle down. They were engaged within weeks and married within months, and for several years it seemed neither of them could be happier.

Annoyed expressions... That could mean complaints, too, he thought. *Jeers? Boos? Beefs?*

Beefs!

He scribbled the word into the grid and read it over again with a satisfied nod. From the hallway he heard the front door open, and the thump-thump of Flora kicking off her boots.

Their first few years of marriage, Reenie had agitated often for them to move away again. They were both still young, she constantly reminded him, and his parents in good enough nick to manage without them a little longer—and certainly he'd considered it. At the same time, though, he'd assumed they'd be having kids before too long, and he didn't want to be away from home for that. Besides, what would either of them *do* somewhere else? He had little taste for further work in the newspaper business, and other than a minor role in the Glasgow student government he'd never held another job; had never even considered another job, really, with the guesthouse always waiting on the horizon. So he'd put off their alleged move month after month, year after year, and all of a sudden he was thirty—his parents almost sixty, and increasingly frail—and it no longer seemed an option.

Children, though, had not been forthcoming. Reenie was assiduous in her birth control and insistent that they wait, and whenever he brought it up she just asked him what the rush was. *We've got our whole lives for children, George—why start so early?* The truth was it didn't feel early to him; as he slowly assumed more of the guesthouse duties, he was growing impatient to fully take on his role as head of household. He yearned for a child—and not just to quiet his mother's constant pestering about grandkids.

He never pressed Reenie, though, not at first, sensing that her leisurely attitude was a cover for some underlying ambivalence whose depths he dared not plumb. It was only after Barry was finally conceived, and she had acted so uninterested, so unmoved— so in denial, almost—that he asked her outright: *do you even want children?* Immediately she'd waved him off. Told him he was being ridiculous, that she was thrilled to be having a child with him, and that if she ever acted otherwise it was only down to first pregnancy jitters—which seemed reasonable enough, so he'd let it slide. And when Barry was born she'd taken to motherhood with such an amazed, devoted sort of glow, George was soon wondering what he'd ever been worried about.

Before long, though, Reenie had slipped into a new, more somber mood. Or maybe somber was the wrong word: listless? Defeated? Even years later he couldn't quite decide. Could only remember the way she'd spend days at a time in an apathetic fog, staring blankly at the walls or peeling dozens more vegetables than they needed because she'd lost count—and then had conceived a second child, with the first barely two and after so many years of carefully planned nothing! Something had to have changed. Something had to be wrong.

Once again she'd told him he was being ridiculous. "Honestly, George," she said, fishing a box of maternity clothes from the back of their bedroom closet. "We've got one child already, that's all— what difference does another make? We're a family now."

He smiled, not quite believing her. "I've started, so I'll finish?"

She held up a tiny knit hat, and laughed. "Something like that, aye."

Flora poked her head through the door, now. "I'm home, Dad." She walked over to where he was hunched on his stool and glanced down at the crossword. "*Beefs* is wrong."

He gave her a warm glare. "And what makes you so sure?"

"Because," she said, patting him on the back. "Six down is *armor*, so that one has to start with an *M*."

He looked down at the grid again, and the clue for six down, and blinked. She was right, of course—she always was. "Fine," he said, erasing *beefs* and wiping away the dust with the side of his pinkie. "Do you fancy bangers and mash for tea? We've got those nice sausages that still need eating."

"Fine by me," she said, leaning forward and kissing him on the cheek. "I'll go get started."

"I'll be through in a minute," he told her. "I just have to get this answer, first."

"I know you do." She winked from the doorway. "Don't be too long."

He turned back to his crossword.

With Reenie so steadfast in her reassurances, he'd again put his concerns out of his head. He had plenty of other things to focus on at the time, anyway: the day-to-day business at the guesthouse, and the continuing diaspora, and without warning his parents' passing away, shortly before Flora's birth and within a few weeks of each other—as if tethered, somehow, even after death. And then there was baby Barry, too. Beyond George's abstract desire to start a family, it turned out he quite enjoyed fatherhood, and would spend hours sitting with the boy in the living room, amazed at what he'd helped create.

After Flora was born, Reenie's mood had worsened again, her retreat accelerating; during her pregnancy with Trevor she seemed to shut him out altogether. Oonagh had more to do with her those nine months than he did, and although the excitement at Trevor's arrival had provided a reprieve from the gloom for a while, once life returned to normal again it began to feel as if their marriage were a matter of course and little else. He fell more deeply into his crosswords, and she, likewise, into her cooking, and though they both continued to muddle through their days with apparent love and tenderness, it began to seem strangely automatic; secondary to some other feeling they were unable to identify, and unwilling to discuss.

Moues, he thought, taking one last look at the grid. *Annoyed expressions a cow might make.* He groaned and filled in the answer, and then stood up to make his way to the kitchen, his back protesting after so long on the stool.

Dinner was much as it had been the other two nights Maureen had been away that week: comfortably silent, he and Flora trading occasional comments and bringing up the absent family members only when one of them sparked a memory. (The time Trevor, for instance, had run from the table in tears, having expected the bangers in bangers and mash to be literal firecrackers.) Towards the end of the meal, however, Flora departed from the usual script.

"I've been meaning to tell you," she said, casually, mopping up the last of her gravy with a heap of potatoes. "There's a gallery in Fort William that wants to show a painting of mine."

George set his fork down. "Oh?" He wasn't quite sure how to respond. "So that's, er...good news, is it?" He hadn't intended to come across as deadpanning, but Flora seemed to take it that way.

"Of course it is, you daft old bugger!" She laughed. "It's fantastic news!"

"Well then," he said with a smile. "Congratulations. Tell me about it."

It was the same gallery that had run the competition she'd won at school, she explained, the Western Eye in Fort William, who were now organizing an exhibit of rising local stars. "Rising stars!" she'd repeated, with a squeal. Oh, it was small fry, she knew that really, the "gallery" not much more than a largish function room in a local hotel and the exhibit itself a moneymaking scheme for them rather than a genuine career opportunity for her—but still, that thrill of recognition! Now she could legitimately call herself an artist, she told him, and though she didn't finish the sentence he could work out from her general demeanor the unspoken second half: *and not just the boss's daughter at some pokey guesthouse.*

"That's why I've been over at the studio so much," she said, standing and starting to clear the dishes. "The show's at the end of next month, and I've been trying to come up with something really special for it."

He coughed. "That's wonderful."

She stopped next to him as she reached for his plate. "You don't seem very excited."

"What?" He blinked. "No, of course I am." He forced a smile. "It's hard to see your little girl grow up, that's all."

She sighed and started for the sink. "Don't worry," she said.

"I'll still be here to do your dishes for many more years."

"That's not what I meant," he said, shifting in his seat. "It's just—"

"I'm joking, Dad. Calm yourself."

To his relief, the phone rang then, and he mumbled that he would get it and hurried from the room. In the hall he paused by the telephone table and took a deep breath. "Fìor Guesthouse," he said, switching to his most booming, professional tone as he picked up. "How can I help you?"

"Ah, Mr. McCloud, good evening." The line was crackly; the voice distant. "My name's Michael Talbot. I wonder if you might remember me—I was a customer of yours a few months ago. The end of August."

George cleared his throat and furrowed his brow, trying to remember a face. "Ah," he began. "I'm not quite sure..."

"Well," said the voice. "No matter. You must get far too many guests to remember us all."

A faint memory clicked into place. "Mr. Talbot!" he exclaimed. "We had to move you to a different room because of those idiots who missed the ferry!" The details were quickly filtering back to him. An Englishman, some sort of finance type. Had clung to Flora a bit. Told them they needed a timetable at the jetty.

There was a laugh at the other end of the line. "That was me, yes."

"Well, Mr. Talbot—what can I do for you today?"

He took a deep breath. "I was wondering," he said, speaking carefully, "if there was any time in the next month or so when I would be able to come see you."

Slipping immediately into his ordinary patter about the season being over, George began to flip through the weekly calendar they kept by the phone, looking for the next year's pages.

"Actually," the other man interrupted, "I'm not really coming for a holiday. I was hoping to discuss a business proposal."

George hesitated. "A business proposal."

"Yes—though I was hoping you could still put me up for one night. I'll happily pay, but I'm not much of a camper."

"A business proposal," George repeated, as in the kitchen the sound of rushing water grew louder. He told himself he had to tread carefully here—these big city types always thought they knew best. (Then again, the timetable had been a good idea, hadn't it?)

"Mr. McCloud?"

"I—what kind of business proposal?"

There was a pause on the other end of the line. "I'd rather leave the particulars until we can speak face-to-face. The phone is so impersonal."

"Surely you don't expect me to agree to a meeting without knowing what it's about, Mr. Talbot."

"No, I suppose not." The man sighed. "I'll cut to the chase, then: I'd like to move in."

"I beg your pardon?"

"Not into the guesthouse itself, of course," he added, "and not full-time—I could live in one of the village houses, maybe six or seven months a year. But I want to be there for a long enough stretch that I can get a proper feel for the place, and then start acting as a kind of...consultant, I suppose. To help you build your business, and improve it, and make sure your wonderful little guesthouse survives for future generations to enjoy."

George let out a choked sort of laugh. "Is that so?" Despite how obviously the speech had been rehearsed, he was curious, now, his defenses dropping. "And what makes you think we need your help?"

"It's not that I think you have a poor operation there, let

me be clear." He seemed to be gaining confidence. "But even in the few days I was visiting I saw several things that could be streamlined—not to mention a few needlessly empty beds losing you money." He took a deep breath. "So you're right, you don't need my help. But that doesn't mean you can't benefit from it."

"And what do you stand to gain from it, Mr. Talbot?" He looked down the hall towards the front door, imagining the empty village beyond it. "Don't tell me you're coming for the social scene."

"I'm twenty-five, Mr. McCloud, and I've been working at the same awful job for too long already. I want my chance to make a mark on the world, and I can't think of a better way to do it."

George hesitated for a few seconds, digesting it all. "Okay," he said, finally. "I'm intrigued." More than intrigued, really. Optimistic. Finally, here was someone to ease the burden on the rest of them. He ran his finger along the days in the calendar. "Would you be able to come the weekend of November twenty-fifth?" That would give him enough time to prepare Reenie for the idea. Ever since the rat catchers, she'd scowled every time the Trust was mentioned—he wasn't sure how she'd react to more outside meddling.

"Whatever's most convenient for you, Mr. McCloud. Thank you."

The water in the kitchen shut off.

"Don't thank me yet," said George. "I'm not guaranteeing anything." He heard Flora push the chairs under the table in the kitchen, and began hurrying the man off the phone; he was hanging up just as Flora stepped into the hallway. She gave him a quizzical look and asked who he'd been blathering away with for so long.

Even lying in bed that night, he wouldn't be able to articulate quite what had suddenly possessed him to lie to her, then; it was one of those decisions that his mind seemed to make without any conscious deliberation. Perhaps with her news about the art show still fresh in his mind, and his nagging worries lately about her losing interest in the guesthouse, he hadn't wanted to give her any reason—like an extra person on board—that might make it seem easier to leave; perhaps he didn't want to risk Reenie finding out before he'd told her himself. Or perhaps he didn't want to say anything yet in case the other man changed his mind—came to his senses, more like—and George ended up looking like a fool for believing him in the first place.

Whatever the reason, he shrugged at Flora's question and shook his head. "Some deaf biddy from the Borders asking about a room. I had to tell her everything three times." He grinned. "And then she didn't even bloody book anything!"

Flora laughed. "Better you than me, then." She nodded towards the pub and asked if he'd like to take another crack at the crossword with her.

"Aye," he said. "Why not?" And putting his arm around her, he guided them down the hallway—wondering, as they walked, what might suddenly be possible.

IX.

The Wednesday night before Flora's show she took the ferry to the mainland; though the opening wasn't until Saturday, she needed to get her piece there a few days early for the setup, so she thought she'd make a vacation of it (the hotel was putting her up for nothing, anyway). In the end she'd submitted a simple pastel landscape, nothing too ambitious—the sorts of people who bought paintings at a Highland hotel probably weren't looking for avantgarde, she decided—but after weeks of tinkering she was pleased with the result, and more pleased still when the manager at the hotel lifted it up and cooed that it was *splendid, Miss McCloud!* Miss McCloud! That alone made her giddy; she smiled herself to sleep that night.

It was a pleasant change, as well, to have some time away from home, where the atmosphere the last few weeks had been particularly tense. Her parents' apparent lack of pride or even interest in the exhibition was bad enough; after her father's flat reaction the night she told him, her mother was downright dismissive, as if Flora were little more than a child completing her first jigsaw puzzle. But far worse was the bitter discovery that they weren't even coming to the opening. When she'd asked, her father's face had turned bright red. *Oh no*, he said. *Your opening is* that *weekend?* Flora gave him a sharp look. *Um, yes, Dad—I told you last week. You circled it in the calendar.*

That was when, stuttering slightly and apologizing nearly every other word, George told her that, no, the date was circled in the calendar for something else. He'd arranged a business meeting for that day. Then it was Maureen's turn to give him a sharp look, and ask what kind of meeting—and his response was the other reason home had felt so uncomfortable lately: he wouldn't tell them. He claimed it was because he wasn't quite sure himself, yet, that some former guest had approached George with a business proposal—probably some retiree who'd discovered he hated his wife and wanted a way out of the house, thought Flora. But her father wanted them to hear this mysterious man out together, instead of saying anything to get them too excited. *Oh, yes*, crowed Maureen, *surprise visitors are always a real bloody excitement. Were you ever planning to mention this, or was it going to be a rabbit out of the hat sort of thing?* George assured them he had just been waiting for the right time, and continued to apologize, but still he wouldn't give them anything else—insisting it would just be speculation. *And I'm sorry about your opening, love*, he added, giving Flora an imploring stare. *I promise we'll make it over later in the month.*

That was some comfort, she supposed. But after the charm of her arrival in Fort William had worn off; after she spent two hours alone in her hotel room on Saturday afternoon, trying on outfits that all seemed impossibly frumpy or outdated; after she spent most of the opening skulking in the corner, her stomach cramping from having skipped both lunch and dinner in anxiety; and after the early train back to Mallaig in the morning, hungover from too much free champagne: she wished there'd been a friendly face to keep her company. Felt, for the first time in her life, that apart from the island itself, there were some things her *family* simply couldn't do for her.

The weather in Mallaig that morning was typical for November, a gloomy swirl of mist and a choking wind, and the crossing was a rough one. Flora hardly noticed, though, staring from the canteen windows in a trance; even once they'd docked at Fìor she took a minute or two to snap back to reality, gathering her things and slipping to the loo only when the crew came through to clear the cabin before the return passengers boarded, and finally hurrying down the gangplank with only a minute or two to spare before departure. As she reached the jetty she thought she caught a whiff of some familiar scent, one she couldn't quite place—until she looked up at the ship and glimpsed a flash of a familiar red coat in one of the windows.

No, she'd told herself, remembering the way that coat had rustled in her arms all those months earlier. *It couldn't be.*

The exhibition, despite Flora's nervousness, was an undeniable success. A red dot adorned her piece's frame by the end of the week, and the sole picture accompanying the show's coverage in the local paper was of her, a nervous grin on her face, left arm drawn protectively across her body and gripping her right elbow. But it wasn't until April, and Bella's return to the island for the summer, that the pull of her artwork became impossible to ignore.

It was still a few weeks before the guesthouse opened for the season, and Flora had escaped to the Stùc for the day to help Bella settle in. At first, as they unpacked her supplies and reorganized the studio to her liking, they chatted away as usual—but then, halfway through tacking a sketch to the wall, Bella abruptly changed the subject.

"You need to apply to art college." She pushed the paper's

last corner to the wall with her thumb. "This year, ideally, to capitalize on your momentum from that sale in the winter." She took a step back and cocked her head, checking the sketch was straight, and finally turned to Flora. "If this—" she motioned to the far corner, where a few of Flora's drawings were yet to be taken down—"is really what you want to do with your life, it's time you started pursuing it more seriously."

Flora objected that she pursued it as seriously as she could, given her other commitments, but Bella waved her off, not listening. "You don't have other commitments, dear, you have guilt, and that's only because your mother actively cultivates it."

"Oh, she does no—"

"There's no reason you have to stay here, Flora, other than that you think your parents can't manage without you. But your brother will have finished school in a year or two, and until then I'm sure they can get by." There was that well practiced smirk again. "Besides, what about Prince Charming? When's he arriving?"

Mumbling, Flora told her it was the next day, annoyed at the reminder; she was far more ambivalent about Michael's return than either Bella or her father. Had spent the months since finding out, in fact, alternately dreading and fantasizing about it. Sometimes it was the predictable lovelorn stuff—long kisses, frantic undressings, that sort of thing—but more often lately she'd found herself imagining the guesthouse growing so successful with Michael's help that she was able to leave it and him behind altogether, and retain an agent, and never have to worry about her parents growing old again.

Of course, it didn't help that the intent behind his return remained maddeningly vague. The few times she'd answered the phone to him, the past few months, her father had rushed her off the line before she could get in more than a few words, and she didn't dare call him herself. So all she knew, still, was that he would be there for *a few months to get a feel for things*, as her father had explained it; she had no idea if it were just for this year or for several, no idea how closely he'd linger, and no idea, worst of all, where she figured in any of it. Because there had been something between them when he'd visited the previous summer, hadn't there? Surely she hadn't imagined it. Surely it had at least crossed his mind when he was drawing up his plan.

"It's not as easy as that," she added, now, after a long pause. "Mum and Dad are barely scraping by as it is, Michael or no Michael. I can't just leave them in the lurch."

Bella waved her off again and reached for another sketch. "Look, I'm no business expert. But it's their business, Flora, not yours. You shouldn't be forced to stay here if it isn't what you want." There were a few more moments of silence as, on her tiptoes, she pressed the drawing to the wall—and when she turned again Flora thought she saw, briefly, a glimmer of sympathy, or compassion, or *something* beyond that cool exterior for a change. "At least think about it," said Bella. "Please?"

"Fine," said Flora, harrumphing. "I will."

And of course she did, at length, reading and re-reading the prospectus Bella pushed on her as she was leaving, until she could recite each of its exciting claims from memory. With only a few years' study she would be able to *innovate! Synthesize! Explore her individual style!* She would work with *renowned international artists*, and receive *complementary lectures in literature and philosophy!* It all sounded utterly wonderful—but that only got her more annoyed at Bella for making her consider it. Because her parents couldn't get by without her, no matter what Bella thought. And even once Trevor returned from school, even if Michael stayed long term, could she really in good conscience swan off to Edinburgh and leave the two of them as trapped here as she was now?

Besides, once Michael actually arrived, she quickly wrote off his potential as a helper around the guesthouse. If anything he made her work there harder, following her around with a spiral-bound black and red notebook, the sight of which she quickly came to dread, and practically demanding that she explain every aspect of her duties, no matter how piddling. *Why do you have a separate grocery order each day? Why do you do laundry so often? What do you do with food scraps when you're clearing meals?* When he wasn't badgering her he was eating up her parents' spare time, insisting on endless meetings about suppliers and room rates and marketing, and a whole heap of other issues they weren't accustomed to considering—never mind justifying. And although he promised he would start to lend a hand once he properly understood how everything worked, that mythical moment remained always just over the horizon, even as the guesthouse leeched more and more from Flora's life. In the entire month of May, she managed to eke out only two afternoons to sit alone with her sketchbook, and the prospect of devoting any serious time to her work seemed less feasible than ever.

As if the dashing of that dream wasn't bad enough, none of her fevered imagined passions with Michael materialized, either. Her previous reservations about falling for him, too fast or at all, had evaporated the moment she'd seen him again, a few specks of grey in his stubble and his eyes the color of black tea. His first week on the island she appeared almost every night at the front door of the old Leslie house, where he'd moved in, and assumed that before long they would fall into each other's arms. But then the cold shower: he greeted her with a polite professionalism each time, as if the Michael who'd visited the island as a tourist were some embarrassing past self to be forgotten.

Logically, Flora told herself she should welcome being spurned, trying to recall all her past hang-ups about her interest in him. But his remoteness instead woke her instinctive stubbornness—reinforced by Bella, who assured Flora he was only playing hard to get—and even as the season moved into full swing she pursued him with ever more brazen tactics, visiting him with bottles of wine, and offering him massages, and pouting with exaggerated disappointment whenever he tried to send her on her way. When at last she elicited a response, it wasn't the one she wanted. It was June, and she'd announced, after another evening in his living room, that she was too tired to go home and would rather stay at his. *Oh, for God's sake, Flora!* He snapped, and told her very firmly that nothing was going to happen between them. That her parents would throw him out in a second if they suspected he was *corrupting their practically teenaged daughter*, and that it was better, surely, to have his platonic company than nothing at all.

She asked him if he really believed they didn't already suspect something—a foolish move, in hindsight, as it only strengthened his resolve—but later his comment gave her pause. Not that she thought her parents would care that much; her mother had only been a year or two older when she'd married, and if Flora had to get involved with anyone she was sure they'd prefer Michael to a man living full-time on the mainland. But it had at least opened her mind to other possibilities with him, beyond romance or nothing at all. *His platonic company*, he'd called it; would that really be so bad? She'd been enjoying the extra person to spend time with, after all, especially one closer to her age than her parents or even Bella, and the idea of a *friend*, she realized, was every bit as appealing as the idea of...what? A lover? A boyfriend? Not that it made any difference for the next few months, as in the wake of their confrontation the few encounters they did have, usually in the pub, were more awkward than anything else.

Once the summer was over, though—once the bustle of customers had died down, once Flora's days had opened up again and she had the time to sit and think—she gradually resumed her evening visits. And now, though he was still impeccably professional, he greeted her more warmly; after so many stiff conversations at the guesthouse they both seemed to exhale—as if the whole, self-conscious summer they'd been saving up stories, knowing that eventually they'd drop the pretense. Which was a relief, for Flora, though it did little to resolve the same old, niggling questions. What did he really want from her? What, come to that, did she really want from him?

Adding to her frustration as the autumn spooled away were the long afternoons she spent working on the Stùc, reclaimed again from Bella. The work itself was a joy, as usual, but that only served, now, to underscore her passion for it, and how inadequately she could pursue it here. Some days she got so happily absorbed she forgot the time and ended up stranded by the high tide, forced to sheepishly call her parents and tell them to eat without her. (Bella continued to keep a working phone year round. *This way I have a number to give out to all the bores who corner me at parties*, she said.)

And at last, caught again and again by the unforgiving one-two of her fantasies of art school and her ambiguous feelings for Michael, Flora cracked. Decided she had to get out, or at least explore the possibility. So one night a few weeks before Trevor returned for Christmas—only one before Michael left until the spring—she announced to her parents at the end of dinner that she wanted to talk to them about something.

"Can't it wait?" asked Maureen, as if the thought of postponing her evening cleaning by even a few minutes left her physically in pain.

"No, Mum," said Flora, steeling herself. "It can't."

"Fine," she huffed, glancing at the clock above the door. "What is it?"

"Well..." She looked to her father, hoping for a supportive smile, but he seemed as anxious as she felt. "Before I say anything," she started again, "please remember this is only an idea. I haven't made any decisions, and even if I did I would make sure it didn't affect you or the business. You know I'd never dream of abandoning you."

Her mother shifted in her chair. Flora recalled, suddenly, the night that Barry had announced he was leaving, right in this very room and at this very table and at this very time of the evening, to her and her mother and Trevor. Remembered the way her own fingers had seemed to ice up, and how her throat had tightened at the prospect of his departure. She cursed herself for not thinking of it sooner—because if she was remembering that scene right now, she was sure her mother must be too.

"You know how much I love my work, though," she pressed on, determined not to lose her momentum. "I've been drawing and painting for as long as I can remember, and I'm getting—I think I'm getting—pretty good at it." She swallowed. Her mother's face was darkening; her father's was still plastered with an uneasy smile. "And to be honest, it's something I can see myself taking further. As a career. That piece in Fort William sold in three days." As she'd rehearsed this speech in her head earlier she'd debated leaving that part out; despite their promises, her parents had kept making excuses and never visited the exhibition, a sore point between them that the intervening seasons hadn't completely healed. In the end, though, she could hardly make the argument without it, could she?

"The thing is," she continued, "there's only so much more I can do on my own, especially with everything I have to do around here. Bella thinks I need to take some time off and go to art school if I want to get any further, and I—I think maybe I want to. I think maybe I should." She sat back in her chair. "What about you?"

"*I* think," her mother said, finally, her cheeks flushed red and her voice as quiet and distant as if she'd been in another room, "that it is entirely out of the question."

Flora gritted her teeth. "Can't we at least discuss it?"

"Yes, Reenie," said George, slowly, his eyes still fixed on Flora. "Maybe we shou—"

"Oh, be quiet, George." She turned to him, her eyes bulging, her voice growing louder. "That woman putting these ridiculous ideas in her head is bad enough—don't you bloody start." She looked at Flora again, her face almost purple now, her breathing heavy. "Real people don't get to run off and be artists whenever they please, Flora!" She wiped her hand across her forehead, where a few beads of sweat were starting to form. "The sooner you accept that, the better."

"Mum, this isn't about running off to be an artist, it's about developing a talent! About making a living doing something that I'm good at and enjoy! What's so wrong with that?"

"Oh, get your head out of the bloody clouds!" She was struggling to talk, now, her breathing labored.

"Fine," said Flora. "Forget I said anything. I'll just go back upstairs and await your orders." She pushed away from the table, sending her chair clattering to the floor, and started for the hallway as her father called for her to wait, standing up to follow her.

But then there was that haunting sound behind them, the sound Flora would never quite forget: her mother gasping, her chair sliding against the floor as she tried to stand up, and the deep *thunk* as she fell against the table for support. Flora and her father spun around in time to see her slump to the floor on her hands and knees, sweat beading across her face like condensation on a glass. "I can't breathe," she croaked, tugging desperately at the collar of her cardigan, and without thinking Flora was running to the phone with a frantic prayer that her mother not die because of *this*.

She didn't, of course. Didn't even come close; when Dr. Nicol arrived from Rum an hour later, and the helicopter paramedics from the mainland a few minutes after that, Maureen seemed already to have recovered. *Probably a panic attack*, the doctor told them, once he'd examined her and sent her to bed. *Good thing, too*, he added, voice dropping; if it really had been her heart, he never would have arrived in time.

Michael, who had come running from his house at the sound of the helicopter, nodded gravely at that assessment, clearly aghast at how suddenly death could stalk the island. He asked if it would be worth buying a defibrillator for the guesthouse, just in case. The doctor laughed. *Not unless one of you wants to learn how to use one!* he said, and that seemed to be the end of it: George went upstairs to check on Maureen; the helicopter buzzed away; and the doctor, with one of his customary wistful remarks about how empty the island seemed these days, said his goodbyes and set off, leaving Flora and Michael alone in the vestibule.

They looked at each other.

"Are you all right?" he asked, putting a hand on her arm.

"I don't know," she said, at last. "That was...unexpected." She shook off his hand from where it still rested at her elbow, and started down the hallway. "Drink?" she said, over her shoulder.

Shrugging, he followed her.

"I only wanted to suggest it," she told him, once she'd explained the whole thing. She was standing behind the bar, drinking one of the more recent elaborate cocktails she'd invented, while he sat in front of it sipping the same beer he'd had his first night there. "Test the waters, you know? See how they'd react." She snorted. "I suppose we answered that question."

Michael tried to convince her that things might not be as bad as they seemed; told her it was unlikely a full-blown panic attack could be caused by something as harmless as a discussion about art school. Probably, he told her, Maureen was under some other stress right now, and Flora's timing had just been unfortunate. The last straw.

"The last straw!" She laughed bitterly. "And what was the first bloody straw, eh? Or the second or the third? It's not exactly one of your high pressure investment banks around here."

Michael gazed down at his drink, in that lost puppy sort of way she'd always found so infuriatingly charming. "I just mean," he said, "that there might be something on her mind you don't know about."

Again, Flora pooh-poohed him. There weren't many ways to keep a secret around here, she said—if anything stressful enough to send her mother into a fit like that were going on, they'd know about it.

As soon as she'd said it, though, she began to wonder. Never mind that night; her mother's behavior the whole year—ever since Flora had returned, actually, if she thought about it—had been so inexplicably different from what she remembered growing up, so dour and pessimistic and solitary, that maybe Michael was right. Otherwise, the only explanation seemed to be that her mother had simply become meaner and more selfish, and despite all the skirmishes they'd had since Flora moved home, she didn't quite believe that was possible.

In any case, her mother's panic attack, whatever the cause, had rattled Flora enough that she was ready to give up on the art school idea, just like that, as she sipped at her drink behind the bar. She imagined the coming years, her time on the Stùc growing shorter and shorter as her parents grew older and more infirm. Imagined Bella giving up on her. Imagined her pictures fading on the studio walls, and finally imagined herself, in her room, withering away alone.

And then she looked at Michael again.

"At least I still have you," she murmured, and reached across the bar. Her fingers brushed against the top of his hand, and she felt the faint thud of his pulse beneath the skin. His eyes dropped, his expression inscrutable—but he didn't pull away. At least, not at first. But after a few more moments he raised his head and met her eyes, and gently withdrew his hand.

"I should go," he said, taking one more sip of beer and setting the glass down, still half full. She fancied she saw his fingers shaking a little. "Goodnight, Flora."

She sighed, and whispered goodnight back as she watched him stand and leave; heard the creak of the hallway floorboards as he stepped into his shoes at the front door. Finally, she reached under the counter and dimmed the pub lights until she could see the faint glow of his torch through the windows, bobbing away down the path, and eventually disappearing altogether.

X.

It was a quiet Christmas that year, the atmosphere awkward, acrimonious. Maureen had no desire to revisit the embarrassment of her panic attack, and Flora none to dwell on the veto of art school, and in the extensive detours necessary to avoid talking about either they mostly talked about nothing at all. Even with George trying valiantly to bridge the long silences between them, their hours together—at meals, and around the tree, and on their habitual Christmas Day constitutional—ended up feeling more like time with their demons.

Trevor also tried his best to right the situation during his few weeks at home, suggesting cards or a board game after dinner the way they'd always done before Barry left, or, when that didn't work, pulling out old photo albums of holidays past—as if to jolt everyone into remembering how happy they could be. None of it worked, though, and the rest of them, George included, were glad when Trevor returned to school. With him gone and the holidays over, they could drop any pretense of familial harmony and retreat without guilt—without as much guilt, anyway—to their own, private corners: Flora to her bedroom or the Stùc, Maureen to the kitchen, and George to the pub and his crosswords.

With the McClouds the only ones left on the island, of course, their silent feuding couldn't last long; some deeper urge for company and conversation forced them, after a few more months, to swallow their misgivings and seek each other out. Flora began to rejoin George in the pub at nights, and she and Maureen began to warm to each other during their dinnertime conversations—and when one evening in March Maureen suggested a game of rummy, George and Flora both agreed without any prodding.

Sometimes, though, it seemed to George as if that meager progress had come too late. In the months since Christmas Flora's routine had absorbed more hours on the Stùc than ever before— she regularly stayed the night there now, stranded or not—and the idea of art school was clearly still sticking in her mind. On a sunny morning in April she brought it up again, this time with George on his own as they carried home the shopping together; asked him if it was really that unreasonable. Asked him if *he* thought it was ridiculous.

For an uncomfortably long time he'd said nothing, listening to the faint shearwater calls over the wind as he tried to come up with a suitably diplomatic answer. But in the end all he could manage was: "Oh, I don't know, Flora. It's complicated." He'd entertained some feeble hope that the vague response would satisfy her, but he was quickly disappointed; she responded without waiting a single beat.

"So you don't think it's entirely impossible?"

He turned to look at her more closely, and replied carefully. "No. I suppose I don't. But do you really want to put this on the table again? After what happened last time? You know your mother has to be a part of this discussion."

"But that's just it, Dad!" she said, her voice rising. "She doesn't want to have the discussion! It's only such a button because she makes it one." He could see the tendons in her neck tensing as she carried on. "What's wrong with wanting to get out and see the world beyond this bloody island and this bloody guesthouse?"

At that, finally, she paused. "Sorry," she said. "I didn't mean for it to come out that way."

He shook his head. "I don't think there's anything wrong with wanting to get out and see the world," he said, "and I won't stop you if you bring it up again." He readjusted his grip on the shopping bag. "But I wish you wouldn't. For my sake, if not hers."

They walked the rest of the way home in silence, after that. And in fact, she didn't bring it up again—but that wasn't the end of it, either.

It was a few days later, and George had gone out for another morning walk, this time on his own, to try and clear his head. Since Flora's outburst he'd been able to think of little else, not because he'd been upset by it but because, to his surprise, he had never considered art college the way she'd put it to him then, as a window to life outside the island—even though his own time at university had been the same thing, really, hadn't it? How had it never occurred to him that his daughter might have that itch as well?

There were a few cottonthreads of cloud overhead as he wandered off the road and into the heather, and in front of him the hillside was a rich palette of color: bright green grass and deep brown soil, and the yellow and purple dots of the spring's flowers. Every few minutes he heard rabbits scurrying away in the brush at his approach, but other than that and the occasional breeze, the air was still and quiet.

It was days like this that reminded him why he loved the place so much. Even in Edinburgh's nicest parks he had always felt sure, when the crocuses and daffodils pushed through the ground each spring, or the trees in Princes' Street Gardens turned golden each autumn, that the island could have conjured something prettier. And that, he supposed, was his biggest reservation about Flora leaving: the suspicion that she didn't feel the same way. More and more since returning from St. Fillan's she'd seemed to outgrow the island, to cultivate sophistication beyond what the place could possibly sustain, and he doubted that if she left she'd ever want to come back. She was seduced by the glamour and charm and apparently limitless potential of the mainland, it was clear. Enjoyed the freedom it promised—the illusion of freedom, anyway.

He was disappointed, just as when Barry moved away, that he'd been unable to give the island a similar allure. Every walk he'd dragged the children on, every story he'd told, every encouragement to explore as they pleased—in the end it had all been futile. It was Trevor, actually, to whom George had given the least attention, who seemed the most attached to home; when he was younger he had constantly collected things from around the island—bird feathers, and strange-shaped pebbles, and flowers that George would find later, pressed between the pages of his ledgers— and George's old photos, when Trevor had discovered them, had left him especially smitten. The little scamp had actually pinched a few, thinking nobody would notice, so they'd bought him his own instamatic for his birthday that year, and he'd spent hours with it out around the village, taking so many rolls of film they'd had to enforce limits on the number he was allowed—it was costing too much to keep sending it to the mainland for development.

George chuckled to himself as he reached the crest of the hill he'd been climbing, and stopped for a moment to sit on a mound of rocks in the brush. He'd always thought *develop film* sounded like crosswordese, and he often tried to write it into clues in his head. *Develop film with no Scots to irritate (7). Most of film developed before drug tale becomes biopic (4,5).* Occasionally he would try out some of them on Flora, who of course saw instantly right through them, leaving him to wonder whether he should be embarrassed for himself or proud for her.

That pretty well captured how he felt about Flora in general these days. Her frequent flashes of brilliance only served as proof that all the other things she did to bewilder him—and there were lots—were simply beyond his grasp. The cocktails, for instance. She was constantly soliciting interesting new ingredients from visitors to the bar, usually some tropical juice or liquor, and when one of them struck her fancy she'd add a bottle to the bar order and spend hours trying it out in new recipes. Then, each month, she'd sit down at the old Remington in George's office and type out a fresh set of drink menus filled with silly-named concoctions: *The Perestroika*, for example, a martini made with lime juice and white rum, or *The Culloden*, a mixture of chartreuse and single malt. Nobody ever ordered the bloody things, naturally, but despite the cost he could never bring himself to put his foot down. It was one of the few things she still genuinely seemed to like about the pub—and anyway, on the few nights she'd persuaded him to try one, it was usually very good.

Worse than the cocktails were the books: she read mountains of them, and not the mysteries and romances Reenie ordered from the supermarket. No, Flora read books that intimidated him, books he remembered seeing in the libraries of his mainland relatives; books those same relatives had lukewarmly recommended to his younger self, with a disdain suggesting they doubted he'd get much out of it. And perhaps, because of that, he didn't. Never finished *Pride and Prejudice* or *Oliver Twist*, never even started *Madame Bovary*, and certainly never came close to enjoying any of the books his daughter now regularly tore through.

Worst by far, though, was her art. It was actually fitting, he thought, sitting there with the sun warming his neck and the

George cleared his throat. There was a pause at the other end of the line, and he could almost hear her reassessing the situation. "Mr. McCloud."

"Hello, Ms. Fowkes. What can I help you with?"

"I need to get in touch with your daughter." She took a deep breath. "I've managed to get her a place at Edinburgh for this autumn."

No. The words settled like a damp cloak on his shoulders as Bella explained the details: she'd shown her colleagues at the art school some photographs of Flora's work and they'd been wildly impressed—and though it was far too late to apply through normal channels, they could guarantee her a clearing place as long as she filed the paperwork within a week.

"This is a fantastic opportunity for her, Mr. McCloud, but she needs to go to the mainland to get the forms first thing tomorrow. First thing yesterday, really." She left a delicate pause. "I know you and your wife have mixed feelings about this, and about me. But I'm trusting you to do the right thing."

George nodded slowly. "I will," he said, letting the numbers on the telephone go blurry in his vision. "I will."

That same morning Flora had woken in a foul mood. This would be her eighth day straight rising early to cross to the studio, where she'd been desperately trying to put the last touches on an oil figure study before they opened the following week. The stupid thing was already taking far longer than she'd expected, a fact she blamed mostly on her parents' incessant piling on of chores—even if in the back of her mind she suspected it had more to do with her loneliness in Michael's months-long absence, and worse, the specter of the approaching season. If she couldn't make progress on her work now, how would she ever manage when they opened?

As she shrugged on her coat that morning she was getting

ready to give herself a typically glum answer, when she opened the front door and came face to face with Michael. "Oh!" Her bag slid from her shoulder. "Hello. How long have you been back?"

He smiled. "Just since last night. I was coming over to make sure you hadn't all abandoned the place."

Flora tried to return the smile, though in her current mood it felt more like a grimace. "Nope—still here."

"And back to the drawing board, it looks like." He motioned to her bag with a wink that she supposed was meant to look rakish. "Excuse the pun."

"Groan."

Rubbing absent-mindedly at a razor nick on his jaw, he asked if he would finally be allowed to see the studio this year. She narrowed her eyes. In more ways than she usually cared to admit, she'd become a lot like Bella, and that was especially true of her sense of privacy about the studio. Nobody had ever been invited to see it, not even Michael, not even when he'd badgered her repeatedly the previous year. Not even when she'd been desperate to seduce him.

"We'll see," she said, at last, moving past him to leave.

"Oh, go on." He took a step to the side to block her way.

"Sorry." She kept pushing past.

He called after her. "No exceptions? Not even for a clueless old Sassenach like me?"

She stopped, sighing, and thought back to the last time they'd been on the Stùc together, in the school, that first summer he'd visited. How exhilarated she had felt. She wondered if he was thinking of the same thing; if he ever thought of it, as fondly and as often as she did.

"Fine," she said, turning to face him. "What are you doing this afternoon?"

His eyes lit up. "Sounds like I'm visiting you! How's three o'clock?"

She shrugged. "Tide should be out again by then."

"Fantastic," he said, and disappeared inside.

It might actually be quite nice having him over, she told herself, dew soaking into her shoes as she trudged towards the beach. Even their short conversation just now had lifted her mood more quickly than anything else that month, and after his winter away it would be nice to catch up. Besides, wasn't she always wishing more people could see her work? If she wasn't going to art school any time soon she might as well start bringing people to her.

By the time she got to the Stùc, though, she was already regretting the invitation. The prospect of his arrival left her too jittery to concentrate, and certainly too jittery to strip naked and sit in front of the full-length mirror as her current painting required—she'd been uncomfortable enough lounging around undressed to begin with, after Bella had insisted that nobody would take her seriously if she couldn't paint a decent nude. But with the thought of Michael walking in on her—even though they'd agreed a specific time, even though the tide was in, even though she'd double- and triple-checked the front door was locked—it was positively unbearable. Instead she sat fully clothed, chipping away at superficial details on the portrait's face, and when her watch passed two she gave up altogether, covering the canvas with a cloth and turning to a book until he arrived, promptly, at three.

Once he'd taken off his shoes—Bella's rule, not hers—she led him to the kitchen, ignoring his eager stares towards the studio and insisting they ought to sit down for tea first. He made some comment about being able to get tea at home, as if he thought she were stalling—but now that she'd admitted someone to her private space, she simply wanted to do it right. She was already planning out the full tour she would give him: the living room, and the sofa where she sat by the fire on the nights she didn't go home; the spot in the orchard where she'd hidden as a child; and the guest bedroom upstairs that she'd now made hers, with a heavy feather pillow from home, and a few books lined up on the nightstand. She would even take him to Bella's room, where she'd lain awake all those years ago, Trevor by her side, listening to the storm outside the windows and Barry's shouting outside the door, and imagining what it would be like to live there all the time.

"So," Michael said, taking a seat at the kitchen table as she fetched tea makings from the cupboard. "This is your secret hideaway."

She laughed. "I don't know that I'd call it secret." The kettle was beginning to rattle as the water heated up inside. "It's not much of a hideaway, either, since Mum and Dad realized the phone was still connected."

As if on cue, the hall telephone began to ring, but she made no move to answer it; when he asked if she was going to she told him she didn't, usually, that it was Bella's line, and that she'd already ignored it a few times that day—and that if it were her parents calling they'd be more persistent. Also on cue, the ringing stopped. "See?" she said. "Not even a minute. Mum lets it ring for ten sometimes."

They chatted for a while longer, but Michael was clearly antsy to get on with it, his leg bouncing up and down under the table and his gaze wandering every minute or two from Flora to the wall clock to the door—so they picked up their mostly full mugs and carried them around the house as she led him from room to room. He seemed pleasantly surprised that he was being shown more than just the studio, nodding intently as she pointed out each of her private landmarks. And just as in the schoolhouse on his first visit, she was in turn pleasantly surprised that he found it all so interesting.

As they made their way downstairs and towards the studio at last, the phone began to ring again.

"You really don't find that annoying?" he asked, shaking his head.

She looked up from her place a few steps below him, and shrugged. "They'll give up eventually."

In the studio itself Flora stood quietly by the door while Michael looked around, remembering Bella's advice before Fort William that she should let her work speak for itself. But Michael's progress from piece to piece was torturously slow, and with each pause, each frown, each silence, her stomach tensed—until she couldn't bear it any longer.

"For God's sake!" she blurted out. "It's not a bloody museum!"

He glanced at her from the corner of his eye and grinned. "I know," he said. "If it were I'd have some plaques on the wall to tell me what I'm supposed to think."

She laughed nervously.

"It's all very good." He turned to face her now. "Honest. I'm genuinely impressed." He nodded towards a messy charcoal still life a few feet away. "I especially like that one. I may have to commission you."

Her spirits soared at that—and then, when he asked if she was still thinking about art college, plummeted again.

"No," she said, walking to the window. A few rain clouds were rolling in from the northwest. "And don't you start." What was it about these bloody mainlanders that made them think she could just up and disappear?

She felt the floorboards shift as he came towards her. Felt his hand rest on her shoulder. "What's wrong?" he asked.

"Nothing," she said, folding her arms. "I just can't go to art college, and I wish people would stop asking about it."

"Sorry." His hand lingered on her shoulder. "I thought maybe with your brother coming back next year—"

"Forget it," she sighed. "It's fine."

He still hadn't moved his hand, and before he could she turned slightly and rested her head on his shoulder.

"You know," he said, finally. "I'm here, too. I'm sure we could cope without you."

"I told you, forget it—I'm not going."

The phone rang again, for longer this time. They waited for it to stop.

"If it's any consolation," he said. "I'm glad you'll be sticking around."

She nuzzled her head against his neck. "Are you?"

There was a faint rumble of thunder in the distance.

"Of course I am." He slid his arm all the way around her; still she didn't move.

"I thought you were only interested in the business," she whispered, her fingers tingling. "I was too young, you said. The boss's daughter."

With her ear still to his neck, his reply sounded strangely amplified. "I don't know." His hand tensed against her ribcage. "Maybe I was kidding myself."

She raised her head, now, and stared at him. "What?"

"Never mind," he said. "Nothing."

"Michael." She turned so that they were face to face, with only a few centimeters between them. She could smell the faint, grassy aroma of tea on his breath; the powdery scent of laundry on his shirt.

"Flora, I—"

She kissed him before he could finish, straining forward on her tiptoes. Stumbled backwards as he pushed his hands against her waist. Ended up pressed to the window.

The phone rang again.

"Oh, for fuck's sake." She pulled away from him; slipped

out from beneath his arms and ran into the hallway. Her fingers were still tingling, and the palms of her hands, and her arms all the way up to her shoulders. She picked up the receiver and growled hello.

"Flora?" It was her father. "I—your mother and I think you should make your way home for the evening."

She groaned. "Why, Dad? What is it?"

There was a long, sad silence.

"Dad?"

"There's a big storm on its way," he said at last. "We're worried about you."

A creamy shade of white began to spread beneath Flora's fingernails as she gripped the edge of the telephone table. "I'm fine, Dad. I'll leave soon."

"Flora, please." His voice sounded strange. Harder than usual.

Michael had come into the hallway, and stood listening as she gave in, exasperated. Once she'd hung up, he shook his head. "Maybe it's a sign."

She scowled. "It's a sign I should take this bloody thing off the hook."

"No." He walked over to her. "You might not mind staying over here for the night, but it would look pretty bad if I did."

She hung her arms around his neck, pouting. "They might not notice."

"Flora."

"Oh, fine." She let her hands drop and pushed past him to turn off the studio lights.

They made the walk across the isthmus in silence, dark seeping down the sides of the sky and their footsteps in the spring grass the only sound between them; their goodbye outside the guesthouse was just as quiet, fumbling, a handshake becoming a pat on the arm becoming a kiss on the cheek, but stopping there, clouds of breath dissolving all around them and the air the color of blue eyes. Inside, she took off her shoes, and had climbed halfway up the stairs, a faint smile on her face and the small of her back still humming from where it had pushed up against the window, when her father appeared in the shadows on the landing.

"We left some soup on the stove if you're hungry."

She shook her head and mumbled that she wasn't, and after mechanically giving him a hug she started towards her room. It was only once she'd flopped down on her bed, that smile still on her face, and lain for almost a minute with the lights off, staring out her window at the streak of the Milky Way, that she finally heard her father's study door click shut.

XI.

Flora often imagined, in the following weeks, what sort of leisurely romance she and Michael might have enjoyed if the circumstances had been different. She pictured months of secret meetings on the Stùc, and brief encounters, when they couldn't bear to wait, under the cover of night by the guesthouse back door; pictured mornings wrapped up in the bed sheets at his cottage, and afternoons spent reading each other their favorite books, and evenings sitting on the studio floor, drinking wine and watching the sunset through the giant windows. After a few months of that—once he'd conquered his silly fear of her parents banishing him forever—they'd have made their relationship public, and quickly entered a pleasant, gradual descent into domesticity and marriage and children, taking over the guesthouse the way her father had always hoped one of the children would.

It might have been nice, she'd think to herself—and then would shudder, relieved, and be thankful things had taken another turn.

The morning after she left Michael on the doorstep, she started awake in her clothes a little before six-thirty, light pouring in through her still open shutters. Rather than leaving for the Stùc she busied herself downstairs with the week's accumulated chores, assuming it would be only a few hours until he returned to sweep her off her feet—but the whole day there was no sign of him. She waited right through 'til the stars were out again, forgoing any time at the studio and her languishing figure painting, and by the time she sat down for dinner she was scolding herself for wasting an entire day. She debated seeking him out at his cottage herself that evening, but each hour she'd sat waiting her confidence from the night before had dripped away, as if a dream, until she was convinced he wasn't coming over because he regretted what had happened.

So doing the washing up that night she was in a bleak mood, standing in silence while her mother passed her dishes to dry and her father, frowning, retreated with his crossword as usual. Or not quite as usual: gone was any suggestion that she join him. Anxious that he too had somehow lost interest in her, she started towards the pub as soon as the kitchen was clean, wiping her hands against her jeans, but as she passed the phone it began to ring and she stopped to answer it; picked up to Bella's voice just as she heard the almighty clatter in the pub, her father practically falling through the door. He stood there watching, a panicked look in his eyes as her confusion quickly gave way to anger, and once she'd thanked Bella and reassured her she'd be on the first ferry the next morning, she slammed down the phone and stalked towards George, who was still cowering in the pub doorway. "What were you thinking?" she screamed, spittle flying from her mouth. "I thought you were on my side!"

"I was going to tell you," he stammered back, looking at the floor. "I was. I promise."

But she didn't listen, couldn't listen, just spun and pushed past her mother—summoned from the kitchen by the commotion—

and stomped upstairs, wedging a chair beneath her room's door handle and ignoring his every entreaty to come out. The next morning she woke with the first light again, this time on purpose, and was out of the house and on the road to the jetty before either of her parents could intercept her. She waited there for three hours, shivering in the damp morning air and watching alternately for the ferry on the horizon and her father coming towards her down the road. He didn't, which somehow infuriated her more.

On the mainland she climbed on the first train south and made her way straight to St. Fillan's, where the delighted career officer supplied her with a university application and talked her through completing it. That done, she dashed straight out again, not pausing until the form was safely in the post at Fort William. Only then did she exhale, and only once she was back at the dock in Mallaig, her mind slowly unwinding, did she realize that she hadn't thought to stop and visit Trevor. And more startling still: had spent the entire day—and the entire restless night before it—without thinking once of Michael. She imagined him coming to see her, finally, and finding her gone, and felt an odd sort of guilt that she'd forgotten him so easily—but when he finally turned up to see her that night it was clear she needn't have. He hadn't even known she'd left.

"I'm sorry I didn't come sooner," he said, sitting down next to her in the living room. (She was pointedly avoiding both the pub and her father that night, after a cursory, mostly silent family dinner.) "The truth is, I didn't really know what I was going to say." He'd been talking to the floor until now, but here he looked up. "I've had some time to think things through the last few days, though, and...I think—I mean, I'd like—"

She didn't let him finish; she already felt so sure in her decision, so serene, there seemed little point in dragging things out.

"I'm leaving," she said.

He stopped, confused. "You're what?"

"I'm leaving," she repeated. "At the end of the summer. I'm going to Edinburgh."

"But..." He shook his head as she continued to stare calmly at him. "But what about your parents? What about all the work you need to do here?" His face flushed. "What about me?"

"I'm sure my parents can work out a way to cope," she told him. "You said so yourself." She cocked her head. "And what about you, anyway? It took you three days to decide what you wanted. Is that supposed to make me feel hopeful?" She thought back again to that moment in the studio those few days earlier, the one that had left her so electrified, but still she didn't waver—because now she thought back, too, to the night of the Leavers' Dinner at St. Fillan's, and the subsequent drunken groping; to the first boy she'd properly, privately kissed, at Maisie's behest, after the lads had raided the lassies' dormitory one night; to her distant, youthful fantasies about Tam. And she asked herself what the difference was between all of it, really, as long as she got out now.

He was looking at the floor again. "I just thought..." He swallowed. "I thought we had something." He shut his eyes tightly for a moment, and then looked up at her. "And I don't mean what happened the other day, I mean everything. Even the first time I came here there was something—wasn't there?"

That confirmation, finally, that she'd correctly guessed his feelings all along, almost made her crack. At least made her consider leaning forward and kissing him again. But she knew that would be the wrong decision, for both of them, so instead she stared back, trying to compose an expression that looked both sympathetic and firm, and took a deep breath. Reminded herself of all the justifications she'd already cooked up for herself, that she wasn't abandoning anyone this way, wasn't *choosing* to apply to art school, wasn't putting anyone second. Was only taking advantage of an opportunity that had presented itself. Reminded herself that if she got to Edinburgh and suddenly had a change of heart, realized she had to drop everything and run home and fall into Michael's arms, well—she could still do that. But it didn't seem very likely.

"I'm sorry," she said, reaching over to squeeze his hand.

He squeezed back, but the room stayed glum, and silent.

Compared to Flora's many departures for St. Fillan's over the years, her send-off to Edinburgh that autumn was subdued. She hadn't, of course, been expecting a party; her departure was still too raw to yield even to feigned optimism. But over the months since her decision, the necessities of living closely knit had as usual dulled any initial animosity, and she had at least expected everybody to turn up.

Her mother announced she was staying at home that afternoon, though, clucking that somebody had to stay and watch the guests, and Michael, to Flora's dismay, wouldn't even answer her last, desperate knocks on his door. And though Trevor and her father were ferryside to say goodbye, neither of them helped drag her trunk on board; neither of them offered words of reassurance. Her father merely pleaded that she stay in touch, and Trevor begrudged her a single, limp hug—and then she was watching the island pull away, and scanning the hills for any sign of Michael.

That tepid farewell left her brooding, through the ferry crossing and the restless night at her Mallaig B&B, and for the entire trip to Edinburgh the next morning, too; from the time her train pulled out of the station at six o'clock, all the way down through the glens and lochs and barren hills of the west coast, she wondered why they were finding it so hard to be happy for her. Wondered why she was the only one to whom this didn't seem like a disaster and a betrayal. It was only when the train emerged from the tunnel below Princes Street, when she saw the black spire of the Scott Monument ahead of her and the castle towering to her right, that her worries drained away. She stepped onto the platform at Waverley, inhaling the smoky must, and it was as if she had been reset. For those next months she was too busy starting her course—and meeting new people, and exploring Edinburgh—to think of anything else.

When she returned home for Christmas, Michael had already left for his habitual months in England, and while she wished he'd been there, to reassure her that he still, at least, considered her a friend, she told herself his absence was for the best; she was glad to be able to focus on her family. There was something this Christmas that seemed different from her trips home from St. Fillan's, something more joyful, in spite—or maybe because—of all the acrimony earlier that year.

In any case, it wasn't until her Easter break that she next overlapped with Michael on the island, and to her relief he seemed pleased to see her. It was almost as if his failure to say goodbye that previous summer had never happened; he invited her to his cottage for a nightcap her first evening back, and they chatted happily for hours. He told her how nice it was to see her again, and how much he'd missed her, and about the pet projects he'd started to pass the time: a reference book about British films he'd always dreamed of writing; a small vegetable patch to supplement George's. Mostly, though, he complained about his lack of progress at the guesthouse, and her parents' stubborn resistance to his proposed improvements.

She'd already heard the other side of his complaints from her parents themselves, who'd grown equally frustrated with Michael's stubborn enthusiasm: *sometimes it's as if he's changing things just to give him something to do!* her mother had grumbled over Christmas dinner, and though her father was as usual more measured in his reaction he still clearly disapproved. *It's not that they're not good ideas*, he'd said—*I'm just not sure they're right for us. What do we need a computer for, anyway?* In her parents' retelling much of it *had* sounded unnecessary, and she'd shared their knee-jerk suspicions, but the way Michael put it now it all seemed eminently reasonable. The computer, he said, his cheeks turning pink, would reduce their costs in the long-term, not to mention saving countless hours of labor, and the new laundry schedule he'd proposed could hardly be any less efficient than the haphazard "system" they'd had before. *And the bloody bacon!* he added, rolling his eyes. *I swear they don't want me to save them any money.* (He'd switched the guesthouse's supplier to a wholesaler on the mainland, who gave them a better deal on the cost of distribution. It was, in fact, exactly the same bacon from exactly the same farmer George had always dealt with, but he and Maureen insisted it tasted odd, and had asked Michael repeatedly to change it back. *There's just...something*, George had said, gravely.)

As they opened their second bottle of wine, she promised she'd try and soften them up a little, and he laughed and wished her luck. *But look at me being rude*, he said, shaking his head. *You don't want to talk about this boring business stuff—what have you been up to all year?* So she told him: regaled him with stories of her tiny room in Bella's Marchmont flat, and the double-decker buses that swooped by on the city streets and left her breathless; about her sunset strolls up Arthur's Seat, and her studio space at the art college, and the intoxicating bustle of *people* that had greeted her at every turn. The only thing she didn't tell him about—not at first, anyway—was Oliver, the handsome, irrepressible boy from the Borders with whom she'd fallen hopelessly in love. They'd met during her first month in town at some freshers' event: he had long black hair and a thin face, the way she imagined Barry might look these days, and he had stunned her into an odd sort of silence. At nineteen he was several years her junior, and yet somehow seemed more worldly than anyone she'd met before, with his designer clothes and wicked sense of humor and stories from his gap year in Malaysia—and she'd been enchanted. Her thoughts of him replaced all her lingering *what ifs* about Michael, and a week after the start of term she'd followed him, puppy-like, from class to the pub to his flat in Tollcross, where they'd fallen into bed together and hardly left since.

Her plan had been to not divulge any of this to Michael—for some murky reason she couldn't quite identify—but while she succeeded for a while he soon forced her hand. Around two in the morning, the third bottle of wine half-empty at their feet, he leaned forward and tried to kiss her. She pulled away, inhaling sharply. "Michael."

He pulled away too, and looked immediately, as always, to the floor. His hair had grown into a messy, side-parted shag while she'd been away, and she thought to herself, as she stared at him staring at the floor, that it suited him; matched his personality better than the professional crop he'd always had before. A little more youthful; a little harder to predict.

"I'm sorry," he said, quietly.

"Don't be." She shuffled closer to him and put her hand on his arm. "I wish I could. I mean, I'm flattered. But—"

"It doesn't matter," he said. "You don't need to explain yourself."

She squeezed his arm tighter. "I just have a boyfriend now, Michael. It wouldn't be right."

He sat there, nodding, still silent.

"I should probably leave," she said, wobbling to her feet.

"You don't have to." He sniffed. "I'm not angry or anything. Not at you. I'm glad you're happy."

She thanked him and left in a hurry, too charmed by that answer to be sure she could resist much longer. For that same reason she avoided him for the rest of the trip, and he seemed to get the message—but while nothing had happened, the mere act of considering Michael again made her feel so guilty that when she returned to Edinburgh she flung herself, out of some twisted sense of atonement, into ever larger commitments with Oliver. Soon they were living together, and she spent the following Christmas with his family instead of hers, and increasingly she wriggled out of spending any time on the island at all, except for the occasional weekend when she knew Michael would be away. She missed the place, of course. Missed the silence of the studio and the long sunsets in July, and most of all, despite everything, missed her evenings with her father in the pub. Each day she spent in Edinburgh, though, each new friend made and each success at school, convinced her more and more that her future lay beyond the island's shores. Pushed her family into the final stages of the slow, inexorable decline that had started, one spring, almost an entire decade earlier.

1988

XII.

It was April, and Maureen was alone in the house: George was taking Flora for her introductory visit to St. Fillan's, and Trevor had gone to the jetty to see them off. Under other circumstances she might have gone with them, or at least waved from the window as they disappeared down the road, but the trip had become such a point of contention the past few days that she'd only stood, arms crossed, as they pulled their shoes on in the hallway—and as soon as the door slammed she bustled off to the kitchen. *Stubborn old sod didn't even say goodbye.*

It had started the previous week, when he came upstairs to bed one night. Maureen had been lying beneath their quilt for almost an hour already, planning what to say while she half-read a tattered Poirot, and when he walked in and began to undress, she looked up, swallowing. "I've been thinking," she said, softly. "Maybe I could take Flora to St. Fillan's next week."

He climbed under the covers next to her. "Why?"

"I don't know," she said, as casually as she'd been practicing it in her head. "I thought it might be nice to go to Glasgow afterwards and do some shopping." A pause—also well rehearsed.

"A few of the bedspreads upstairs could do with replacing."

George grunted, trying to find a comfortable spot on the pillow. "Why do you need to go all the way to Glasgow to get bedspreads?"

Sighing, she set her book down on the bedside table, next to her old, brass alarm clock. "I don't." She'd been prepared for this too, even if she'd hoped she was being pessimistic. "But there's a public lecture at the university next week I'd like to go to. A history professor who's just back from Morocco."

"Well, I've got banking to do next week," he said, reaching across her to turn out the bedside lamp. "And we can't leave Trevor on his own—so I think you'll have to miss it, this time."

Calmly, resigned, she'd turned towards him, though in the dark she couldn't see anything except the light's lingering neon afterimage. "I could take Trevor with me. Or do the banking for you."

"Let's talk about it in the morning," he yawned. "I'm shattered."

She felt her jaw clench. "Fine," she said. "Goodnight."

But predictably, they didn't talk about it in the morning; she wouldn't bring it up, waiting with equal parts hope and bitterness to see if he'd do it himself, and he, of course, had already made up his mind. Her, doing the banking? What a ridiculous suggestion! It was bloody typical: he was so particular about the guesthouse errands that he never let anybody else take over. Or never let *her* take over, anyway. His monopoly over mainland visits was so absolute it had been years since she'd been anywhere other than her cousins' house in Perth, or the pub in Mallaig for Sunday lunch—and though in the past she'd sometimes visited Glasgow on days out with the other island ladies, Mrs. Kilgourie was the only one of them left, now, and lately she didn't have much appetite for travel.

Whenever she broached the issue with George, however, he always gave the same, silly excuse: *you've not spent as much time on the mainland as I have, Reenie. You don't know how to handle yourself.* What cheek! And whose fault was that, anyway? One of these days she should just go without telling him—spend a week living large and then waltz back and see what he said! Except the fear always nagged that maybe he was right—that if she disappeared by herself she *would* end up in a gutter somewhere, and with nobody back home having the slightest idea where to look for her. When she was fifteen she'd stowed away to Mallaig, thinking she would travel the world, but she'd had no real plan, no money, and when she'd arrived she only stood there on the dock, paralyzed—until one of the ferrymen recognized her and asked if she needed any help, and she burst into tears and asked to be taken home. And despite her many years of experience since, she'd always wondered if, faced once more with the prospect of self-reliance on the mainland, she'd freeze just as she had then.

Still, in bed again the night before George and Flora were due to leave, she'd made one last attempt to change his mind—and one last time, he had instantly dismissed her. Frustrated, she'd tried to take a firmer stand, but he just snapped at her to let it be, and they started to argue, and only stopped when Trevor appeared at the door to ask if everything was all right.

In the kitchen, now, she sighed, walking to a shelf above the sink and pulling down a recipe book. She would put her foot down next time, she told herself, settling into a chair at the table to decide on dinner—even as, in the back of her mind, she suspected that probably she wouldn't.

At the jetty, George and the children found Mr. Kilgourie also waiting for the ferry. "My my," said the man, with his usual chuckle, when he noticed Flora's overnight bag. "It seems like only yesterday we were saying farewell to Barry."

"She's not leaving yet," mumbled Trevor, fidgeting with the life preserver hanging next to him on the sea wall. "It's just a visit."

George patted Trevor on the head, and smiled at Mr. Kilgourie. "And what brings you over today?"

He laughed. "Oh, nothing much. A few bits of business."

Trevor saw his father raise an eyebrow at that, saw his forehead wrinkle as he asked what sort of business, but then he returned to staring at the life preserver, uninterested in the conversation and too upset at Flora's departure to talk to her. Even as they hugged goodbye, Trevor's gaze stayed stubbornly on some vague point behind her, and it wasn't until the rest of them had climbed aboard and the ship was reversing into the sound that he let himself look up. Flora, smiling, waved at him from the foredeck; he gave a reluctant half-wave back, and then watched as she turned and disappeared inside.

Spring had come early that year, on the heels of a mild winter. Already the island was dotted with primrose and coltsfoot, plus a few shearwaters that had returned early for the summer, and instead of walking home Trevor took advantage of the mild weather and turned off the road from the jetty, skirting the island's shoreline in the breeze off the water. A ways down the beach he passed one of the intrepid shearwaters, perched alone on a rock; it gave him an inquisitive caw.

Mr. Lewis had told Trevor once that when the Vikings visited the Hebrides they had been so terrified by the birds' calls, in full tilt a ghostly, roaring wail, they'd assumed the islands were full of trolls. Trevor snorted at the thought as he stared at the bird now, its head a downy grey and its beak a gleaming stick of charcoal, and wondered how anyone could ever find the things scary. As if to prove his fearlessness, he picked up a pebble and pitched it towards the shearwater's perch, but the throw landed short and the bird, unfazed, only stared back. In the distance the ferry's foghorn sounded, a long, bassoon lament.

There had been talk of Flora leaving for months, but until his sister started to pack the night before Trevor had remained impervious to even the slightest unease; it was only now, with the ferry disappearing, that the truth completely struck him: soon, he'd be on his own. The island's final child. He pictured Flora's room back at the house—the heaps of clothes draped over every chair and bedpost, the creeping mess of toys and colored pencils—and imagined it getting gradually tidied away over the coming months, after Flora's departure proper. Imagined it emptied out completely. Imagined himself standing in its doorway, alone.

If he'd been older than seven-and-a-half, he might not have cried. Might have tried to keep the tears in, or to pretend they were down to the cool wind blowing in his face. If he'd been older, too, he might have been better able to rationalize, to tell himself that he didn't see Flora much these days anyway, between her art lessons with Bella and her evenings in the pub with dad and their mysterious little word games—and that after a day or two he'd barely notice her absence. But all he could do now was think of their walks to school, and of listening to her hum as she dressed each morning, and of all their rainy day projects together since Barry had left for St. Fillan's; just a month ago they'd written a book, concocting a story in the cave of Flora's bottom bunk and transferring it to paper page by page, illustrations by her and smudged, wobbly lettering by him. Who would he do that with now? Who would he talk to while his parents worked? Angry, he kicked at a lone dandelion that had strayed into the sand from the grass bordering the beach, and plopped to the ground to tear at its leaves. After a few minutes of that he just sat drawing spirals on the ground until eventually, light fading, he returned home.

His mother greeted him in the hallway, hands on hips and expression stern. "Where have you been?" she clucked. "The ferry left two hours ago."

"Sorry." He looked at his feet. "I was at the beach."

"Well come along, no more dawdling—I need your help with dinner."

He followed her obediently to the kitchen, where three giant pots bubbled on the stove and a mess of cookbooks, cutting blocks and vegetables covered the table. In the past she'd often tried to get him and Flora to help with the cooking, but they were so good at distracting each other with side games—peeling designs into potato skins, making up songs to go along with their chores—that usually she ended up excusing them. So was *this* what was in store for him, he wondered, with Flora leaving? Endless evenings spent actually helping his mother, bored and on his own? He felt his eyes tearing up again and quickly shut them, letting the room's humid, fragrant air wash against his face.

"Now what?" she asked. When he opened his eyes she was staring at him and tightening her apron, a few new reddish stains down its front. "Come on, we haven't got all night."

This military cooking regime of hers was a recent development, one that Trevor had watched with curiosity. Though his mother had always been in charge of food at the guesthouse, both for customers and for the family, in the past year or so her planning and freezer restocking had become increasingly elaborate. Where once she'd used the off-season to pursue other projects—mending clothes, reading books, spending evenings with the children—now she seemed to see that extra time as the principal front in an ongoing campaign against famine. Each week her grocery orders swelled as she experimented with exotic new recipes, and each week the pantry shelves would fill with cooling jams and pickles and preserves, their jars dark-colored and full of shadows—like the shelves, Trevor imagined, of some mad scientist's laboratory. A few months earlier she had completely filled the chest freezer, for the first time ever, and after many nights of squabbling had convinced George to buy a second for the overflow.

The thing had finally floated across on the ferry just a few weeks ago, and had taken most of the day to get home because the dolly they normally used to shift heavy supplies wasn't big enough. Instead George, Mr. Kilgourie, and Mr. Lewis had taken turns carrying it in pairs, sweat freckling across their backs as the sun burnt off the morning mist and Trevor, giving occasional shouts of encouragement, cleared the path ahead of them. By early afternoon, when at last they'd reached the hillcrest overlooking the village, Mr. Lewis had burst into giddy laughter at the task's absurdity, quickly setting the rest of them off too, and amidst their guffaws they decided it was time for a break; they sent Trevor home to fetch some sandwiches, and when he returned he found them using the freezer as a bench, still giggling to each other and squeezing sweat from the hair behind their ears. When at last they deposited the monolith at the guesthouse's front door, the sun had almost set, and they immediately stumbled to the pub—where George set a line of pints along the bar and told the other two to drink up.

"What should I do?" Trevor asked now, flopping into a seat at the table.

"Stand up again, for a start," his mother replied, dragging her finger down a recipe and leaving a faint, glistening trail on the page. "Keep an eye on that stew on the front burner for me. It needs stirring, and I've carrots to chop."

Without a word, Trevor got up and pulled his chair over to the stove.

"And once that comes off the heat," she continued, still

peering at her cookbook, "you can clear the table and set out some plates."

Now he managed a quiet *Yes, Mum*, and climbed onto the chair, staring into the muddy, mahogany goop in the pot. Behind him, a knife began to clack-clack against one of the cutting boards, and with a sigh he began to stir.

Later, at the dinner table, they ate in silence; even with the others gone they had taken their normal seats out of habit, Maureen at the head of the table and Trevor two places down and perpendicular to her. That odd configuration made conversation seem unnatural, stilted, and after a few half-hearted questions and answers about Trevor's homework they simply gave up, listening instead to a clock tick in the next room and the creak of the table as they mopped their plates with bread.

As they cleared the dishes Trevor asked hopefully if they could play a board game, desperate not to go upstairs to the empty family rooms, and to his surprise, his mother quickly agreed. When they moved to the living room and dug through the toy cabinet there, though, they realized that almost everything they owned required four players.

"We could try Monopoly," Trevor said, starting to pull it from the stack.

Maureen shook her head and told him it would take too long. Instead she reached into the back of the cupboard and dislodged a dog-eared deck of cards wrapped in a brittle rubber band. "Why don't I teach you rummy?" she said, waving the cards from side to side. "Your father and I used to play that all the time before Barry was born."

They returned to the kitchen to sit at the table, this time huddled together at the corner nearest the sink. Maureen explained the rules as she dealt the first hand, and though she faltered over several of the finer details Trevor was a natural, falling into the rhythm of the game almost immediately and thoroughly trouncing his mother, six hands in a row, until she announced it was time for bed. He couldn't stop chattering about it as they marched upstairs—*I was good, wasn't I, Mum? Do you think Dad'll be impressed, Mum?*—and even as he brushed his teeth on tiptoes at the sink, he kept mumbling through the minty foam: *can we play again tomorrow?* It was only after she'd tucked him in and he was lying alone in his darkened room, his excitement wearing off, that he realized she hadn't given him her usual kiss before turning off the light. Suddenly he found himself missing Flora again, wishing she were there so he could sneak across the hallway, as he'd often done before, and ask her what she thought that meant. With a muffled cry he lifted his arms and slammed them into the mattress beside him, whispering angrily to himself about how much he hated that stupid mainland school. He spent another hour, almost, lying there clenching and unclenching his fists in frustration, his quiet tears returning and warming the pillow against his face, until finally, some time past eleven, he drifted off to sleep.

In the kitchen, for different reasons, Maureen was also upset. Or not upset, exactly; unsettled. Every few minutes she would blink and find herself staring at a ribbon of carrot skin on the floor or lost in the woodgrain of the countertop, her mind miles away and her brow sore from frowning.

It was the rummy. Years had passed since she'd last seen those cards, the peeling gloss at their corners and the kitschy photographs on their versos, and finding them again had reminded her of the day she and George had bought them. It was during a rare trip to Edinburgh, long before the children were born, for the wedding of some wealthy cousin of his to which they nearly hadn't gone; George ignored the invitation when it came, and only after Maureen discovered it, emptying the bins just days before the RSVP

camping headlamp from the drawer beside the sink and slipped it over her head, fiddling with the strap as she moved towards the counter and the waiting stew. Once she'd switched on the bulb she took a deep breath and picked up the two tubs, and finally hobbled from the kitchen and into the garden. At the gate she turned onto a small path that ran behind the village buildings, an old byway for the locals from the days when boatloads of tourists would clog the main road. The guesthouse floodlight clicked off and slowly dimmed behind her as she shuffled along, the brush on either side darkening until the halo from her headlamp was all that lit the ground at her feet. Her shoulders ached from the weight of the stew.

When she finally reached the Braithwaite house she carefully bent her knees and set the containers down by the back door, leaning against the wall for a minute as she caught her breath. In the distance she could still make out the dark silhouette of the guesthouse, and was glad to see no light coming from Trevor's window; he'd been so worked up after their game tonight she'd been afraid he might not sleep.

Shaking out her arms, she turned to the cottage door and pushed it open. The new freezer was right there, just beyond the threshold, an enormous white coffin sitting in the middle of what had once been the Braithwaites' kitchen—where Maureen had sat herself, more times than she could remember, chatting with Gillian and looking through mail order catalogues. When George carried it over here with Mr. Kilgourie, shirt drenched in sweat again, he'd refused to move it any farther than the door, and she hadn't been able to come up with a good reason why he should. But she still hated that the thing had been plonked there so carelessly, not even flush against a wall. It made the place feel less like anything that had been a home, once; seemed to seal its fate as derelict.

The Braithwaites had left years earlier, when Barry was only a few years old, but in fact Maureen had been here much more recently: when the rat trappers had reappeared two Januaries ago to start their cull, there had been too many of them with too much equipment to accommodate the whole lot at the guesthouse, so instead they'd camped out in several of the old village homes. The Braithwaites', the closest to the guesthouse, became their unofficial headquarters, and Maureen stopped by almost daily with news and mail from the mainland. Out of good manners she always tried not to linger, but David, the team leader, a tallish man with silver hair in his temples and large oblong glasses, would often stand and chat with her on the doorstep—about the weather, or the team's progress, or whatever else happened to occur to him.

They were there for months, toiling away at their gruesome task, and if they'd seemed a nuisance on their first visit, now they were out-and-out invasive. Their giant metal traps cluttered the island from edge to edge, laid out every few yards as if some strange new weed had taken root, and whenever Maureen walked to the Stùc to collect the children—a necessity, with the bridge blown away—she would hear the things snapping shut around her, chunks of bloody carcass flying out of the grass. At the peak of the cull, when the cleanup crew was struggling to keep up, she would smell the rotting flesh almost everywhere she went.

What struck the islanders more, though, before long, was the constant presence of the trappers in the pub: they were like a whole new set of regulars, appearing every evening for the home-cooked dinners Maureen provided or, when they opted instead for instant noodles by their sleeping bags, for a post-meal drink to soothe the aches and pains of work. *It's nice to have the place full again*, Peter Manning whispered to her one night. Mr. Kilgourie, eavesdropping from the next stool, nodded vigorously, and so did Maureen. Though the crowd was clearly smaller than it often could be on busy summer weekends, this felt more like a community than those streams of day-tripping tourists, and it was nice to have people to talk to beyond the Kilgouries and the Mannings and the Pikes. (The Thomases, the only other hangers-on, had moved to Dundee a few weeks after Christmas.)

That May, near the notional start of the season, and after a full three weeks of empty traps, David had appeared in the pub one night and declared the cull complete. *Rejoice!* cried George, who was so relieved they'd be able to open on time that he announced free drinks for all and sent Trevor and Flora to fetch the other islanders. Soon the room was churning with bodies and roaring with cheer, and the party carried on for hours, through a whole keg and a late summer sunset—until eventually, sometime past midnight, the guests began to trickle away. Maureen was at the front door seeing off the Pikes when she heard the commotion.

When she hurried back to the pub she found that one of the trappers, a little too merry, had thrown up in the middle of the pub. David was kneeling beside the man and apologizing repeatedly to George, who meanwhile was standing feckless behind the bar—and with a brusque step forward Maureen took charge, waking Flora from where she'd dozed off in the corner and commanding her to fetch the mop, and snapping at George to keep on serving drinks.

"And you and I," she said, turning to David, who was still on the floor, "are going to get this dope to bed."

"Oh, there's no need for that," he said. He got to his feet. "One of the lads can help."

"Nonsense," said Maureen, wobbling, a little tipsy herself. "No need to tear anyone from the party."

Behind the bar, she saw George raise an eyebrow.

"If you're sure," said David, pulling the drunk man up and slipping an arm around his back, and waiting for Maureen to do the same. "Okay then. Off we go."

They guided him down the hallway and out of the house, and then along the main road towards the Braithwaites' cottage. As they reached the front door, David made his umpteenth apology.

"Ach, don't be silly," she replied, "We were all young once."

He laughed. "Once?"

"I'm forty, Mr. Cox—I can hardly call myself young anymore." Without thinking she'd shaved a few years off her actual age, though she wasn't quite sure why; she'd long ago grown comfortable with the idea that her youth had totally escaped her.

"Forty!" He shook his head. "I long for those days. I'm pushing fifty."

"Oh, but you don't look a day over forty-five," she said, smiling.

The drunk belched between them.

"Charming," said David.

Inside, he settled the man in his sleeping bag while Maureen searched through the old store cupboard for a bucket to leave next to him, and finally, standing together in the kitchen, in the exact spot where the freezer now hummed, she looked hopefully at him and asked if he would come rejoin the party.

He shook his head. "No, I think I'd just as well be calling it a night. We old fogies have to look after ourselves, you know." The laugh lines around his eyes seemed to deepen a little.

"Goodnight then, Mr. Cox."

"And goodnight, Mrs. McCloud."

In one of her romance novels, she thought, that would have been when he leaned forward and kissed her. In her memory, sometimes, it still was. But at the time he only smiled, and she, still teetering on her feet from the drink, squeezed his arm and turned to leave. It had been enough, though—that sordid, impulsive desire—to shake her from her rut. No, nothing had happened, it was true, and during the trappers' remaining week there were no further incidents. But she had wanted something, hadn't she? Had followed him home out of more than her hostess's desire to keep the party going?

Of course, there was no question of pursuing anything serious. Even if she felt less sure of that now than she had at the time, she couldn't bear the thought of leaving the children. Besides, beyond her intermittent fears about handling herself on the mainland, she had real, practical problems to consider: where would she live? What would she do? She had no money of her own, no job experience, and the few ex-island friends with whom she kept in touch seemed to be having a hard enough time scraping by as it was, without having to help Maureen as well. Assuming they even would, if she fled her family in disrepute. At best she might have been able to stay with her cousins in Perth until she found her feet, but she wasn't sure she could depend on them, either; she'd always been convinced they liked George better.

So after David left she buckled down and put him out of her head. Whatever she'd felt that night was just a silly fantasy, she told herself, and if she was sensible there was really nothing about life at home that was particularly bad. Predictable, maybe; boring from time to time. But never bad. Yet despite those rationalizations, the bugbears and discontents continued to collect, each one transforming David into more of a panacea. She even wrote him a letter a few months later, explaining how much she missed him and suggesting that perhaps she could come visit. But in the end she only dropped it off the end of the jetty and watched it float away with the waves—and then spent the whole of the following week terrified it might wash ashore again for the children to find.

As she closed the freezer now, her cheeks still tingling from the cold air, she took a wistful look around the empty kitchen, seeing herself again in the spot where they'd stood that night, and imagined that fanciful, romance novel scene for the thousandth time. She wasn't sure she'd ever quite be rid of it.

XIII.

August, and the long trailing off of summer. It had been a brisk season, the guesthouse full most nights and the day-trippers turning out in large numbers thanks to the mainland media's coverage of the cull. George in particular found the headlines hilarious (*Scottish Island Smells A Rat* his favorite), and started a collection of cuttings that he would proudly show off to anyone who asked. He even discussed framing a few to hang up around the pub, an idea that Maureen hated. *It sets the wrong tone*, she told him. *The wrong tone for what?* he replied.

Despite the surge in customers, though, the guesthouse was running smoothly. Trevor was finally at an age where he could help with the easier chores, and Barry, back for the summer as usual, was more than happy to take on the daily hikes to the jetty for supplies, freeing up George for other tasks. The boy's trips were often longer than his father's, but Maureen let the tardiness pass without comment; it was the only job Barry would reliably do with good humor these days, and besides, his arrivals at the back door laden with packages were more or less all she ever saw of him. Even compared to his first hermitic Christmas, he'd grown so reclusive on visits home that some days felt scarcely any different than when he was away at school. She cooked him a special dinner for his birthday in June, all his favorite things, and invited Mr. Lewis—and still the boy had stayed downstairs for as little time as possible before retreating, as always, to his room.

It was a surprise, then, on his last night home at the end of the summer—Flora's last too, this year—when after dinner he didn't immediately disappear. Instead, when Maureen asked, as she did every night, out of some hopeless, automatic reflex, whether he wanted to stay downstairs and play a game with them, he shrugged, and mumbled an awkward yes. (Flora and Trevor, who had been bickering about something at the kitchen door, froze instantly in surprise.)

"Well, then," said Maureen, clearing her throat. "Why don't you go pick one out?"

So while she carried dinner through to George, manning the bar as always, the children retrieved a battered set of *Cluedo* from the living room, and when she returned they arranged themselves around the board at the kitchen table. As she dealt out the cards she found herself studying Barry, himself studying the tabletop intently, and wondering if there were some special reason he had consented to spend time with them this evening—or if it was simply the pre–St. Fillan's jitters that, despite his usual withdrawal, she often noticed on his last night home.

"It's nice of you stay down here tonight," she said, distributing the players' tokens around the board. He nodded, not looking up from the splinter he was picking at on the table's edge. When it became clear he wouldn't offer anything more, she sighed and handed the dice to Trevor. "You're the youngest, dear," she said. "You go first."

As the game progressed the mood grew lighter, the outlandish mansion generating inevitable cheer at their discoveries, and good-natured despair at Flora's eleventh-hour break for the finish, and groans of defeat as she triumphantly unveiled the killer. But as they packed everything away the uneasy quiet once again descended.

"Well," said Maureen. "It certainly has been nice having you here this summer."

No response.

She dropped her blue piece into a small plastic bag with the others, and the dice, and replaced the bag in the box. "And so much easier getting things done during the day." She smiled. "It'll be quite a relief having you back here full-time once you finish school. Your father's got a list of projects a mile long he's been waiting for your help with."

She saw his shoulders tense. "Aye," he said, fidgeting with the miniature lead pipe. "I suppose."

"Come on," she continued. "You must be a bit excited about finally coming home for good." Even as she said it she realized how unconvincing it sounded; these days he didn't get excited about anything. And why should she expect him to miss the island, really, when she probably wouldn't either?

He shrugged.

"Maybe we can redecorate your room when you get back," she added. "Make it feel a bit more grown-up for you."

He hesitated, clearly weighing something up, and at last wet his lips. "Thing is," he said, "I'm not really sure I *am* coming back."

She frowned. "What?"

"Yeah," said Barry, replacing the lead pipe in the box. "I'm leaving school next year, and not coming home." He picked up the candlestick; Flora and Trevor gawped at him and then, after a few seconds, at Maureen.

"What?" she repeated.

He coughed. "I'm going to get a job."

"A job." Her voice was rising now. "A job!"

Flora slowly squared the cards she'd been shuffling and set them down in the box. Trevor's face was flushed red. "What do you mean you're getting a job?" he said.

Maureen shushed him, eyes still fixed on Barry. "I'm afraid that's entirely out of the question," she said, chest tightening. "You'll still have a year of school left, for a start! And where are you getting this supposed job, anyway?"

"I'll be sixteen next summer," said Barry, his voice firm. "I can leave school if I want. And one of my mates knows someone in Aberdeen—reckons he could get me signed up on a rig."

"An *oil* rig?" Too furious to look at him, now, she began snatching up the other murder weapons still scattered around the table. "Absolutely not!" She flung the pieces into the box and dropped the board on top of them. "No son of mine is going to work on one of those North Sea death traps. You'll stay at St. Fillan's and finish school, and then you'll come home and work for us here." She turned back to him, waving towards the pub. "You know your father's always planned to pass the business onto you eventually. What do you think he'll make of this?"

"It doesn't matter," said Barry, the expression on his face serene in its defiance. "You can't make me stay."

"Oh, we bloody well can!"

"No," he replied. "You can't." And as if to prove the point, he started for the door, ignoring his mother's screams that he stay, and marched quietly upstairs.

Safely in his room, Barry climbed into the top bunk and exhaled, his entire chest shuddering with each beat of his heart. He lay staring at the ceiling for several minutes trying to calm the pounding, trying to reassure himself he was doing the right thing, while downstairs he could hear his mother continuing to bang around.

A showdown like this had been precisely what he'd hoped to avoid, when he settled on his decision to leave; upsetting his parents, and particularly his mother, didn't bring him any joy. But the truth was, he was tired of school and tired of home—or tired, anyway, of always yearning for the home of his childhood—and he knew he couldn't stay. Couldn't sign onto a lifetime of dimly wandering around this tiny, haunted place; couldn't bear the thought of his few remaining happy memories being forced out by years more of bitter ones.

So when his geography teacher had shown the class a video that March about the Scottish oil fields, he'd been mesmerized, not just by the isolation of the oil platform or the hugeness of the ocean, but by the riggers' way of life: no people, no trouble, and no responsibilities beyond getting up each morning and starting work. Compared to Tam and his cronies, compared even to his family's endless, eager pleas that he cheer up, the idea of an anonymous bunk in the swells of the North Sea was too appealing to ignore. He could picture himself lying in bed on his days off and reading, uninterrupted, for hours on end, or sitting on the edge of a platform, legs dangling, watching as the sun set and the sky surrounded him with orange. It would be bliss.

Still, his plan had been to avoid telling his parents until the last second and then slip away with as little conflict as possible, which was why he'd kept even more than usual to his room this summer: the fewer conversations he had with them, he reasoned, the less likely it was that his post-school plans might accidentally come up. Because he'd resolved he wouldn't lie about it if they asked, would at least grant his family that one, tiny courtesy. Indeed, it was that same distorted filial loyalty that was stopping him from running off tomorrow, even though, a few months earlier, he'd been looking up train schedules to Aberdeen as the spring term had drawn to a close.

But then: Flora's visit.

He shuddered even thinking of that day, of the cold glint in Tam's eye as he watched Flora sit down across the dining hall.

"So, Baz," he said, noticing Barry watching her as well. "That's your sister, eh?" The sneer Barry had come to dread so much crept across the other boy's face. "Quite the looker, isn't she?"

"You can fuck right off, Tam," he replied, and he marveled, still, that he'd had the nerve to talk to him like that. "You don't go near her."

Tam laughed, and the rest of the boys joined in. "Touched a sore spot there, have I? Well don't worry—I wouldn't want your sloppy seconds. The way you islandfolk carry on the two of you probably have three spastics of your own at home already."

More brays of laughter.

"Aye, well," Barry said. "We can't all be blessed with a wanking hand like yours."

"Ho ho!" said Tam, his mouth a thin, flat line. "You're a proper Billy Connolly, aren't you, McCloud? Maybe when we get outside later you can have a taste of that hand in your cheeky face."

"Do what you like, Tam—just leave her alone. She's off limits."

And oh, how he'd meant that. That same fear he remembered from his early weeks at school had instantly returned that afternoon, its hard, icy edges pressing into him as he tuned out the other boys' asinine banter and looked again at his sister across the hall. She was smiling meekly at another girl, with a heartbreaking, nervous naïveté, and all he'd wanted to do was leap across the room, tabletop by tabletop, and whisk her away.

So one more year, he'd resolved to stay, until Tam himself had graduated. He would keep Flora in his sights at all times,

186

would follow her or stick to Tam or some mixture of both, always making sure they were never alone together, not even for a second. He'd make sure she kept that innocence. He had to.

The door to his bedroom opened, now, and Flora stepped quietly into the room. Sitting up halfway, Barry looked down at her from the top bunk. "What?" he said. She glared at him, then stomped across the room and began rooting around in the closet; he sat up further. "What do you *want*, Flora?"

She turned for just long enough to tell him curtly she didn't want anything, then continued digging through the closet. But even without seeing her face, Barry could picture her cheeks flushing and her nostrils flaring—the same look she always got when she was lying.

"You can't change my mind," he said, sinking back into his pillow.

She let her arms drop to her sides, and for a moment stood completely still. And then, suddenly, she turned again—he'd been right, her face was flushed—and began to shout. "Maybe I don't want you to change your mind! All you do is upset Mum, so you might as well not come back!" He thought he might have seen a few tears appearing in the corners of her eyes, but she was already looking away again now, and grabbing a stuffed bear from one of the closet shelves. She tossed it across the room at her new trunk, packed and ready for the trip to St. Fillan's the next day, and hurried towards the door again, eyes on her feet. With her hand on the doorknob, she paused. "You don't even like us anymore, do you?"

He didn't answer immediately; the question caught him too off guard. He had never imagined that the compulsion he felt to leave might boil down to something quite so simple. Of course he still loved his family—how could he not? But did he really *like* them anymore? Was that why home had become so unbearable?

Clearly he took too long to consider it, because Flora let out a frustrated sigh and opened the door. "I thought so," she whispered—and before he could say another word, she'd vanished.

Flora leapt down the stairs three at a time, still fighting tears, determined not to give Barry the satisfaction. Outside the pub door she stopped and wiped her eyes dry with the heel of her palm, blinking tightly to marshal some composure, and with a deep breath pushed through the door and strode behind the bar to join her father.

"Dearie me," he said, as she yanked the newspaper from his hands and started scanning the crossword. "First it was your mother huffing around, and now you too! Is there something in the water?"

She ignored his comment and continued looking for any clues she could decipher. "You've got this one wrong," she said, finally, smiling faintly as she remembered her earlier *Cluedo* victory. "*Gathered for hearing of accused colonel?*, eight letters? It's *mustered*. Gathered. Like Colonel Mustard. One of those sound-alike clues."

"All right, all right." He took back the paper. "I'll be getting you your own copy if you keep this up." He erased his original answer from the grid and filled in the new one. "Now come on—what's got everyone so upset?"

Flora shrugged. "Barry."

"Big surprise there." He rolled his eyes. "What's he done now?"

"Nothing." She could feel the heat of her tears returning.

Her father shook his head. "Not feeling very talkative tonight, are we? Okay, I won't pry. What are your thoughts on eight down?"

Flora sniffed and studied the puzzle again, but already she

was losing her concentration. It wasn't only Barry's announcement; she'd been feeling out of sorts since she woke up that morning. Since the beginning of the week, really, as she fretted about her departure for St. Fillan's. Or, more accurately, about her arrival there; about opening the door to a new room and the metal bunks and the flimsy fake wood desk she'd seen on her tour in April. About meeting the girl she'd be living with. About meeting another girl at all.

She'd met others before, of course: her distant relatives in Perth, and the Kilgouries' airy-fairy niece, and a few more who'd passed through the guesthouse over the years. But taken one at a time like that it had never occurred to her that girls as a group existed as something materially that different from boys. Even after the sex ed primer she'd had from Mr. Lewis, conducted just as Barry's had been with Trevor kept unwillingly at home, she hadn't really given it much thought. It was only when she visited St. Fillan's in April, and witnessed firsthand how effortlessly the kids from larger schools drew those strange, invisible boundaries between each other, that the difference finally made itself clear: she smiled at one of the boys in her tour group, out of nervousness and nothing else, and immediately another of the girls—Maisie, she'd later introduced herself—pulled her aside, a shocked look on her face, and asked what Flora had been thinking.

"You don't fancy him, do you?" Maisie's eyes bulged. "He's pure minging!"

Unsure what the girl meant, Flora simply shook her head from side to side, hoping it would be an acceptable response.

"Well," said Maisie, "if you don't fancy him you don't want to be smiling at him, or everyone will think you do."

At that point the teacher, who was explaining something or another about the dormitories, shushed them—but once they were sent to lunch they were right back into it (or rather, Maisie was), scanning the dining hall for *lookers*, and speculating about *willie size*, and assessing their competition from any *hoors* among the crowd. Flora, meanwhile, continued to nod or shake her head as seemed appropriate, still in a daze, and staring at where she'd spotted Barry across the room. She'd been hoping for some sign of reassurance, but it never came: their eyes met just once, and all he did was scowl and turn away, towards the other boys at his table.

Seeing him in a big group like that, fitting with everybody else into the school's strange social divisions, was unsettling as well, as if she were watching an actor play her brother—badly. This was a change on an entirely different scale than the times Barry had come home to visit, because yes, perhaps he'd been more sullen the past few years, more withdrawn, but he had still recognizably been Barry. Now everything about him was different, his mannerisms and his posture and the shape of his mouth as he talked, and she doubted, suddenly, that even a warm smile would have been that comforting.

All those baffled fears from that first visit, though, amplified by the past months of anticipation, had faded into the background tonight, as they sat down for dinner and she realized with a jolt that, unlike when her brother left for school, there had been no special notice made of her departure the next day, no night off for her parents, no festive farewell dinner. Only the usual bread and soup, with her father not even there. It didn't matter that the Kilgouries were the only people they might have invited, now, and that she didn't particularly like either of them and would have complained about it endlessly if they'd been there—she couldn't understand why her parents hadn't even tried.

George patted her on the shoulder now, nodding towards the crossword. "No luck?"

Flora shook her head and mumbled sorry.

"Well, no matter. Shouldn't be relying on you anyway, now

that you're flying the coop."

She sniffed.

"Are you sure you're all right, love?" He frowned. "Nervous about tomorrow, maybe?"

Looking at the ground, she shook her head again.

"Come on." He took her chin in his hand and lifted her head to look her in the eye. "Out with it."

She took a deep breath. "Will you miss me?" Another tear slid down her cheek.

"What!" His hand moved from her chin to her crown, now, and he gently stroked her hair. "Of course we'll miss you, Flora! Whatever would make you think otherwise?"

"I don't know," she said, thinking: *because we don't miss Barry anymore.* She nestled her head against her father's chest. "Nobody seems that bothered that I'm leaving."

He wrapped his arm around her and squeezed tight. "We're very bothered, Flora, I promise. Especially me." He glanced up, at the few guests seated at tables around the room. "It won't be the same around here without you."

Face still pressed against him, she smiled weakly, and finally sat up again, wiping her eyes.

"Does this have anything to do with Barry?" he asked, giving her a searching look. "Did he say something nasty to you?"

"No." She glanced at the door, then began explaining what had happened after dinner: the game, and Barry's plans to leave, and his defiant escape upstairs. As her father listened his expression quickly changed from mild concern to total dismay, and when at last she'd finished he surveyed the room again, sizing up the half-dozen stragglers still nursing drinks, and patted her on the shoulder.

"Tell you what," he said, handing her the paper. "We're not busy, so can you keep an eye on things while I nip through and make sure your mum's not too upset? News like that and she might be about to break something." He stood up. "I'll be back in a flash."

She nodded and watched him hurry out. When she looked down at the page again, the black and white squares were shimmering.

When George found her, Maureen was in the kitchen, viciously wiping down a cutting board. She looked up at him as he walked in. "Pub empty already?"

Still walking towards her, he shook his head. Then: "I hear Barry's been making grand plans."

At that flippant summing up of the situation, she actually laughed, feeling a pang of relief that, in addition to all his stubborn little habits that drove her up the wall these days, the sense of humor she'd always loved about him was as reliable as ever. Small solace, though, given her despair at this further proof of Barry's drifting away, and, more than that, at her inability to convince herself motherly concern was behind it. Because her terror picturing Barry on an oil rig had come only second, tonight, after a rush of other feelings that she could only describe as selfish: anger, dread. The sense of an opportunity snatched away.

She'd had those same feelings just a few months earlier, on an otherwise uneventful night just a few days after Flora's visit to St. Fillan's. Mr. Kilgourie had been at the pub late, stretching out his last pint interminably as she and George cleaned up around him. Once Mr. Kilgourie was finished he sat at the bar not moving, portentous, until the lights were off and the chairs stacked, and George and Maureen practically screamed at him to tell them what was wrong. *I've given up the house*, he said, staring into his empty pint glass. *We're leaving at the end of the summer.*

Maureen listened in disbelief as he explained how far their

finances had fallen; how they'd never completely recovered after the rats, and how they needed to move to the mainland now while they still had any money left. *Does Oonagh know you've done it?* she asked, certain it was impossible, certain her friend would have said something if she had any idea—and shocked when Mr. Kilgourie nodded, and said his wife had been the one to insist. Maureen poured herself a whisky, then, leaning on the bar, aghast: with the Kilgouries gone, and the Mannings and the Pikes having given up over the winter, her family would be it. The last ones left. The fate of the island would rest entirely on them. Already she could hear George's rallying cry as he took her hand in bed that night, his declaration, proud and desperate and firm all at once, that it was up to them. And with Barry leaving now, that fate seemed all the more certain. Without him at the guesthouse there was even less chance of a reprieve for her, less chance of her ever slipping away, for a holiday or for good.

But to George now, all she said was: "That boy will be the death of me."

He'd moved next to her at the sink while she'd been thinking, and now put his hand in the small of her back. "Ach, don't worry, Reenie. I'm sure he'll come around. This is just bog standard teenage rebellion." At last she stopped scrubbing at the cutting board, and looked at him, and told him that she hoped so. He laughed. "Trust me, that boy'll take one look at a rig and wilt like a daisy. Before you'll know it he'll be begging to come home and peel the tatties for us."

"Maybe." She dropped her scouring pad at the edge of the sink and began to dry her hands on the tea towel slung over her shoulder. "It's just...He can be such a stubborn brat sometimes."

"It'll be fine, love. Really." His hand slipped further around her waist and he pulled her closer, her body a tensed bow in their awkward half-embrace—until she slumped, finally, and kissed him through the sleeve of his shirt.

"I'd best get back to the bar," he said, squeezing her hipbone. "Flora's probably giving away drinks."

Maureen took a step back. "Didn't you come in here for something?"

He winked. "I was going to hide the knives, but you seem calm enough."

She still just stared at him, and his playful expression disappeared. "I wanted to see if you were all right," he said, walking to the door. "That's all."

"Oh," she replied, but by the time she thought to utter a belated thank you, he had already started down the hall.

It was sad, she supposed, that she'd assumed his looking in on her must have some other motive. Sadder still that such an assumption didn't strike her, even in hindsight, as particularly unreasonable. Even before her most recent malaise, before the Kilgouries' announcement and David and the rats, their marriage had slowly transformed—out of circumstance, really, rather than malice or neglect—into something more like curatorship; between the children and the guesthouse and the village, their interactions now were more functional than tender. Still, there was something else on her mind tonight that she thought probably explained her distracted response.

The night before she'd been lying in bed waiting for him to come upstairs, much as usual, the satisfying flap of her mystery novel's pages the only sound besides her occasional sighs. She hadn't looked up when he padded in, skimming forward instead to reach a good stopping point, and when finally she did raise her head he'd already undressed and was taking off his watch.

"Late one tonight," he sighed.

She set her book down. "You are the owner, you know—you can close whenever you want."

"As long as they keep buying drinks..." He crossed the room and climbed into bed. "By the way," he said, "the wildlife chaps were on the phone today." She instantly felt a burst of heat at the back of her neck. "They wanted to sort out when they were coming for their follow-up on our furry friends."

Her breath caught. "And?"

"I put them in for the first week of October. Books were clear then anyway."

She exhaled. "You scheduled it without even asking me?"

He tugged the blankets towards him, and she felt a corner of her thigh come uncovered. "Why would I ask you?"

"I don't know. I—I might have had something planned." She pulled her nightie down to cover the exposed skin.

"Then it would have been in the books," he said, turning over to face the wall.

"I just like being kept in the know. Is that too much to ask?"

"No," he said. "That's why I'm telling you."

After you've already bloody decided everything, she thought, but she let it drop. She wasn't even sure what she was that upset about: nobody had seen a rat all year, and the trappers' visit was bound to be short and uneventful; George might as well have been booking guests in for the weekend. And wasn't the fact that he'd treated it like any other business precisely what she'd wanted? Didn't that prove she'd hidden her feelings about David perfectly?

She sighed, now, taking some paper and a pen from a drawer next to the sink and sitting down at the table to make a list. The real problem, she told herself, was that she still had feelings about David at all. And clearly she did—that much was obvious from her fluttering heartbeat the night before, her churning stomach and her lying awake 'til three. The last time she remembered feeling that way about George had been years ago.

She scribbled out a heading on the page in front of her, but before she could actually begin the list, she was looking at the wall clock and cursing under her breath: it was a few minutes past Trevor's bedtime, already, and she hadn't even been upstairs to get him ready.

Trevor, meanwhile, was sitting alone on his bedroom floor, reading in a splash of eggshell light coming off his bedside lamp. Other than that, and the faint teal glow of dusk in the windows, the room was dark, and when his mother bustled in she immediately switched on the overhead bulb, clucking that he'd make himself blind.

Nodding glumly, Trevor stood up and crossed the room to where she was now pulling a pair of pajamas from his dresser.

"You can read for another ten minutes," she said, glancing at his alarm clock, "but I want your lights out by the time I come upstairs again." She was already back at the door, her hand on the knob. "Understood?"

He nodded again, and listened to her clomp off down the hallway before moving to the door himself, to check the latch was firmly shut and switch the ceiling light back off. Once he was changed he returned to the spot where he'd been reading, and stared down at the book still lying on the rug. It was *George's Marvelous Medicine*, a Roald Dahl he'd read before and not one of his favorites—but with Barry locked up in his and Flora's room tonight, as he had been so often this summer, Trevor hadn't been able to raid their shelves for fresh material. He stood for a few more seconds and considered picking it up again, but finally he shook his head and knelt down next to his bedside table. Reaching behind it, he felt for a piece of skirting board he knew was loose, and carefully pried it back to pull out a small photograph. The image was difficult to make out in the darkened room, but he knew it well enough from memory: a family portrait taken when he was still a baby, the five of them arranged around a Christmas tree in the living room, Barry and Flora glancing at each other from the corners of their eyes.

He'd found the picture about a year ago, in a desk drawer in his father's office. It was tucked away in a ratty yellow envelope with a few dozen others—landscapes, mostly, and a few group shots of relatives on the mainland—but it was this particular portrait, just two or three down in the pile, that really captured his attention: Barry looked impossibly young, and Flora, her hair longer and thicker than Trevor had ever seen it, was practically unrecognizable. Until then he'd always thought of his sister as unchanging, permanent, and to be confronted with this strange other version of her, staring him in the face as if from another world, had been captivating. He snuck the whole envelope to his room and spent the afternoon studying its contents, spread out around him in an ocean on the floor.

The landscape shots, it turned out, were almost as fascinating as the people ones. They'd all been taken on the island, it looked like, and yet there were several that he couldn't place: close-ups, mostly, the frames filled with heather in bloom or strange rock formations in the brush. He took to studying them before bed each night, and hiking around with them during the day, consulting their fading images every few minutes as he tried to figure out their origins. Then, a few weeks later, his father casually mentioned over dinner one night that a few of his photographs had gone missing; Trevor blushed, he hoped not too conspicuously, and the next day replaced them all in the drawer. But he'd kept that one family shot he was gazing at now, unable to bring himself to part with it.

The thing he loved most about the picture was seeing everyone together. Though he had a few memories from before Barry had left for St. Fillan's—his brother slipping him a sweetie under the table one lunchtime; the sight of their mother weeping at his departure—generally he thought of the household as himself, his parents and Flora, and there was a charming novelty to the idea that at some point they had shared the space with Barry, too. Indeed, as the weeks had passed with the picture hidden in the walls, emerging only every few evenings for Trevor to study it again, he'd started fantasizing about reuniting the family in that harmonious, pre–St. Fillan's state—and the more he'd thought about it the more he'd convinced himself it was possible. Until tonight. Though he had only the vaguest idea what an oil rig was, and the North Sea was nothing more to him than a blue patch on the other side of Mr. Lewis's Scotland map, something about the tone of Barry's announcement earlier, and his mother's reaction, had left him certain of one thing: his brother wasn't coming back.

Caught up wondering why, he missed the sound of his mother's footsteps in the hallway; only as she turned the door handle did he realize she'd returned, and he frantically shoved the picture under his bed to hide it.

"Time's up, young man," she said, as he spun his head to look at her. Apparently she hadn't noticed anything. "Into bed." Hands on hips, she waited for him to climb beneath his covers, then tucked him in and retreated to the door, whispering goodnight as she stepped into the hallway.

"Goodnight, Mum," he called after her, and once the door was shut he clicked off his bedside lamp and lay there in the dark, forgetting all about the photograph, now, and wondering instead why she hadn't made him brush his teeth.

XIV.

There was barely time to breathe after Barry and Flora left that year: with September raining in and extinguishing the summer, the family's attention turned quickly to the Kilgouries' impending departure. The last of the couple's crops for the year were harvested and shipped away; a buyer from Inverness relieved them of their sheep, rustled chaotically to the jetty with the help of George and Mr. Lewis; and after that their house was all that remained, and its lifetime of furniture and crockery and clothing—which Maureen and Trevor helped pack over a lingering, nostalgic week. With no children of their own, the Kilgouries had no old toys to dispose of, no baby shoes or clothing, and none of the boxes' worth of drawings Maureen knew would have slowed her own departure. But in the absence of all that they'd made their belongings into offspring, their attic a mess of cast-off memories as sentimental as any parent's. Several times she found them whispering sadly to each other in the corners of emptying rooms. *The old covering from the armchair, Jack! Oh! And the paint left over from our bedroom!* They seemed bizarrely caught off guard by their attachment to the place, and when at last it was empty they sagged with relief, checking into the guesthouse for their final night ashore.

"So this is it, eh?" said Mr. Kilgourie over dinner, his voice softer than usual as he stirred his soup. "The last supper." He and his wife were at the kitchen table with Maureen and Trevor, while George kept an eye on the season's last visitors in the pub.

"Surely you'll be back to visit," replied Maureen, glancing more towards Oonagh than her husband. The woman had a sickly expression and hadn't touched her soup; she seemed to have aged ten years in as many days.

"Aye, well," said Mr. Kilgourie. "We'll have to see."

"We'll do our best, of course," added his wife, quietly. "Once we work out"—she cleared her throat—"how much time off our jobs will give us."

"You've found something, then?" Maureen asked, though she instantly regretted it. Whenever she and Oonagh had gone shopping in Fort William, her friend was always making snide, under-the-breath remarks about working wives. *Can't her husband support her?* she would always whisper, on spotting a sales assistant's wedding ring. *Has she no dignity?* Maureen never really agreed with the sentiment—she actually saw something quite thrilling in the idea of earning her own wage—but she doubted Oonagh would want to discuss her own employment prospects now.

The woman bowed her head. "Well, no. Not yet. There's not much I seem qualified for over in Dundee." She adjusted her napkin ring so it was in line with the tip of her butter knife. "Unless I want to work at the Safeway, and I'm hoping I'll not have to." Maureen nodded, trying to imagine Oonagh scanning groceries. Trying to imagine doing it herself. "Jack's had some luck, though—haven't you dear?"

Mr. Kilgourie shrugged, and explained that he'd found some work as a farmhand outside town. "I always thought I'd be hiring farmhands one day," he added with a sigh, and after that the table fell silent, apart from Trevor slurping down his broth. Maureen glared at him, irritated by his indifference, and once he'd finished and waited the requisite minute or so before asking to be excused, she snapped.

"It's Mr. and Mrs. Kilgourie's last night!" She banged her hand on the table. "Can't you stay and sit awhile?"

He gave her a hurt look. "I've homework to finish, Mum. I already told you." He had frozen in place, halfway through sliding from his seat.

"Ach, don't worry about us," said Mr. Kilgourie, with a wistful smile in Trevor's direction. "We're not much company tonight, anyway."

Trevor looked to Maureen again, and she told him through gritted teeth that he could go. He quickly deposited his dishes in the sink and scurried from the room.

"He's a good lad," said Mrs. Kilgourie, still staring sadly into her untouched soup. "It's a shame we won't be here to see him grow up."

Maureen wished she could grab the woman by the shoulders. *It's not that bad!* she wanted to scream. *You should be happy you're getting free of this place!* Of course, free probably wasn't quite the right word, given the duress of their departure and what sounded like a dismal outlook in Dundee—and yet she couldn't help but feel jealous of the uncertainty they faced and the potential it contained, and dread at her own, inevitable future. After the next day, she and George would be alone on the island, except for Trevor and Mr. Lewis, and once Trevor finished primary school the two of them would be gone too. And if Trevor and Flora decided not to return, as Barry had, it would be just her and her husband, forever, and this blink of stone in the giant sea.

George stuck his head into the kitchen, now. "How about

we swap places for a wee bit?" he said, his eyes fixed on her. "Give me a go with the dearly departing?"

She stood up and told him that was fine, carrying her own bowl to the sink and placing it on top of Trevor's. On her way out, she stopped where George had sat himself at the table, kissing him on the cheek, and told him to take all the time he needed.

Upstairs, Trevor had already finished his homework. Had already finished it, in fact, even before he'd excused himself from dinner—but he'd discovered that "homework" was one of the few excuses for hiding in his room that his parents left consistently unchallenged, and in the weeks since Flora's departure he'd tried to spend as much time there as he could. The dismal, wordless dinner with the Kilgouries tonight had been painful enough, but since Flora had left even time spent with his parents felt uneven, somehow. Off kilter.

The week before, for instance, his father coaxed him to the pub to help with one of those secret word puzzles he'd always reserved for Flora. Naturally, after so many years of curiosity, Trevor jumped at the chance, but within minutes of his father's long-winded explanation the evening quickly soured. *Think, Trevor!* his father urged him in frustration. *What words fit in the space?* Trevor kicked the side of the bar, equally annoyed. *Who cares, Dad! It's just a stupid game!* The dispute escalated: George warned his son to watch his tone, told him Flora had never behaved this way, and Trevor, already showing signs of the temper that would hobble him in later years, yelled that they *shouldn't have let her leave, then!* and swept his father's glass to the floor.

Nights with his mother were just as bad, if less dramatic. On the few occasions he strayed downstairs to find her he'd ended up helping clean the kitchen or doing more infernal cooking, and when he subsequently tried to weasel away she firmly called him back. *But Mum*, he'd whined once, *you cook every night! Don't we have enough in the freezer already?* She gave him a dour look. *It doesn't fill itself, young man.* And then, more tender: *besides, it's good to have so much stored up. You never know when you might need it.*

So his room it was. He'd even started asking Mr. Lewis for extra homework—*to make sure I understand*, he said—and if the man had nothing else to assign him Trevor would repeat the work they'd done in class, going through the day's sentence exercises and arithmetic problems from memory. When he tired of that he'd curl up by his bedroom window and dissolve into a book, or lately would cross the hallway to Barry and Flora's room, and sift through their belongings. At first he was driven by a bored sort of curiosity, but quickly he found himself drawn in. One night he discovered an old sketchbook of Flora's, jammed behind the dresser by their window; and of Barry's, in the flyleaves of an old *Boxcar Children*, a scribbled piece of what looked like years-old spelling homework. Neither item was particularly noteworthy, and clearly they hadn't been missed, but to Trevor they were a window to his sibling's secret lives; another piece of proof that the island had been more vibrant, once. A shred of hope that it might someday manage it again.

That night, after escaping from dinner with the Kilgouries, he stood in the center of his room with his fingers linked on top of his head, schoolbag in front of him and packed for the following morning, and contemplated what to do next. After a moment he let his arms drop and walked over to his closet; on tiptoes he reached up and inched an old shoebox from the top shelf, guided it carefully to the floor, and removed its lid. Inside were all the things he'd found in his siblings' room the past few weeks, plus the photograph he used to keep behind the skirting board (an ugly crease down its center from when he'd rushed to hide it the month before), and on top of that a dozen or so other items filched from the Kilgouries' house as he helped them pack: a page from an ancient farm ledger, its cream-colored pages filled with line after line of Mr. Kilgourie's sloping, inky script; a heavy mortar and pestle, fragments of oat pressed permanently to its surface. And then there was the discovery that fascinated Trevor the most, the one that had prompted him to start the collection in the first place: a postcard, silken from wear, the pigment fading in its decades-old picture.

He'd seen postcards before, of course; his parents kept a small supply on hand for guests. But the ones they sold now were of scenes from elsewhere in Scotland, bought in bulk from Mallaig, whereas the one he'd found last week showed a picture of *the Kilgouries' house!* The caption on the back confirmed it: *Traditional croft house*, it read; *Eilean Fìor, c.1968*. Thrilled, he called over his mother, who studied it for a moment with a mournful look. *Yes*, she said, handing it back to him. *The McKenzies used to sell these at the general store.* A company in Fort William had produced them, she explained, but after the McKenzies left the contract lapsed, and since it was cheaper to get the generic ones she and George hadn't bothered to renew it. She turned back to whatever she'd been packing as if no further explanation were required, and that was when Trevor slipped the card beneath his shirt. Since then he'd taken it out to look at every night, still in awe of the world it suggested.

After a few more minutes he replaced the shoebox in his closet and moved to the window to read until bedtime. The Kilgouries popped their heads in to say goodnight when Maureen came to put him to bed, but it was as he walked out the door for school the next morning that he said his last goodbyes, enduring awkward hugs and kisses as they wished him well in life. *I remember the day I delivered you*, Mrs. Kilgourie sniffed, patting him on the head, and her wording caught him off guard; he'd always known that she'd been there at his birth, but that she had delivered him—that she was somehow responsible for his existence—was not something he'd ever dwelled on. The thought stayed with him all week, her farewell repeating in his head each morning as he left for school. *I delivered you*, she'd said. *And now*, he thought, *I'm gone*.

Soon, however, his attention turned again to other things. A week into October the rat men returned, a smaller troupe than during the cull but still enough of them to fill the guesthouse's upper floor. Trevor looked up from his book one afternoon to see them approaching through his window, and crept to the head of the stairs to watch his mother meet them in the entryway. There were a few new faces in the group this time, but most of them Trevor recognized from their previous visits: a bearded giant, shoulders hunched beneath the weight of his rucksack; a lankier man behind him, with a gaunt face and a grim line of a mouth. And at the back of the crowd was the one who'd been in charge before, his silver-framed glasses glinting as he nodded at Maureen.

"You're sure you wouldn't rather we stay in the cottages again?" he was saying, as Trevor's eyes finally landed on him.

"Ach, no," his mother replied. "There's only a handful of you and we've no guests this week anyway. Make yourselves at home." She smiled at the man—the first sign of happiness Trevor had seen from her since Flora'd left—and he smiled back as he thanked her.

"It's our pleasure, Mr. Cox," she said. "Let me know if you need anything." And to Trevor's surprise, she reached forward and touched his arm then, a gesture of affection he recognized even at eight years old.

And more intriguing still, a few days later: the phone call from St. Fillan's.

It came in the evening, while George and Trevor ate in the kitchen and Maureen, having volunteered to give George a rest that night, manned the bar—so it was his father who hurried to the hallway to answer the phone.

"Yes, this is Mr. McCloud. Yes...What about Barry?" Trevor gently laid his fork down on hearing his brother's name and strained to listen, though his father was interjecting only occasionally, between long stretches of silence, to grunt or ask a question. After a few minutes there was a click as he set the receiver down, and a long, drawn-out sigh, and perhaps, Trevor thought, unless he was imagining it, the sound of his dad running his hands down his face. Then his footsteps moved further down the hall, and the pub door opened and shut, and only in that sudden quiet did Trevor dare to take another bite of dinner.

A few moments later he heard footsteps re-emerging. "What is it, George?" his mother said, sounding irritated. "I shouldn't leave them too long."

"I'm sure they can spare you for a few minutes, Reenie." A pause. "It's Barry."

"Barry!" Her voice quavered. "What about Barry?"

"He's been in a fight at school. They just called. Broke a lad's nose, apparently."

"He *what*?"

"Broke a lad's nose! I can't quite believe it myself, but the headmaster is livid. Wants us on the first ferry there tomorrow, he said, to discuss Barry's 'future at the school.' His words."

"Tomorrow?" said Maureen. "We can't go anywhere tomorrow! Who'll look after the men? And Trevor?"

The sound of floorboards creaking.

"Don't worry, Reenie, I can go on my own. I've some banking to do, anyway."

Silence.

"What has got into him lately, George? First all this oil rig nonsense, and now a broken nose?"

"Boys will be boys, Reenie. I dished out a few healthy knockings when I was his age, too. I'm sure it'll pass."

"I hope so." A sniff. "I should get back in there."

And as the pub door re-opened, and the floorboards began to creak again, Trevor rushed to pick up his fork as if he'd been eating all along.

George left the following morning and called home late that afternoon. Maureen ran to answer from the kitchen, where she and Trevor had been preparing for dinner, and took the handset between ear and shoulder while she dried her hands against her pinny.

"Crisis averted," said George, his voice echoing on the line. "Managed to persuade them to let Barry stay on, though he's suspended for a week and on probation after that. But I've had words with him—he'll behave."

"He'd better." She took the phone in her hand, now, her eyes drifting towards the pub door. "Are you coming home, then?" It was a Friday, so there'd be a second ferry that night—one of the season's last.

"No," he said. "The next train won't get me back to Mallaig in time. I'll have to spend the night and catch the ferry first thing."

Her heart beat a little faster. "Oh," she said. "What a nuisance." Another glance down the hallway. "I'm sorry you had to go on your own."

He assured her it was nothing, and after a few more pleasantries they hung up, Maureen's pulse now thumping in her ears. She started for the pub.

David was there, as she'd expected, sitting at his now habitual spot and going through some paperwork. As the operation's head he wasn't doing much actual reconnaissance this trip, and had taken instead to spending the days by a window in the corner, poring over maps and his subordinates' reports, his chair tipped back, his brow ever so slightly furrowed, and an almost regal look of concentration on his face.

"It looks like you're getting the all clear," he told her now, glancing up as she entered. "We've still not found a thing."

"That's a relief," she said, pausing by the bar while simultaneously, in her head, she was walking towards him, and sitting down at his table, and taking his hand in hers. "Can I get you a drink before dinner?"

"Oh, no. Thank you." He shook his head. "Have to set a good example for my rowdy lot." As if not to disappoint her, though, he added, with one of those kind-hearted smiles she'd come to love so much, that he was getting a bit peckish for a pre-dinner snack.

"Tsk, tsk," she said, looking away from him even as she smiled back. "You'll spoil your appetite, young man."

"Ah, yes, of course. And what spectacular culinary feat will I be depriving myself of tonight?"

"I'm afraid only shepherd's pie—but I've a whole salmon coming with the messages Monday." She frowned, suddenly, and met his eyes again. "If you'll still be here."

"With a prospect like that," he said, "we may well be."

She kept staring at him even as he returned to his work, her hands shaky, and her shoulders, and her stomach light and airy. It was the same way she'd felt when he arrived that week—and this morning, too, when George had left, leaving her standing in the kitchen on her own, with a hint of opportunity suddenly in his place. On a whim she'd rushed upstairs to change, pulling an old Sunday dress from deep in the closet—a relic of the days when she'd regularly gone to church—and was relieved to find it still fit.

She managed a few strokes of mascara, too, though to her dismay her rouge had grown a thin layer of mold. *My*, David said, when he saw her at lunch. *Should the rest of us be dressing up as well?* She'd beamed. *What, this old thing?*

"Mum!" Trevor was calling her from the kitchen, now, and with a start she realized she'd left him in there peeling parsnips. Flustered, she hurried away to help.

She and Trevor returned to the pub that evening, though, at her suggestion, to eat dinner with the men—a raucous meal that, as it had most nights since they'd arrived, devolved into a lengthy bout of drinks. Even Trevor stayed downstairs for a change (a curious lack of homework tonight, Maureen noticed), the visitors reveling in his attention just as much as he seemed to revel in theirs. And while the room hushed when she finally dragged Trevor to bed a few minutes past nine, it still showed no signs of emptying, and she happily alternated between pouring drinks and clearing up until, around eleven, a few of the men finally began to drift upstairs. She dimmed the lights; the voices softened. She glanced at David. And then her mood instantly sank: he was gathering his things and standing up. Walking towards her with his empty glass.

"Goodnight, Maureen," he said, setting it down and patting her on the arm. "Thank you for another wonderful meal." She grinned helplessly and said goodnight back, her skin buzzing where he'd touched her.

"And you lot," he said, louder, turning to the room. "This is your last round, understood? We've still got work to do tomorrow." There were grumbles all around at that, but half an hour later the last of the men dutifully trooped upstairs, leaving empty drinks and full ashtrays, and Maureen alone in the pub. After tidying their mess and mopping the floor, she switched the lights off completely and walked through to the kitchen, retrieving a binder labeled *Inventory* from a shelf above the sink and standing over the table as she skimmed through it. Once she found the entry she was looking for she noted down the details on a scrap of paper and neatly scored through the line in the book, and then made her way to the back door and the path to the deep freeze.

When she reached the Braithwaites' cottage, she stopped. Here she was again, she thought, at the place where so many of her fantasies had started. Except that tonight, unexpectedly, they were more than fantasies; they were possibilities. Possibilities, she decided, as she stepped over the threshold, that she was going to pursue. It had begun to seem so simple that evening, as she replayed each encounter she'd had with David the last few days. His compliments on her appearance, his interest in her cooking... And when she set that drink in front of him, earlier, his hand covering hers as she withdrew it—that had been no accident, she was sure. She could still feel the condensation on the glass against her fingers; the absence of the wedding ring on his. It was too perfect to ignore! And though she still felt a pinch of guilt as she opened the freezer now and her own wedding ring pressed against her skin, that guilt seemed unimportant, somehow, blurry beside all she stood to gain: escape from her increasing discontent at home, from her even greater guilt at the same. The life elsewhere she'd always wanted. How could she not do it? The family would get by somehow without her.

Stepping back outside, a heavy tray of food balanced against her stomach, she looked towards the guesthouse and saw the light still on in his window. She imagined him in bed there, leaning against the headboard and knees bent under the blanket, turning, captivated, through a novel—his face arranged in that same thoughtful look he got while working in the pub, and his features casting handsome shadows in the reading lamp's golden light. And then she was there, above him, gently pushing the book away as she climbed over his waist, pressing her hands against his shoulders and leaning forward.

In the guesthouse kitchen again, she shook her head, trying to keep herself collected as she laid down a cloth on the counter and set out the food to defrost. That done, she glanced around the room one more time, then moved to the door and switched off the lights. Still moving as calmly as she could, she stepped into the hallway and started towards the stairs.

She paused again as she reached the first landing to let her eyes adjust to the dark; picked out the hazy, monochromatic outline of the *Do Not Enter* sign across the door to the family rooms. There were no sounds behind it. No sounds upstairs. No sounds at all except her own breathing and the rush of blood in her ears. In her head she kissed him, let her hips slide further down his body, let her spine straighten as she pressed against his chest. She put her foot on the next step. Paused again. Took a last fleeting glance at the *Do Not Enter* sign. And then she started to climb, quietly, weighing each step so as not to let the wood groan, but still going, frantically, as fast as she could. Now that she'd made her break for it, she had to cling to that momentum.

As her head came level with the floor of the upper hallway she surveyed the carpet for stray slices of light from other rooms. To her relief, the only one shone out of his, and with renewed determination she pressed forward until, outside his door, she stopped—swallowed—and knocked lightly on the wood. The seconds seemed to slow and draw together, gathering like a drop of water on a leaky faucet's lip, but no one moved behind the door. She knocked again, louder this time, and when still there was no answer she turned the handle and pushed inside.

The room looked as it usually did: a small dresser to her left, a wardrobe to her right, and in the far corner, flush against the wall under the eaves' sloping ceiling, a single bed and nightstand, and the reading lamp whose light she'd seen outside. But then the crucial difference: him, lying underneath the covers.

He'd been reading, just as she'd imagined, and had fallen asleep, book flopping against his chest. And just as she'd imagined, too, his knees were bent, and in his slumber had drifted sideways to lean against the wall. She closed the door softly behind her, not taking her eyes off him for a second, luxuriating in all the details of his body: his mouth hanging just slightly open; his plain white undershirt bunching around his shoulders; his glasses fogging in his steady breaths. She wondered if it were a sign that she'd pictured the scene so exactly, or if the sign instead was that he'd fallen fast asleep; if that one, simple difference was a warning she should turn away.

No, she thought. This far, she had already come. She would have the rest.

With a nervous shiver she moved forward again, striding towards him, no longer concerned with the sound of her footsteps. He stirred as she neared the bed. Opened his eyes as she knelt down beside him.

"Hello," she whispered, and smiled at him, resting her elbow on his mattress.

He blinked a few times. "Maureen! What—?"

And there it was, the kiss she'd seen a thousand times that night, that sigh of lips together and her eyelashes flickering against his skin. Hardly pausing, she pushed herself up, still on her knees, keeping her mouth to his, and reached across his body so she could plant her hands on either side of him. Her whole face was tingling, and the nape of her neck, and her entire back, and instinctively she was standing up, still without pulling away, and sliding her leg across his body so that she sat straddling him on the bed. As she held her arms out behind her and began to wriggle from her cardigan, his hands crept up her waist. She could feel his erection pressing into her thigh.

But then.

Suddenly he was pushing her away, his hands on her shoulders and their lips finally coming apart.

"What?" she whispered, breathless, tossing her cardigan behind her. "What's wrong?"

"I won't do this, Maureen." His face a pained frown. "I'm sorry."

"I—I'm...What do you mean? Why not?" She felt her face flushing and tried pushing towards him again, but he kept his arms braced against her.

"You're a married woman, Maureen. And a mother! Your son's only one flight down, for God's sake!" He squirmed, trying to slide out from beneath her.

"I'll leave them."

His eyes bulged. "Come on, Maureen, don't be silly—you barely know me. Besides, I'm a contractor here. If your husband found out I could lose my job."

"He won't."

"He might." For a moment his face seemed to soften. "You're a charming woman, Maureen. Maybe if we'd met in other circumstances..." He stopped, apparently thinking better of finishing the thought. "Please," he said, instead. "You have to get up before one of the men hears us."

She stared at him. "No."

"No?"

"No. You don't mean it. This isn't what you want." She felt a tear run down the side of her nose. Tasted it when it broke at the corner of her mouth.

"It is what I want."

But she felt his arms slacken slightly, now, and let her whole weight fall against them so that his elbows buckled and her torso finally pressed against his. "You didn't push me away," she whimpered, nestling her face in the vee between his shoulder and his neck. "Not at first." She felt the worn, velvety fabric of his t-shirt against her cheek. "Please."

He was silent for a moment, and then said, again: "I'm sorry."

All of a sudden she felt ridiculous, sprawled there simpering on this almost total stranger, for seriously thinking anything might happen. For hoping that he'd throw his arms around her and ask her to run away with him, or provide her some rapturous moment, played out in so many of her books, of *feeling alive again*. For wanting something smaller, even: a soft *I understand*, with a stroke of reassurance along her back. An absolution. A promise that even though she loved her family, loved George (and she did, somehow, didn't she?), it was okay to want to leave this place. To wish for something else.

But she knew, now, as David squirmed beneath her again, that she would never leave; as he told her firmly that she had to go downstairs, she heard her final lot. She *would* go downstairs. She would sleep on her half of the bed, would get up when her alarm told her to, and would go through the next day and the next and the next knowing that she'd taken this, the biggest risk of her life, and failed.

So, numbly, she allowed him to roll her to one side, and get her to her feet, and guide her to the door with his hand between her shoulder blades. Numbly, she allowed him to ease her through the door.

"Goodnight," he said, when she turned to face him from the hallway.

"Goodnight," she whispered, hoping one last time he might change his mind and kiss her again. But instead he only stepped back and disappeared behind the closing door, behind the faint click of the resetting latch—behind the final thunk, this time, of the deadbolt sliding into place. She heard his mattress squeak as he climbed into bed across the room; watched the light around the doorframe vanish. And then, a few more tears starting down her cheeks, she simply stood there in the dark, and on her own.

2002

XV.

On a sunny morning in April, Trevor came downstairs for breakfast and found his mother dead. She was sixty-one.

It was a no-nonsense, practical sort of death, whose restraint she might have admired if she hadn't been its victim. She simply got out of bed as usual that morning, and dressed, and stopped at the landing on her way downstairs to adjust a crooked picture—a painting Flora had given them a few Christmases earlier, the guesthouse viewed from a nearby hill and not much more than a speck in one corner, lost below the sky's giant watercolor sweep. She looked at her reflection in the frame, the black of her pupils swallowing up light and letting the image beneath shine through, but paused for only a few seconds before she continued, dutifully, towards the kitchen. And it was there, preparing porridge for George and Trevor, that she first acknowledged the painful twitch in her chest; there, as she sprinkled brown sugar into the bubbling pan, that at last she fell to the floor. By the time Trevor found her, fifteen minutes later, a tiny grimace on her face and wooden spoon still gripped in her hand, the porridge was smoking on the stove; by the time the doctor arrived, half an hour after that, the whole house stunk of burnt oats.

Michael was the one to call Flora, and the rest of Maureen's relatives in Perth; Michael was the one who arranged for the body to be sent away and cremated. Michael handled everything, really, as if managing bereavement were just another part of his remit. Which in fact, they soon discovered, it was: when he contacted the family solicitor he was told that Maureen had changed her will a few months earlier and named him as executor. *She didn't think George could manage it anymore*, the lawyer told him. *Said his illness was getting to be too much.*

Under other circumstances Trevor might have been piqued that his mother hadn't chosen him. Did feel, actually, when Michael explained it to him, the familiar spark of anger that would normally have set him shouting. *I'm her son, for fuck's sake! The only one who bothered to stick around! And this is what I get for it?* But a sudden flicker of regret, at so many similar outbursts inflicted on his mother over the years, left his temper dampened, and all he did was listen vaguely as Michael went through the will's few, straightforward provisions: her engagement ring to Flora, an old Stewart family portrait to Trevor, and anything else not shared with George to whoever wanted it or charity.

The only surprise came at the end of the list, when Michael hesitated, and wet his mouth, and added that there was a savings account, too, a private one, in Maureen's name only, at a bank in Fort William instead of their normal branch in Mallaig. There wasn't much in it, Michael explained, barely £300, deposited in dribs and drabs over the past four or five years—but nevertheless, there it was, to be divided evenly among the three children. Trevor had stared at him, a blank expression on his face, and asked why she would have opened a secret bank account. *She probably wanted to keep some money separate*, Michael told him, shrugging, keeping any speculation to himself. *In case your father did something silly with their joint account.* Trevor nodded, repeating that single, collusive word. *Probably.*

The obvious difficulty with disbursing the account was Barry: in recent years he'd fallen completely out of touch, and the drilling company for which he'd last claimed to work had long since closed up shop—as they discovered when a Christmas card sent via the main office came back *Return to Sender.* And though Michael assured Trevor he'd do everything he could to track his brother down, that amounted to little more than leaving messages with every Aberdeen oil company that had a listing in the phonebook and hoping, as each day passed with those messages unreturned, for a miracle.

Trevor hardly cared, though; felt neither sadness at the sibling lost nor frustration at his absence. Felt very little at all, in fact, in those weeks following his mother's death, beyond a tangential awareness of the basic happenings around him—Michael's tireless funeral organizing, and the mourners trickling into the village again, and the countless flowers arriving from those who couldn't make the trip. Each day passed in an elaborate, whisky-soaked dream, so much so that weeks later he would think back and wonder if any of it had really happened. How many of the details he might have missed.

The only thing that kept his attention, in those final days before the funeral, was the village chapel. Although Michael's plan, initially, had been to hold a small memorial in the guesthouse garden and then retire for a wake inside, Trevor was seized one night with the idea that they should use the old church instead. Not because he thought his mother would have wanted anything religious, but because it would be the first time in a decade that anyone had been inside—easily another decade before that since it was last used for worship—and opening it again seemed to him an appropriately grand gesture to mark his mother's life.

So he told Michael, anyway. Mostly, though, he was hoping

he could block out his despair by indulging his curiosity. For as long as he could remember the chapel had been shuttered, the synod having decreed before his birth that it was too expensive to keep Fior in the pastor's weekly rounds of the archipelago. Since then it had been opened up only a handful of times in his memory, mostly for the rat hunters to lay traps and later collect them, empty—and once on a single day ten years ago, when the Trust sent an engineer to assess a crack along the outside wall. That time Trevor actually managed to creep inside, but was quickly shooed away.

On the morning before the funeral, when the key from the Trust arrived with the early ferry, he went straight from the jetty to the chapel, stopping only to leave the rest of the deliveries on the guesthouse's front doorstep. Perhaps as much as curiosity or distraction, he was glad for the brief respite from his father, too. Or at least from his father's *condition*—a word he hated, but one for which he could never find a suitable alternative. *Condition* made it sound like something transient, easy to get rid of. Fatigue was a condition, he thought, or obesity, or low spirits. Not whatever was wrong with his father. Yet none of the doctors they visited on the mainland had been able to agree on a specific diagnosis, dithering between Alzheimer's and Parkinson's and Lewy Body, and settling most often for the hopelessly vague *dementia*, a symptom rather than a disease in itself, but one of the few problems they could consistently identify.

The decline started innocently enough, with a few occasional memory lapses that everyone assumed were little more than a sign of age. Who *would* expect a sixty-year-old to get by without ever writing anything down, without waiter's pads or recipes or to-do lists, the way George always had when younger? Soon, though, there were other symptoms, too: he would drift in and out of his monthly meetings with Michael, increasingly unconcerned with the well-being of the business; he would fall asleep at odd times of the day, or at the dinner table, or even in the middle of a conversation; and he would regularly forget his chores, letting a whole batch of supplies blow away in a gale one day, for instance, because he never went to fetch it. And then his trouble moving started. Maureen called him down as usual for breakfast one morning, and when after ten minutes he'd failed to appear she went to look for him and found him on the stairs, stuck mid-step, gripping white-knuckled to the banister with a look of impossible concentration. *Like he was walking against a riptide*, Maureen described it to the doctor later—and stranger still, when she asked him what was wrong, he looked at her serenely. *Your husband's having trouble walking, it seems*, he said. Only a few seconds later did he frown, as if snapping out of a trance. *Perhaps we should call the doctor.*

The most unnerving thing was that most of the time he still looked and acted like himself—had all the same mannerisms and facial expressions, told all the same jokes—even as that well-practiced exterior masked his steady disappearance. By that winter he was nothing but a charming, hollow automaton, incapable of anything beyond hard-wired routines, growing anxious whenever conversation strayed from the usual topics of the guesthouse or the island, and giving them unconvincing smiles to gloss over his recurring confusion. For a long time the only thing that seemed not to have suffered were his crosswords, at which he continued to toil away—until Flora came to visit one Easter and sat down with him to help, and discovered he was filling the grid with mostly nonsense. Trevor wondered how long he'd been completing them that way, cheerfully scribbling down words without any idea why. Wondered what part of his mind was compelling him to carry on.

It haunted him, seeing his father so diminished, made him want to run away and cower; to preserve, at least, a memory of the functioning person who'd brought him up. Worse, though, and more often these days, his father simply irritated him, so that increasingly Trevor found himself snapping at innocent acts of incompetence, or sighing loudly whenever he had to repeat himself. It was hard to tell if George noticed anything—his jovial publican's persona was his default, now, regardless of the circumstance—but every now and then Trevor was sure he caught something in the man's eyes, some distant understanding of what was going on. As the months passed Trevor tried more and more to withdraw altogether, leaving the day-to-day care to Maureen. It was better for everyone that way, he told himself, and perhaps until his mother's death it had been. Now, though, they'd been forced back into an awkward, faltering reacquaintance that, entering the chapel that morning, Trevor was glad to temporarily escape.

The inside of the building was smaller than he remembered it, as if after so many years the walls had contracted at the presence of a person. He'd forgotten, too, its smell of damp stone and the bizarre arrangement of the pews, different from the chapel at St. Fillan's or any other church he'd ever seen: instead of facing the pulpit, the seats ran lengthwise down the small chamber, so that parishioners were forced to stare at each other or swivel uncomfortably to watch the pastor. The light, though, was exactly as it had been when Trevor snuck in as a boy, the greyish-white of elderly hair and not quite bright enough to illuminate the hall's far corners.

Over the years a few patches of mold had grown around the joints on the wooden seating, and a thin layer of dust covered everything else, and Trevor swept and scrubbed so diligently now he was in there well past lunch. His reward was the countless artifacts he discovered as he went: a black coat button and a ballpoint pen and a hair ribbon among the pews, and near the pulpit an old Bible, pages mildewed and disintegrating, and a sheet of file paper on which were scribbled and intermittently crossed out the notes for a sermon on self-reliance. And most beautiful of all, on the floor by one of the windows: the desiccated corpse of a moth, the pigment of its wings faded and its body curled inward on itself. He added it to the pile he'd started by the door, and on his way out, once the chapel was finally ready, he scooped all of them into his hands and carried the lot back home.

When he arrived at the guesthouse, though, he found a pair of paint-flecked canvas trainers in the vestibule, and instantly forgot about his collection. *Flora.* He looked at his watch; the ferry had arrived while he was gone. Calling out her name, he started down the hallway, and when she called back he carelessly dropped his trinkets on the telephone table and bounded for the stairs, telling himself he'd come back for them later. By the time he remembered that evening, though, it was already too late; in the frenzy of extra, helping hands around the guesthouse that weekend, somebody else had already cleared them away.

The service was short the next day; Flora wasn't sure it could even be called a service, technically, since the archipelago's new pastor, a young fellow who'd never known Maureen anyway, hadn't been invited. Instead Flora, as the oldest child present, officiated a more secular remembrance, and anyone who wanted to share a few words was welcome—which in the end meant Trevor, and Maureen's cousin from Perth, and a handful of the older islanders who'd returned for the occasion.

The chapel air was cool as the two-dozen or so guests filed in that morning, and Flora vaguely worried about her father catching a chill. But once the heavy doors were shut and everyone was seated, the walls began to trap the heat coming off their bodies—and by the time she stood up to start the proceedings, hands shaking and neck drenched in sweat, the room was warm and still.

"Good morning," she said, gripping the sides of the lectern. "Thank you all so much for coming." Her voice cracked as she carried on reading from her notes, explaining how much the turnout meant to her and how touched Maureen would have been, and introducing the first speaker of the morning: the cousin Susan from Perth. She, in turn, made much of being the only member of Maureen's extended family to stay in contact over the years, and then told a few dull but well-meaning stories—about the first time they'd met as children, about the long letters they'd began to trade in recent years, and about Maureen's visit to Perth with George and Trevor the Christmas past, their first in years, and how happy a reunion it had been. Flora barely listened, alternating instead between tinkering with her notes and trying not to cry, and with each subsequent speaker—Gillian Braithwaite, a childhood friend, and Bobby McKenzie from the old general store—the routine was the same: she would stand, thank one person while introducing the next, and then return to her seat between Trevor and her father and shut out anything that threatened to break her composure.

To her surprise that didn't mean the familiar stories, the ones she remembered herself or could easily imagine: her mother mending a torn dress mere minutes before a wedding; her mother single-handedly taking over the general store's scone-baking while Mrs. McKenzie recovered from a broken wrist. No, it was the stories she *couldn't* picture that brought tears to her eyes: the book club Maureen had started for the island women, and her girlish fantasies about Richard Burton, and the impromptu ceilidh she'd thrown on the beach for her twenty-seventh birthday (or her twenty-eighth; Gillian couldn't quite remember). So while the rest of the crowd chuckled ruefully at their memories, Flora felt only regret, both that she hadn't known her mother better, and that she wasn't sure she'd ever really tried. It was a relief when at last she called Trevor to the podium for the day's final eulogy, and she returned to her seat imagining the stiff drink they could soon retire to. Her neck ached from sitting in the odd, sideways pews all morning.

Trevor began quietly. "My mother," he said, shuffling his feet, "was a wonderful woman, and I wouldn't be who I am today without her." He cleared his throat and swallowed hard, and when he continued his voice was louder, more self-consciously projected. "But actually, I don't think any of our lives would be the same if it weren't for Maureen Elizabeth Stewart McCloud." There were a few approving nods around the room at that, Flora noticed, and they seemed to give Trevor some extra confidence as he went on, explaining that although he was devastated to have lost a loving parent, his own loss was insignificant compared to the one suffered collectively by this crowd, and by those who hadn't been able to attend, and by the island's countless future visitors and residents who would never gain, now, from her remarkable gifts. He extolled a long list of her virtues; he told another story or two about her heroic feats helping others; and then he moved on to a reverent description of all the things she'd done with him when she'd visited for his half-term breaks at St. Fillan's: afternoons in tearooms, and evenings in nice restaurants, and the time she'd taken him to Glasgow for a new exhibit at the Burrell.

It was a touching speech, Flora thought, unlike anything she'd expected. Since she'd left the island she'd missed, it seemed, her brother's transformation, from mercurial teenager to thoughtful, mature young man—and she cried at that clear proof of her neglect, these recent years, as much as at the speech itself. She hadn't even come home for Christmas the last three winters—part of the reason, she was sure, that the rest of them returned to Perth last year after so many more at home—and what a bloody mistake that was!

Instead she'd spent the most recent holidays with Oliver at his family home in the Borders, out of some misguided sense of her own maturity, even after it had become clear that a break-up was inevitable. *Why can't we spend Christmas with my family for a change?* she'd asked him as they'd shopped for gifts that year, along a chill Princes Street struggling to project normalcy among the ghosts of the autumn's tragedy in New York. *We've been together for years and you've never even seen where I grew up.* He'd given her a bored glare, familiar from so many identical discussions in recent months. *Because,* he said, *I don't want to spend Christmas on some godforsaken rock in the middle of nowhere.* The remark, much harsher than anything he'd said before, had stung, and she'd stormed off into the dark winter's afternoon, leaving him on his own in the middle of Marks & Spencer—and though ultimately she'd skulked back and given in, as always, the argument flared again and again, most spectacularly at his parents' house on Christmas Eve. After that they sat through a painful Christmas dinner, the next afternoon, and she left on her own on Boxing Day; when he returned, a whole week later, to their cramped flat near the Meadows, they made the split official. Flora moved into Bella's spare room again while she looked for somewhere of her own.

As Trevor finished his speech, now, she heard a sniffle beside her, and turned to see her father crying, dark splotches on his shirt where a few tears had already fallen. *Thank God*, she thought, as she stood up to return to the podium; she'd been afraid the day's meaning might escape him.

As she crossed paths with Trevor she whispered that he'd been brilliant, and kept her eyes on him as she addressed the room one last time, abandoning her notes and saying that she didn't have much to add: Trevor had shared a portrait of their mother more perfect, she nodded emphatically, than anything she could ever paint. She cringed as the words left her mouth—they hadn't sounded as trite in her head—but the sentiment was met with more approving nods around the room, and, grateful for that opportunity to wrap things up, she thanked everyone for coming one last time.

Michael had slipped out as she was talking to go set out the food for the wake, and Trevor joined him now, leaving Flora to stand at the chapel door, arm-in-arm with her father, and see off all the mourners. A woman whose name she couldn't remember stopped and patted her on the arm.

"You did very well dear," she said. "I'm sure your mother would have been proud." She looked to George, who greeted her with a cheerful *how do you do?* Her face fell. "We'll talk more later," she whispered to Flora, and hurried away.

The wake was more of the same, streams of old islanders seeking out Flora and Trevor to applaud their poise in such hard times, and ending up grieving for their father as much as their mother, as he sunnily chattered away with no idea who anybody was. Flora found it exhausting, and by the time the sky was darkening that afternoon, the visitors slowly disappearing to their cottages or their rooms, she was glad to spot Michael sitting alone at a table by the window.

"Penny for them," she said, coming up behind him.

He looked up. "Just...thinking."

She smiled and asked about what, stumbling over her words and realizing that she'd had more to drink than she'd intended. (Everyone who spoke to her that afternoon insisted she take a dram.)

Michael shrugged; paused. Looked around the room. "Things seem to be winding down."

She nodded but didn't say anything, scared now of slurring her words more.

"I suppose we ought to start cleaning," he said, with a sigh. He stood up and stretched his back.

"Not yet," she said. "Let's take a walk." She put her hand on his wrist. "Before it gets too dark."

He frowned, looking around the room again, and told her they shouldn't leave Trevor on his own, which she knew was true—but in that moment she simply didn't care, overwhelmed by the desire to get out of there as fast as she could, and to take Michael with her. She squeezed his wrist where she still held it. "Please?" she said. "Humor me?"

And like that, weakly, he gave in.

She told Trevor they were going to the kitchen and they snuck out the back door, taking the old byway past the chapel and away from the village. When the trail ended they crossed over to the main road for a while, and when that ended too, at the Kilgouries' old crofthouse, they carried on beyond it, into the grass, up a faint rise and over an old fence to the edge of the gentle cliffs on the island's north coast. The sky was a crisp, vernal sunset, a wash of pinks and silvers behind the clouds rolling in across the sea; their cheeks blushed in the wind.

On their left the land sloped down to the pass between the village and the Stùc, half a mile away, and to the land bridge still bulging from the water. From this angle it looked much smaller than usual, dreamlike, the merest of threads connecting the two islands.

"I didn't think it would be low tide right now," said Flora, huddling close to Michael and wrapping her arm around his waist. She remembered, briefly, how only a few months earlier she'd wished she could stand here with Oliver; remembered the emotionless expression on his face as she told him she was leaving. Remembered how even then—even after so many years!—her first thought, walking out the door, had been of Michael. Of what she might have thrown away with him. Of whether she still had a chance to get it back.

"We should go down there," she said.

He was quiet for a moment. "We don't have time," he murmured, putting his arm around her. "It'll be dark soon. And the tide's coming in."

"Ach," she said, letting go of him. "You worry too much." She took a few steps forward, and when she reached the lip of the cliff she knelt down, sizing up a rocky shelf a few feet down the cliff face and then smiling at him over her shoulder. "Live a little."

She hopped over the edge.

Letting out a yelp, he rushed forward, stopping sheepishly when he realized she was fine. "My God, Flora! You should be more careful! You've been drinking!"

"It's nothing," she said, already scrambling onto another shelf, lower still. "I've done this before—there's a path all the way to the beach." She tested her footing on the next ledge and stepped across. "Sort of."

Michael repeated his admonition to be careful and told her this was a terrible idea, but when it became clear she was carrying on regardless he lowered himself over the edge, following as she practically skipped ahead of him. When she reached the bottom he was still only halfway down, and she flopped on the sand to wait, watching as he took his slow, measured steps down the rock face.

She'd been thinking about him a lot since her break-up. If she was honest, she'd been thinking about him even before that, because in Oliver's latest recalcitrance about visiting the island the comparison between the two was too tempting to pass up. Why was she wasting her time, she'd asked herself, with this selfish pipsqueak who didn't care if he even met her family, when she had an admirer back home who'd already given himself entirely to their cause? Not just an admirer—someone she'd previously lusted after, for months! Why had she ever passed that up? After all, it wasn't as if she wanted to abandon the island and never return; she was glad to have gone to art school and liked the prospect of living in Edinburgh long term, but this place would always be home.

A disgruntled shearwater shrieked and flew away as Michael reached the bottom of the cliff and jumped the last few feet to the ground. Flora smiled and stood up.

"See?" she said. "That wasn't so bad."

He laughed. "Still took a few years off my life."

"Oh, wheesht." She came up beside him and took him by the elbow. "Come on, look: the crossing's still here. Let's make a dash for it."

"Flora." He looked at her imploringly. "We can't go over there. We'll get stuck."

He was right, of course—rationally and responsibly and emotionally she knew that. But at the same time she knew she'd never wanted anything more, not when she'd wished that Barry would suddenly show up today, not when she'd decided to go to art school, not even on that day at St. Fillan's when she'd yearned to run off to Tam's room and give into whatever he asked. So she looked at Michael, now, at his eyes, charcoal in the twilight, and she shook her head.

"I don't care," she said, and, still holding onto his elbow, she raised herself onto her tiptoes, just as she had in her studio that rainy afternoon all those years ago, and kissed him. And, just as in her studio, he kissed her back. This time, though, it didn't feel like a surrender, like she was settling for plan B; she simply felt calm, and happy, and decided. And for a minute or two that feeling, and his hipbone beneath her palm, and his chapped lips on hers—that was all she knew.

"I'm glad we met," she said, when she finally pulled away. "You've been so good to me. To all of us." He nodded, but before he could say anything she was dragging him down the beach again, towards the land bridge, and this time he didn't try to stop her. As they crossed, a thin sheet of water spread over the isthmus, breaking in tiny waves against their feet and then their ankles and then their shins, and by the time they reached the other side the path had mostly vanished. They were already looking ahead of them, though, joining hands as amethyst clouds gathered overhead, and breaking into a run—towards the old orchard, and sanctuary, and each other.

XVI.

Trevor spent the whole night worried sick and bellowed as much at Flora when she returned the following morning, Mrs. Kilgourie and several of the other elderly ex-islanders cramming into the pub to join him—not even their previous day's sympathy was enough to quell their love of a good scandal. They upbraided Flora for *running off like some lovestruck teenager*, and whispered disbelievingly to each other, when she weakly defended herself against whoever's turn it was to scold, that it had been *the day of a funeral, for pity's sake*. A row of shaking heads saw off Michael as he skulked back to his cottage. *I'm just glad your mother wasn't here to see it*, Mrs. Kilgourie muttered to Trevor, as Flora finally disappeared upstairs to shower.

And yet as the day wore on, as Trevor exchanged apologies with Flora and forgiveness seemed to settle, he wondered if they should be glad of his mother's absence not for her sake, but for theirs; when he really stopped to ponder how she might have reacted, he doubted their resolution would have come so easy. There would have been far lengthier recriminations, and a week of stubborn silence, and instead of the happy dinner he had with his sister that night, all giggles and nostalgia, Flora would have pouted through the rest of her visit under Maureen's disapproving stare, hiding in her room or on the Stùc, and then escaped back to Edinburgh for months without a peep.

As it was, actually, he still didn't see much of Flora before she left, but for different reasons. Even after the other mourners trickled away, and despite a few unplanned days tacked on at the end of her visit, she spent most of her time with Michael. But Trevor cared less for now about the number of hours she passed with him, than about the number she spent simply on the island, contented, and acquiring more reasons to come back—because if she and Michael became seriously involved, it seemed to him, they were both more likely to keep ties to the island. More likely, in coming years, to settle permanently.

He had obvious reasons for wanting Flora back, of course: with Barry gone and George demented, she was effectively the last survivor among his immediate family. But he'd long been searching for a way to ensure Michael's continued presence, too, because in the man's peculiar obsession with the island Trevor felt he'd found a kindred spirit—someone else, at last, who understood that the guesthouse, and the floundering way of life it represented, were both things worth preserving. And while Trevor was more than willing to bear that responsibility on his own, with his father's decline in recent years he'd realized that, unfortunately, it was much more than a one-man job.

Not that Michael showed any sign of leaving. On the contrary, he'd gradually raised the amount of time he spent on the island each year, of his own accord, from the six or seven months when he'd started to almost eleven now. Partly it was pragmatic: letting his London flat, purchased a decade ago at the edge of what was now a trendy, gentrifying neighborhood, brought him enormous profits. But mostly, as he'd spent more time on the island over the years, he'd developed some sense of belonging there, if not alienation from the hedonistic lifestyle he'd left behind. Or so Trevor liked to hope.

The turning point had been a few years ago—sometime between Flora leaving and the start of his father's illness—after Michael had cut another month off his time in London and some of his friends, in response, decided to finally visit the island and see what all the fuss was about. Michael was unusually anxious at the prospect, and when they arrived Trevor could see why: they were lager louts, all of them, a pair of men and a pair of women, drinking too much and too loudly for his tastes or anyone else's. And then the real disaster: one of the men threw up all over the bar, their last night, and when Maureen went to fetch a mop and bucket she found the other man with one of the women in the public loo, she half-naked and perched on the sink, legs wrapped around him, and he telling her slurringly to *fuck off and let us finish*. Maureen screamed for Michael, who came running, aghast, and sided against his friends—and that was when the fight broke out. It took both Trevor and George and another male guest, pulled groggily from bed, to finally break it up.

Once Michael's friends left the next day he apologized profusely, even offering to give up his post in penitence—though Trevor managed, thank God, to dissuade him. *Thank you for understanding*, he'd replied, more grateful than Trevor had ever seen him. *You see why I prefer it here. Every weekend's like that back home.*

And from then on Michael's whole mindset seemed to change: he installed internet on the island, both at his cottage and the guesthouse, and built a website for the latter; he began a project to replace their costly diesel generators with wind and solar power; and he persuaded the ferry company to install a phone line at the jetty to help visitors who'd missed their crossing. He even talked, though never did anything, about petitioning the Trust to rebuild the bridge to the Stùc—he wanted to convert the old schoolhouse into a museum.

For Trevor, though, the scandal that night, and Michael's reaction, was a sobering reminder of how easily the man could choose to leave—and a relationship with Flora seemed like the perfect way to permanently close off that opportunity. Abandoning a business partner was unfortunate, perhaps, but justifiable; abandoning a girlfriend's family—or a brother-in-law, thought Trevor, his imagination running away with him—was inconceivable. And in the meantime, their relationship would provide an equally perfect way to reel Flora back in. He was giddy at the possibilities.

When Flora finally left the week after the funeral, though, it began to look as if life on the island, at least temporarily, would be a struggle. Trevor and Michael and George—the island's three remaining residents—went to the jetty to see her off, each one giving her a long, wretched hug, and as the ship pulled away Trevor instantly felt the island grow emptier, larger, the uncluttered landscape ominous, suddenly, and the quiet claustrophobic. The other men felt it too, he was sure, because as they trudged back to the guesthouse they made incessant small talk, Michael about some new idea for the website, and George about what the weather might do that night, and Trevor about anything he could think of, really, to hold the creeping void at bay; back at home, too, they clung to each other, moving from room to room together as they busied themselves with cleaning and then sharing dinner in the pub, frittering away the evening with more forced conversation. Despite their best efforts, Trevor lay in bed that night staring at the ceiling and dreading another day of the same anxious hyperactivity. And then another. And then another.

Which was precisely what he got: when Michael showed up

the next morning—after a similarly restless night, it looked like—it was with a notepad, and a thermos of coffee, and a manic, focused energy. With Maureen gone and George less helpful every day, he told Trevor, sitting him down at the kitchen table, they were going to have to make some drastic changes—and for those last weeks before the season they threw themselves into it, updating their operating manuals and filing systems and spreadsheets, and stocking the freezer past Maureen's already ample backlog, and filling every spare hour beyond that with brainstorming sessions to refine their vision of a new, improved guesthouse. Many of their changes were little more than damage control, for the time being, limiting bookings and altering duty rosters and a hundred other tweaks and stopgaps to make the place more manageable. But looking forward they cooked up more ambitious plans, of clearing out the guestrooms upstairs to make way for self-catering suites; of opening up a few old cottages as more of the same; of contracts for frozen meals from mainland suppliers, and summer interns scouted from hospitality programs, and partnerships with B&Bs in Mallaig.

To some extent it helped, actually. During the days Trevor even began to believe their plans would work, that the guesthouse would soon be great again, that years from now he'd look back on their work here as a triumph. On those lonely, sleepless nights in bed, though, he grew glummer, succumbing again and often to his funk. So what, he asked himself, if they got the place on its feet again? It still wouldn't be the guesthouse he remembered, the one he'd long pictured himself inheriting. All the improvements Michael had made the past few years were one thing—the computer, and the redecorated guestrooms, and the modern, energy efficient window frames throughout—but now the very spirit of the place seemed dangerously in flux, transforming into something he neither cared for nor completely understood. Why would anyone even want one of these self-catering suites Michael was so excited about? Who would want a holiday absent the care his parents had always lavished on their guests, and in a setting so sterile? The smell of soup and soapsuds from his mother's kitchen, and his father's vegetable patch, and the old half-finished Monopoly games tucked beneath the coffee table: it was all gone, his family vanished, and even if Flora did return now he doubted it would make much difference.

When they finally opened for the year and some approximation of normality returned, those concerns faded for a while; forced to assume the role of proprietor, something his father could no longer manage, he perked up considerably. In fact, despite the many extra hours cooking and cleaning, and markedly fewer asleep, he enjoyed the job that summer more than he ever had. Even handling complaints, of which inevitably there were several that year, left him with an odd sense of satisfaction.

The summer's happy reprieve, however, only made the autumn's crash more pronounced. Trevor's days seemed to settle in front of him without end, like those days of thick white fog he remembered from his childhood, and he spent his spare hours moping around the house, lost among specters of his mother. All her little routines the first weeks after the season stuck out now in their absence: the paperbacks she'd start, and then leave open to her place in strange spots around the house; the rich smells from the kitchen and disappearing stack of storage tubs in the pantry; and the sound of the radio drifting from the kitchen, tuned to classical music or the world history programs she'd more recently grown to love.

In the meantime, George was getting steadily worse, as if Maureen's death had shaken him from his moorings. One day in November Trevor went to the jetty to fetch supplies, and returned to his father standing motionless by the hallway telephone.

"Call heard for you as you were out," he said, when Trevor asked him what was wrong. (His faintly garbled sentences had started a few weeks after the funeral—or at least, that was when Trevor started noticing them.)

"Oh?" His stomach clenched at the thought of a potential customer getting his father on the phone. "Who was it?"

George blinked. "Barry," he said. "A number left to call him up."

Trevor's heart emptied at his brother's name, but when he hurried to the telephone table and looked at his father's message on the notepad, he found only gibberish. *Barry*, it read. *Arby R. Y Arab? Bay ar(ea)*—and below that a string of numbers sloping downwards for twenty or thirty digits. Shoulders slumping, Trevor wondered if the phone had even rung. Several times in the past few weeks his father had claimed to see and speak with his dead brother James, and a handful of other islanders who had long since passed away—and even, once, to Maureen. This was probably more of the same. Rolling his eyes, Trevor ushered him back to his chair in the living room.

And yet it did seem strange, he thought, as he unpacked the shopping, that his father would imagine Barry; usually his hallucinations involved people from his childhood, the memories most firmly cemented. Barry seemed too recent. And his father had never imagined any of the children before, as far as Trevor knew. Or a phone call.

So once everything was put away, Trevor returned to the telephone table and studied the message again. The first ten digits in the string of numbers did look as if they could be a phone number...He looked up and towards the living room, where he could hear his father humming to himself.

It couldn't be.

Fingers trembling, he picked up the handset and punched in

the number. There was the normal, brief silence as the call made its way to the exchange on the mainland—but then only the scolding, three-tone noise of a non-existent circuit, and British Telecom's haughty matron telling him the number had not been recognized. Handset still pressed to his ear, he ended the call with his thumb and frowned at the message pad again. Tried dialing another set of the numbers, and then another, each time with the same result, until at last, on his fifth attempt, he heard ringing. Held his breath.

"Hello?" It was a man's voice.

Trevor hesitated. "I—um..." He hadn't thought what he might say if someone answered. "May I speak to Barry McCloud please?"

He braced himself.

"There's no Barry McCloud here, pal. Think you've got a wrong number."

Trevor's eyes shut; his head sagged. He muttered sorry and slammed the phone down, suddenly furious—at himself for entertaining the possibility and at his father for putting it in his head in the first place. Down the hall the senile old coot was still humming his constantly remodulating tune, oblivious to what he'd done.

With a sigh, Trevor tore off the message and tossed it in the bin, and began yanking open drawers on the telephone table looking for some place to hide the pad. But the first two drawers were too full of phonebooks and the miscellaneous stamps and postcards they kept on hand for guests, and in the mostly empty third he spotted something else. He moved his head closer, squinting to get a better look.

The objects he'd collected from the chapel.

He'd never looked for them again after they disappeared in April, partly because he assumed they'd been thrown out but mostly because, in the commotion with Michael and Flora, he'd forgotten all about them. Yet apparently they'd been here the whole time, thoughtfully put away by someone, and waiting for him to find them again. He fished them from the drawer, one by one. Their slight weight in his hands was soothing, somehow, disarming, temporarily squeezing out his anger. Calling to his father that he'd be down shortly to start on lunch, he started towards the stairs, telling himself he ought to put these somewhere safe before they disappeared again.

In his room, he made straight for the closet and pulled out the most current box from his collection's three. Out of habit he sat down on the floor beside it, to sort through and savor some of its other recent additions before he added the new ones. There was his invitation to Flora's degree show at ECA; the fuel cap from the guesthouse's old diesel generator, now replaced by Michael's solar panels; and a gnarled piece of driftwood, a rusted nail lodged in one end the only clue that it had once been part of the bridge to the Stùc. As he picked up each item, holding them to the light to look a little closer, or running his hands along their surfaces to wipe them clean of dust, he felt his temper subsiding even further, and when he came across his mother's old alarm clock he even found himself approaching a regretful sort of happiness.

The clock was an old-fashioned model, with Roman numerals on its face and two brass bells on top. A few weeks before she died it had broken, as if prompting her to give up just as insistently as it woke her each morning, and they'd replaced it with a modern digital one she hated. This clock, though, the one that had sat by her bedside since Trevor was a baby, still felt decidedly like his mother's—and, inspired, he started rooting more purposefully through the box for anything else of hers, quickly reaching the bottom and pulling out a second. To his delight he found a few of the letters she'd sent him at school—mostly news about whichever ex-islander she'd heard from most recently—and a beat-up pair of the nicer shoes she always wore to see him on the mainland; beneath all that was a lock of hair from one of the trims George sometimes used to give her, and, wrapped in plastic to prevent its smell from spreading, the wooden spoon he'd found her gripping when she died, a few dried specks of porridge still caked on the handle. He'd amassed a relatively impressive pile of stuff by the time he got to the last box—or the first one, really, the one he'd started with.

As he pulled it from the shelf he realized he had very little idea what was actually in it, anymore; he'd filled it by the time he was fourteen or fifteen—*coming up on ten years now*, he realized—and since then had hardly touched it. Unfortunately there didn't seem to be much more of his mother in it, and in the end he found only a few more things: the faded, family photograph he'd often stared at as a child, image crumbling away around the crease down its center, and a painted Easter egg the two of them had made one year. And last of all, rolled up and stuffed tightly in the corner of the box, one of her old, flimsy cardigans.

He almost missed the cardigan, actually, assuming it was a blanket until he noticed the bulge of a button in the fabric and shook the thing out. As soon as he realized what it was, his spirits leapt, and he brought it to his face, eyes closed, snuggling against the soft fibers. After so many years in storage it smelled overwhelmingly of cardboard and mildew, but beneath that he thought he could still detect a few bursts of his mother's scent: the dried lavender she kept in her dresser drawers to ward away moths, and a muddy mixture of sweat, talc, and the fancy perfume she wore for special occasions. He let out a contented sigh. This was exactly the sort of find he'd been hoping for.

Letting it drop to his lap again, he tried to remember how it had come to be in the collection. There was nothing wrong with it, no stains or tears that might have made her throw it out, which struck him as particularly odd—most of his items were salvaged from the rubbish, and he would have expected his mother to miss a perfectly good piece of clothing. So where had he found it? He rubbed the collar between his thumb and forefinger, trying to jog his memory. A faint image of one of the guestrooms came to mind. *Yes*, he thought, as the details began to rise out of the murk: Flora had just started at St. Fillan's. His dad had gone to the mainland to tend to some trouble Barry'd been in at school, and with the guesthouse full of the rat-catchers his mother was leaning on him for extra help with the chores; he found the cardigan when she asked him to make the beds one morning. He remembered balking at the job, because he'd been young enough that he'd never made one before and wasn't sure he'd know how—but his mother had shown little sympathy and sent him sternly upstairs. He remembered, too, how confused he'd been at finding the cardigan there, bunched up between the bed and the wall in one of the single guestrooms; remembered rubbing it between his fingers as he was doing now, and the thrilling, seductive mystery of an object out of place. It was relatively dressy, not one his mother would have worn for cleaning the guestrooms, and at the time he hadn't been able to think of any reason it might be up there.

Now he found himself wondering again. His mother had rarely fraternized with guests, and certainly never upstairs; *if they want our company*, she'd always told the children, *they'll come to us*. So what on earth could she have been doing up there in her nice clothes—removing her nice clothes, even!—on a night when her husband was away? A grim theory began to congeal as he struggled to remember more details, an uncomfortable lump forming at the back of his throat. He'd seen enough soap operas on the common room television at St. Fillan's that he could fit the pieces together well enough. A long marriage; an attractive outsider. An affair.

He shook his head. Tried to tell himself it was absurd. She had been a loyal wife and an exemplary mother; she couldn't possibly have done anything so sordid. And yet...Now other memories were surfacing, too: her late nights in the pub while the catchers had been there; how she'd insisted she couldn't go to St. Fillan's herself that week, despite her usual fondness for the mainland. And why *was* she always wearing those nice shoes of hers when she came to visit? Who had she been trying to impress? Where had she been stopping on her way?

His earlier anger was returning now, accompanied by a growing sense of horror. Which of the rat catchers was it? How many times? Were there others, too? He flung the cardigan away from him, now, tears burning in his eyes. There had to be another explanation, he told himself. There had to be!

"Trevor," his father called from downstairs. "It's lunchtime."

Letting out a frustrated sob, he banged his fist against the floor. *Not now!* He took a deep breath. Slowly stood up and walked to the door. "I know, Dad," he replied, trying to keep a level voice. "I'll be down in a minute."

"Barry phoned."

"Yes, Dad, of course he did. You already told me." He could feel his last shreds of patience slipping away, his blood pressure rising. His hand, still gripping the doorframe, squeezed the wood tighter, until the bones in his fingers felt like they might snap.

"Trevor," his father repeated, after a few more moments. "It's lunchtime."

With another exasperated roar, he stepped into the hallway. "Fine!" he yelled. "It's fucking lunchtime!" He jogged down the stairs, head pounding, and shoved his father out of the way as he passed him at the bottom step. That contact—his tense hand against his father's soft, ageing flesh—stirred a brief feeling of guilt, but even as he tried to take a deep breath, to remind himself it was only the Condition talking, the dementia, whatever it was, he was turning around to the sight of his father still cowering by the staircase, a pathetic look on his face, and for some reason that only incensed him more.

"Trevor—"

"Don't tell me!" he shouted. "Fucking lunchtime, is it?" He stalked back to his father. *Not his fault, Trevor.* He grabbed him by the wrist. "Come on then," he said, "I'm not bloody feeding you out here!"

He can't help it, Trevor.

In the kitchen he pushed his father into a chair at the table and fetched a few ingredients from the cupboards. As he began furiously chopping an onion he could see the veins in his forearm bulging, could feel his teeth grind painfully together, and was asking that reasonable voice in his head why it wouldn't be better to just throw the old coot off the end of the jetty and put him out of his misery, when behind him his father croaked again.

"Trevor."

He spun around. "*What!*"

There were a few tears running down his father's cheeks. "I'm sorry."

And then, as if a valve had opened, all the pressure that had been building in Trevor's chest seemed to rush up towards his face, and tears began to form in his eyes, too. *Put him out of his misery?* the voice asked, fading away. *Or put you out of yours?*

It wasn't long, after that, until things with Michael began to slide too. Though in past winters he and Trevor had seemed like close friends—spending the long evenings in the pub, or at grandfather McCloud's old card table, pulled from beneath the stairs, or simply reading side by side in the living room—now the man was too preoccupied with Flora to do much else. Most nights he spent at his own cottage either at the computer or on the phone, making what Trevor could only assume were noxious declarations of eternal love. (He'd never had much taste for romance, which perhaps explained his lack of success with the opposite sex while at school.)

His waning enthusiasm for the relationship wasn't down only to Michael's withdrawal, however, or even to Trevor's subsequent loneliness: he'd also realized that, contrary to what he'd hoped in the spring, it wasn't bringing Flora any closer either. She hadn't come home any more often, and it certainly didn't seem to be increasing her attachment to Trevor or the business; the few times she did visit, for the occasional long weekend, and an entire ten days around Christmas, she didn't even spend the time at home, sleeping instead at Michael's cottage and moving her things there the way she'd once done with the mansion on the Stùc. When she wasn't there canoodling, she was sketching or on the phone scheduling some event, and Trevor, mostly on his own or chatting vacuously with his father, seemed not even to exist.

Throughout it all he stewed about his mother, too, swinging back and forth almost daily from knowing her infidelity was impossible to knowing, just as surely, that there was no other explanation. That was the worst part: the never being sure. No longer could he call up some happy image of her to remind himself what he was fighting to preserve, or how idyllic the guesthouse had once been, or why his solitary nights in the pub that winter, crying bitterly into his whisky, were still worth struggling through—because all of them, now, came with unpleasant questions attached.

By the time the summer rolled around, Trevor and Michael's second on their own, running the guesthouse had predictably lost much of its allure. Trevor toiled through without much charm or pleasure, and Michael, his attitude towards work suddenly lackadaisical, came to view the guesthouse as more of a nuisance, it seemed, than anything else. Their weekly planning meetings grew curter and less productive, Trevor frequently losing his temper at what he now saw as Michael's arrogant obsession with the bottom line, and Michael condescending to Trevor about his untenable nostalgia. When October arrived and they finally closed again, exhausted, Michael announced he'd be upping his time on the mainland again that winter, spending December through February in Edinburgh with Flora—and Trevor began to think he'd be better off after all if the two of them just left him alone and let him do things his way. Began to realize that, like it or not, that might soon be the case anyway.

So when the letter from the ferry company arrived a few weeks later, informing him they'd no longer be operating their separate summer schedule to the island—that after the usual mid-November drop to three crossings a week that would be it, all year round—he didn't mention it to Michael. Not so much because he feared that this would finally make the man give up, but from some stubborn determination to face the problem without any help. Even as he re-read the letter a second and third time after his father was in bed that night, he decided he had to prove to them, or to himself, or to *someone*, that he could manage on his own. So he simply hid the letter in his bedside table and went for a walk to clear his head.

It was getting late as he wandered onto the path towards the Stùc, and even with the faint light on the horizon the landscape had turned a velvet black. He'd left the house without a torch, something his father had always scolded him not to do, but he enjoyed the novelty of seeing the island this way—his eyes adjusting to the dark, the twilight giving the hills a fleeting, luminescent depth, and in the distance the whisper of the ocean growing to a roar.

Once the path opened up to the glimmer of water, he sat

down on the sand and began to ponder his options. His only chance, really, was to come up with a way to change the ferry company's mind: the guesthouse itself was barely scraping by as it was, and cutting out the pub's income from summer day-trippers would be the deathblow he'd dreaded for years. And yet each idea that came to him—a letter-writing campaign, a plea to his local MP, some offer of sharing the guesthouse's (non-existent) profits— seemed more hopeless than the last, and before long he'd been reduced to asking himself, sourly, what Michael would do. And worse, after that: asking himself whether Michael's help would even make a difference.

With a sigh, at last, he looked out across the water, towards the horizon, where there was still a wispy ring of gasflame blue— as if somehow, far away, the sea had caught alight.

XVII.

*The light goes out and...*What? *Title hgh. High lett. Eighth lt?*

"Fuck!"

Eighth lt. goes towards death (3,5).

A clatter; Trevor walking into something in the dark.

The light.

"The light."

"Yes, Dad, the light. I know. I'm trying to fix it."

He shifts nervously in his chair. "What's wrong?"

A sigh. "I'm not sure yet."

They had been eating dinner in the kitchen, when suddenly the light above the table went out. Not just the light: the numbers on the microwave, and the faint glow around the door, and the illuminated dial on the countertop radio. Other than the hiss of rain outside, all the sounds stopped, too.

In the hallway he hears Trevor jiggling the light switch up and down. Swearing again. He leans back in his chair. *It's dark to eat like this (?).*

"Sit tight, Dad," calls Trevor. *Gorge?* "I have to check the generator." *Biliously?* "Dad?"

"Okay, Trevor. I'll sit here."

Listen: make it darker to eat less (4).

The front door creaks open; slams shut.

Diet.

Trevor's so good to be looking after him like this. Such a splendid young man. And he's taken the reins around the guesthouse quite brilliantly, too. Has the place running like clockwork. Not many guests these days, mind. But things will pick up soon.

The front door slams again.

"Well," says Trevor, stomping into the kitchen, a flashlight in his hand. George can smell the rain on him. "Looks like we're finishing by candlelight."

"Candlelight?"

Trevor walks towards him, slowly, careful not to hit anything in the dark. "The electricity's fucked somehow. Fantastic thing to happen in the middle of January."

There is a gloating gust of wind outside.

"I'll take a proper look in the morning—I can't see a thing out there right now." He sighs. "I don't suppose you remember where the candles are?"

Candles. Torches, lamps, flames. Wicks.

"I'll take that as a no." He rummages through some of the kitchen drawers, then disappears into the hallway. Five minutes pass. Ten?

"Found some," says Trevor, reappearing with two shot glasses from the bar, a candle standing crookedly in each. "They were under the stairs." He places them carefully on his side of the table. Away from George.

They finish eating; sit awhile. Before long Trevor puts George to bed. ("Not much else we can do tonight, eh?" he says, nodding towards the shrinking candles.) He lies there for hours, not tired. It's still too early to sleep. Isn't it? These days it's so hard to tell. Time seems to stretch recently, contract, spill over, days bleeding into hours bleeding into weeks. Whole seasons sometimes pass him by.

It isn't as bad, though, as everyone seems to think. The way people talk to him now—talk *about* him, as if he isn't there, or look at him with misplaced pity—you'd think he was already dead. But what's a little confusion every now and then? No, maybe he's not as sharp as he used to be, and he knows he's forgotten things he shouldn't—and the trouble moving is a worry, too, if only because he doesn't notice it happening half the time. He'll be standing up from the table, or buttoning his shirt in the morning, and it will be as if his mind has wandered: he'll start to daydream about a flower he saw once, or a room he stood in long ago, and all of a sudden whole minutes have passed and he's still stuck mid-motion, Trevor or that nice young fellow from down the road staring at him in concern. But give him some credit, damn it! He still gets through the days in one piece, still carries on a pretty decent conversation, still manages to get a few clues in the crossword every night. As long as he sticks to his routines, he's fine.

"The only thing I feel bad about," he says, softly, "is Trevor."

In the dark, his wife perches next to him on the bed. "What's wrong with Trevor?"

"He's unhappy."

More than unhappy, really. Something harder to define. A change in the way he talks, and the way he moves, a sort of doleful blandness to his manner. Signs—signs he knows he should understand—of something Trevor won't say, but wants to. And this is where George really does rue his mental slowing down, because even if he hasn't always been the perfect father, he feels sure that in the past he would have *got it*, would have known exactly what to do—whereas now he just watches as Trevor lopes helplessly along, and feels in response some elusive, intangible remorse.

He says goodnight to Maureen, and then it's morning. Red numbers flashing above his head.

He dresses himself and goes downstairs.

"Dad," says Trevor, standing over a pot on the stove. "I was about to come get you."

The fridge is humming again.

"I borrowed a part from Michael's cottage to get the power working," he explains, dipping a ladle into the pot, "but we'll need to pick up a new one in Fort William." He hands a steaming bowl to George. "Just as well we're going over today."

George stops as he takes his breakfast. "We're going to Fort William?"

Trevor sighs. "Yes, Dad, we're going to Fort William and staying two nights—I must have told you fifty times. I have a meeting with the ferry people."

Perhaps this does sound familiar. Ferry people. Yes. *Ferry people not starting to run off (5).* He's been dreading it.

"Why do I have to go?" he asks.

"Because I can't very well leave you here alone, can I?"

"You leave me here alone all the time."

"That's different, Dad." He laughs, though it sounds more bitter than amused. "You can't get into much trouble when I'm gone for half an hour to pick up the shopping. This'll be three days."

"I can cope."

Trevor pours the rest of the pan's contents into a bowl of his own. "No, Dad, you can't, and you're not going to convince me now any more than the last three times we had this conversation."

Have they really discussed this before? "But Trevor, I—"

"Enough, Dad!" He flings the pan into the sink, where it lands with a loud clatter. His face is red. "Now eat up. We have to leave in an hour."

George sits, sullen, and begins to eat. This is precisely the sort of coddling he can't stand. More distressing right now, though, is the prospect of the mainland—because if his routines are all he has to orient himself, now, then the mainland is a break from those routines beyond all others: the place is terrifying, a mess of people and places and customs as impenetrable as the radio soaps he now listens to joylessly, out of habit. The last time he went to the mainland was a year ago, for a hospital visit, and he felt so vulnerable there, so hopelessly dependent on Trevor, that he doesn't wish to repeat the experience.

He scrapes up the last of his porridge. "Why can't you just talk to the ferry people on the phone?" he says.

But Trevor isn't in the kitchen anymore; he's banging around upstairs.

George quietly takes his bowl to the sink and washes it: one of his routines, and a hard-earned one. As his seizures and tremors had worsened the past few years, Trevor tried to stop him doing dishes altogether. *At best you'll break something*, he'd said; *at worst you'll take a finger off*. But George wasn't having it: *I'm not an invalid*, he'd bellowed, and very fluidly, he thought, had banged his fist against the table. They settled, in the end, on George doing his own dishes at the end of every meal.

He places his bowl in the drying rack, now, and shuts off the faucet. Routine.

Trevor appears in the doorway telling him it's time to go, but still George lingers. Asks again why Trevor can't just call the ferry people on the phone.

"Because, Dad," he replies, his cheeks flushing, "this is pretty much the last thing between us and having to close up for good, and I want to make it clear how serious I am." He squeezes his eyes shut; rubs the bridge of his nose. Tells George to put his shoes on.

George does as he's told, but sitting on the staircase's bottom step and tying his laces, he looks up at Trevor, looming over him and leaning on the banister, and makes one last plea. "What if Michael looks in on me?"

Trevor's face darkens. "He can't. He's fucked off to the mainland to visit Flora." He looks over his shoulder. "Everyone's fucked off to the mainland."

George stands up. "Let me stay here by myself, then. I'll be okay."

Trevor turns to face him again, staring for a few seconds without reacting. Finally he lets out a frustrated yell. "Fuck sake, Dad! You're like a child!"

"I—"

"Okay! Fine! You want to stay here so much, fucking stay here! It'll be easier without you, anyway." And then he reaches out with both hands and shoves George backwards, sending him stumbling on the bottom step and falling against the stairs. A sharp edge digs into his spine, and he yelps, but Trevor is already turning away, luggage in hand; the front door has slammed shut before George can think of anything to say.

He lies there without moving, back throbbing, for what feels like several minutes, but when he eventually stands up, gingerly, and makes his way to the living room, he can still see Trevor in the distance, stalking away in miniature. A fine drizzle, the remnants of last night's rain, is blowing all around him.

Trevor hit him! *Every other blow a choker (3).* But he only did it because he was annoyed, George knows that, and everybody gets annoyed sometimes. Anyway, George is safer now because of it, at home with no trip to make after all. And he *can* look after himself for a few days, easy-peasy, no matter what Trevor says.

He looks around the living room. Sometime recently—he isn't sure exactly when—they moved his armchair from its old position, facing into the room with the other furniture, so that now it looks out the window, over the village glen. A few of the old cottages are visible a little ways off, towards the left of the glass; behind them the grey-green landscape curves and rises up into the ridge of a hill, and behind that the sky is almost white. He sits down to watch the island come awake, as he does every morning. Routine.

The rain intensifies, hissing lightly against the window. He closes his eyes. Listens. Opens them again and sees the clouds have darkened. Swiveling in his chair—his back protesting after the fall—he tries to see the time on the mantel clock, but the hands seem not to have moved since he sat down. He closes his eyes again. His stomach gurgles.

For some reason, Trevor hasn't brought him the newspaper yet. And where has Trevor disappeared to, anyway?

He's on the mainland. He's not coming back for a few days. *He's over back between the tower walls (6).*

So no paper today, no skimming through the increasingly opaque news. No arriving greedily at the crossword. No routine.

Hmph.

Should he go get it himself? No. The clouds are even darker, now, the hiss of rain a growl; he shouldn't go to the jetty in that. So what instead? His stomach gurgles again; he squirms in his seat to look at the clock and sees it's almost noon. Lunchtime.

There's no food on the kitchen table, of course, nothing prepared; Trevor isn't here. He'll have to find something for himself. In front of the open fridge he frowns, and tries to think what he can make. On the top shelf he spots a plastic container labeled *Spag bol*, which he pulls out—*excellent*, he thinks, *just reheat and serve*—but once he's put it in the microwave he can only stare blankly at the controls, unsure how to start it. Eventually he gives up and eats the noodles cold.

In his armchair the sky is darker again. Sooty. The rain is still rattling against the window frames, and the wind still smacking against the walls—and as he watches, the blackness outside seems to creep in, smoke-like, around the edges of the glass. Time isn't passing; it's circling. He closes his eyes. The room is empty.

He pulls himself out of his chair and goes to the pub. The furniture is in stacks around the edges of the room, covered in dust tarps, and he twirls the lights on, full strength, to bring them out of the shadows. The air gleams.

It's the middle of the off-season, that much he knows, but he needs something to occupy him—so he moves to the closest table and carefully removes the tarp, guiding it up and over the chair legs so it won't get caught. That done, he folds it in half, corner to corner, three times, four times, five. He places the resulting bundle on the bar. Then he's back to the table again, taking down chairs, standing them right-side-up on the floor; he's pulling the table to the center of the room and arranging the chairs around it. This is good: he's calming down again, focusing on the task. Routine.

Ringing.

Routine. He moves to another table and begins the process again, tarp off, chairs down, table out. The ringing stops.

He carries on until the whole room is set up and ready to receive guests, then moves to the doorway and admires his handiwork. The clock above the bar reads almost five. He nods. Shuts off the lights again. Outside, night has fallen, and he moves from room to room, closing all the curtains. The ringing is back.

He saves the living room for last, the black window there still worrying him. When at last he has no choice but to foray inside, he turns on the hallway lights first so that when he flings open the living room door a yellow rectangle flaps down across the floor. Quickly, he reaches around the frame and feels for the switch, and then the lights are on, expelling the darkness, and he moves to the window to pull the curtains shut. Much better.

He sits down in his chair. That bloody ringing starts again.

The phone!

He doesn't answer the phone much anymore; Trevor doesn't like him to, and usually gets to it first. But George can still put on a good public face when he needs to, so out of the chair now and into the hallway he lifts the receiver from its cradle.

"Fìor Guesthouse, how can I help you?"

"Dad! Thank God! I've been trying to call for hours!"

He blinks. "Hello?"

"Is everything okay there, Dad? Are you hurt?"

"Hurt?"

"Look, Dad, I'm sorry about before. I'm so sorry. I was just angry, and I wasn't thinking straight, and as soon as the ferry pushed away I knew I'd made a mistake—but they wouldn't go back. Said they had to get to Mallaig before the weather turned." He swears. "And I got off at Rum to hitch a ride back with the doctor, but with this storm, and in the dark..."

"Would you like to reserve a room?"

"Oh, Christ." The voice pauses. "Dad, listen to me: this is Trevor. Your son. Do you understand?"

"Trevor?"

"Yes, Dad. I'm on Rum, and I'm trying to get someone to bring me home, but the sea's too rough. I'm probably stuck here 'til morning."

"You're stuck there 'til morning."

"I need you do exactly what I say, okay Dad? I need you to go upstairs to bed, right now, and try to go to sleep."

He looks at the hallway clock. "It's dinnertime."

"I know Dad, and I'm sorry. I shouldn't have left you there like this. Fuck. I'm so sorry, Dad. I was just so frustrated...Dad? Dad!"

"Fíor Guesthouse, how can I help you?"

"Oh Jesus fuck." He sniffles; perhaps he's ill. "Dad, please, it's Trevor. Do you remember? Your son, Trevor." He's almost whispering.

"Trevor."

"Yes, Dad, Trevor. Now go upstairs, please. Do you understand me? You have to go upstairs. You'll be safe that way, and I'll be home as soon as I can. Okay?"

"Okay."

"You're going to go to bed right now?"

"Yes."

He seems to choke. "Good. Fantastic. I'll see you soon, Dad. As soon as I can."

"Okay, Trevor. Goodbye."

He hangs up. Tries to concentrate. It had been Trevor on the phone. He'd said to go to bed and wait.

He looks at the clock again. It's still dinnertime, not bedtime.

I've misunderstood, somehow. I've misunderstood him again.

His stomach rumbles and he goes to the kitchen thinking he should fix dinner, though he isn't very used to cooking anymore. Something easy, then. An omelette. He can still make a simple omelette.

He goes to the fridge, trying to remember what he needs. *Omelette. Let me toe. Eel totem. Motel Tee. Motel Tee confuses breakfast order (8). Breakfast spelled out in chrome lettering (8). Let me toe scrambled egg dish (8). Egg dish.*

Eggs!

The mixing bowls aren't where they should be, so he retrieves his porridge dish from the drying rack and begins whisking together three eggs in it. The whisk *had* been in its proper place, in a ceramic jug on the counter, along with all the ladles and wooden spoons and a potato masher. The jug—glazed in a flaxen white, with thistles painted around its sides in thick streaks of navy blue—had belonged to another family, but when they'd moved away they'd given it to George and Reenie. *The Leslies!* They hadn't wanted to take it with them, they said; were afraid it might break in transit. Were afraid it might remind them of all they'd left behind.

He blinks again. He's standing over the table, the whisk gripped in one hand and the bowl, tipping imperceptibly towards him, in the other; egg is dribbling over the edge and onto the table and down his front, and he rights it violently, dropping the whisk as he does so. More egg spatters against the cuff off his trousers. Behind him, Reenie tuts.

"Egg makes an awful stain, you know. Trevor'll have a time getting that out."

"I can do it myself," George mumbles. "I don't want to trouble him."

She shrugs, and is gone.

He needs the cheese grater.

A wall of cupboards and drawers towers up in front of him, white panels and metal knobs. A few of the doors are still gaping from his search for the mixing bowls, and the dark squares and lines seem to shuffle around in front of him into a giant, lopsided puzzle grid.

No; *routine!*

He lurches forward and begins throwing more doors open, trying to rein in the kitchen. The damn grater has to be somewhere! *We hear it's better to shred all sorts of things (6).* Frantic, he reaches deep into the cupboards, shifting around plates and casseroles and cake tins, greasy jars of mace and nutmeg; soggy boxes of bicarbonate of soda. A food processor, an electric mixer. A coffee grinder.

"Bloody hell!" he yells, slumping, his hands still hooked on the bottom lip of the cupboard. He leans his forehead against the frame.

"Calm down," says Reenie. He spins around.

The grater is on the table.

Routine, routine, routine.

He fetches some cheddar from the fridge. Puts a pan on the stove and turns on the heat.

"Trevor wanted you to go upstairs," Reenie reminds him, leaning on the counter.

"He's just being a fusspot."

"He wants to look after you."

"He shouldn't have to!" George looks up as he shouts this, hands trembling against the grater. "I should be able to look after myself! I should be able to make myself a meal and put myself to bed without him holding my hand!" He struggles for breath.

The ringing has started again.

"Fior Guesthouse," he says, in the hallway. "How can I help you?" But only the dial tone hums back. *Dial tone for your noggin? (3)*

The ringing is still there.

He's in the kitchen again.

Smoke is overflowing from the pan on the stove, its skin of egg black and blistering. When did he even pour it in? He lunges for the stove and throws the pan in the sink, where it clangs against the porridge pot from that morning. There's blood on the counter. Blood on the floor. A menacing trail of pearly drops leading from the sink to the stove to the table. The grater is covered in blood too, the cheese a crimson mess. *A crimson mess. Mr. Casino. Omnicars. Minorcas!*

He looks down at his hands, now covered in a cross-hatching of cuts and gruesome flaps of skin, and smeared all over with sticky, drying blood.

These birds are a crimson mess (8).

"You need help, George," says Reenie, still in her chair.

He groans and runs his hands down his face. It stings. "What will Trevor say when he sees all this?"

"He told you to go straight to bed."

"I know!" A few, discouraged tears creep into his field of vision. "I know."

The ringing has finally stopped.

"You need help, George," Reenie says again, and folds her arms.

And then he's by the front door, pulling on his boots. That Michael down the road is always fixing things—maybe he can help. Or Jack Kilgourie. Or Kenny Burke or John Braithwaite or that fellow who used to run the general store—there must be *someone* who can get everything sorted out. If they hurry, they can even finish before Trevor gets home, and he'll never have to know what happened.

He opens the front door. A swarm of rain and hail blows in at him.

It's dark outside. Too dark. After what feels like only a few steps, he loses his nerve, turns back to the house—but behind him, through the wall of raindrops in the sky and streaming down his face, he can't see any sign of it.

Panicking, he tries to retrace his steps, his woolen sweater clinging to his shoulders, sodden. Weighing him down.

He's shivering.

The last time he'd been out in weather like this was that night years ago—or was it only months?—when the bridge had blown away. He remembered how the mud glommed to his feet, then, and how the terror crept up his neck, and how his skin felt as if it were peeling away in the wind. He remembers the wretched look on Reenie's face when he returned, and the sex and how surprised he'd been, not by the act itself but by the sense of closeness it brought him—the intimacy he hadn't realized he'd been missing. He remembers his relief when Mr. Lewis called, and his happiness at seeing the children the next morning, Trevor's enthusiasm and Flora's fealty and even Barry's awful sullenness; remembers his grief, in the years that followed, as the elder two disappeared again. Remembers his guilty fear, especially with Flora, that he was the one to drive them away.

He's standing still, struggling to move his legs forward, whether against the wind and rain or his own failing synapses, he can't quite tell. His lower back is throbbing.

"Reenie," he gasps, and falls to the ground.

"You should know better than to leave the house without a coat at this time of year," she says, kneeling next to him. Stroking his hair.

"Tell the children I'm sorry," he says.

She frowns, and somehow he can see her face perfectly, even in the dark. "For what?"

"For making them feel responsible for me," he tells her, teeth chattering. "For making it so hard for them to stay." He smiles, sadly, at the touch of her fingers against his scalp. "I suppose you must have felt that way yourself, sometimes."

But she says nothing in response, and when he looks up again she's gone.

Reenie! He half sits up, looking desperately from side to side, but he can't see a thing in the squall. With a grunt he tries to lift his arms, to turn onto his front, to crawl after her wherever she's gone and find her one last time. But his body only seizes, stuttering, and he crumples to the ground again, into the stream of rainwater trickling beneath him, and the wet grass flocking around his head. Black clouds swirl above. His legs begin to numb.

And that's it; he won't get up again. Won't be there when Trevor returns in the morning, sprinting from the jetty and stumbling every few yards as the waterlogged ground gives way beneath him; won't be there when his son cries out at the blood smeared all around the kitchen, at the single stove burner still flickering a mournful blue, at the pub set out perfectly for business; won't be there in the coming days when Barry, swallowing his pride at last, and his shame, phones again and this time Trevor answers; won't be there when all three siblings return for one more funeral, or when afterwards they leave. Instead he'll simply lie there in the dark a little longer, and finally, whispering apologies, he'll let his eyes fall shut.

Author's Note

I'm afraid I must disappoint anyone hoping to visit Eilean Fìor and see the place with his or her own eyes; the place exists only in my flawed and rather questionable imagination. However, astute readers may notice similarities between my imaginary island and several other locations around the west of Scotland, from where I freely admit to having drawn inspiration: Tom Steel's excellent history of St. Kilda, appropriately titled *The Life and Death of St. Kilda*, provided many valuable and haunting details about life in extreme isolation and at the mercy of the elements; Anna Blair's *Croft and Creel*, and particularly its history of Lewis, was instrumental in filling in the details of Fìor's past; and numerous other books and articles supplied the narrative with flashes of colour and atmosphere far more vivid than anything I could have come up with on my own.

More than anything else, however, Fìor owes its essential features to the Small Isles, the group of four Hebridean islands to which it putatively belongs. In particular it shares many traits with Canna, which claims the real title of "smallest and most remote" in the archipelago. Canna also struggled with a mysterious rat infestation in the last decade, and Canna, too, occasionally finds itself split in half depending on the tides. (Sanday, Canna's "Stùc", is also home to the schoolhouse in real life, and the footbridge connecting them was torn away in a storm—though there's still an easy road crossing when the tide is in.) Saddest of all, in the six years since I began this book, Canna's inhabitants—none of whom, I hasten to add, bear resemblance to the characters in this story except by extraordinary coincidence—have been reduced in numbers from thirty to just twelve.

I can't comment, though, on how the Cannans feel about all this. Indeed, given the pitiful amount of time I spent on Canna doing research, I can't really comment on their real-life plight in any capacity. Instead, I encourage anyone wishing to find out more about life in the area to take the trip and ask the Cannans personally. It is most certainly worth the effort—and, if camping isn't your thing, you will be thrilled to know that Canna, like Fìor, has a guesthouse where, at the end of your journey north, you can rest your weary feet.

Acknowledgments

Above all I must thank Kathryn Davis, the judge of the AWP 2012 Prize in the Novel, and Kate Bernheimer, one of the contest's initial screeners, both of whom picked this manuscript from a field, I'm sure, of many other deserving entries. Thanks also to the Association of Writers and Writing Programs, and all at New Issues Press—particularly Kim Kolbe and Elizabyth Ann Hiscox, who were very patient with all my silly first-time author habits, and Megan Lappe, who provided the beautiful illustration on the cover.

Dozens of people also suffered through earlier drafts of this manuscript, most notably Margot Livesey, my amazing MFA thesis chair and an editor more thoughtful, generous, hard-working, and dedicated than any writer could hope for. Thanks also to Jessica Treadway, my thesis reader, as well as Lise Haines, Kim McLarin, and the many students in their respective writing workshops, for their valuable advice on preliminary drafts. And Barb, from David Emblidge's Book Editing class—I'm ashamed to admit that I've forgotten your last name, but I will never forget your admonitions to stop explaining everything twice and not to start so many sentences with "And then..."

While I'm thanking the people who have suffered through my

first drafts, one group of people deserve a paragraph all their own: the members past and present of Write Club, in all its incarnations. Heinz Healey Schaldenbrand, Erica Dorpalen, Michelle Fernandes, Akshay Ahuja, Annie McGough, Kim Liao, Kirstin Chen, Bridget Pelkie, Taylor Shann, Jill Gallagher, Mike Dunphy, Alex Sharp... And, in the years before Write Club, Anca Szilagyi, Julian Smith, Ilya Zaychik, Danny Spitzberg, and the other members of my various writing squares and heptagons. You are all saints—even those of you who only ever made one meeting.

Dozens of people also suffered through me as I wrote earlier drafts of this manuscript, and they deserve the biggest cheers of all: my family, immediate and extended, living and deceased, as well as my friends in Boston, Edinburgh, London, Montreal, New York, and elsewhere.

Endless and enormous thanks are also due Michael Kay, whose slashingly vicious editorship when I was fifteen made me the writer I am today; to Miss Carter, my high school English teacher, whose report card my penultimate year—the one that said "I wouldn't be surprised to see Andrew's name on the bestseller lists in years to come"—I wish I could find because I would frame it and stare at it daily for inspiration; Sean Michaels, whose own beautiful prose always makes me feel like I could be doing seven hundred times better; and everyone else who I've forgotten and forgives me for it.

And Mallory, of course. Mallory Mallory Mallory. I couldn't have done it without you.

Photo by Maureen Cotton

Andrew Ladd is the blog editor for *Ploughshares*, and his work has also appeared in *Apalachee Review*, *CICADA*, *Memoir Journal*, and *The Rumpus*, among others. He grew up in Edinburgh, Scotland, and has since lived in Boston, Montreal, and London; currently he lives in Brooklyn with his wife and cat.